The
Future
Of The
Future

The
Future
Of The
Future

JOHN McHALE

GEORGE BRAZILLER / NEW YORK

The author and publisher wish to thank the following for permission to reprint certain materials included in this book from the books and periodicals listed below:

The American Sociologist—"The Sociologist and the Study of the Future" by Henry Winthrop. Northwestern University, Evanston, Ill., May, 1968.

Adelbert Ames, Jr.—Institute for Associated Research, Hanover, N.H.

Annals of the American Academy of Political and Social Sciences—"A New Orientation in American Government" by Bertram M. Gross and Michael Springer. Syracuse, N.Y., May, 1967.

George W. Ball—From an article appearing in *Time*, November 24, 1967.

Basic Books, Inc.—*The Art of Conjecture* by Bertram de Jouvenel. New York, 1967.

Bedminster Press, Inc.—*Language and Literature in Society* by Hugh D. Duncan. Totowa, N.J., 1961.

Bollingen Foundation—*The Myth of the Eternal Return* by Mircea Eliade, Bollingen Series XLIV. New York, 1954.

George Braziller, Inc.—"Subjective Time" by John Cohen, from *The Voices of Time* edited by J. T. Fraser. New York, 1966.

Arnold Buchholz—Draft manuscript. Germany, 1958.

Bulletin of the Atomic Scientists—"The Speed of Change" by Ritchie Calder. December, 1965.

Center Diary: 17, Center for the Study of Democratic Institutions—"Futuribles: Innovation vs. Stability" by John Wilkinson. Santa Barbara, Calif., 1967.

Christian Science Monitor—Editorial by Robert C. Cowen. Boston, Mass., February, 1968.

Columbia University Press—*Little Science, Big Science* by Derek J. de Solla Price. New York, 1963.

Current—"The Future as Present Expectation" by Daniel Bell. New York, November, 1967.

iv

v *Acknowledgements*

Daedalus, Journal of the American Academy of Arts and Sciences—"Twelve Modes of Prediction" by Daniel Bell. Cambridge, Mass., Summer, 1964.

Daedalus, Journal of the American Academy of Arts and Sciences—"Utopia for Practical Purposes" by Bertrand de Jouvenel. Cambridge, Mass., Spring, 1965.

Daedalus, Journal of the American Academy of Arts and Sciences—"Communications Technology and the Future" by John R. Pierce. Cambridge, Mass., Spring, 1965.

Daedalus, Journal of the American Academy of Arts and Sciences—"The Year 2000-Trajectory of an Idea" by Daniel Bell. Cambridge, Mass., Summer, 1967.

The Free Press—*"The End of Ideology": On the Exhaustion of Political Ideas in the Fifties* (1960) by Daniel Bell. New York, 1965.

The Free Press—*The Division of Labor in Society* (1893) by Emile Durkheim, translated by George Simpson. New York, 1947.

The Free Press—*Machine Age Maya: The Industrialization of a Guatemalan Community* by Manning Nash. New York, 1958.

The Free Press—*The Sociology of Georg Simmel* translated and edited by Kurt H. Wolff. New York, 1950.

James M. Gavin, Chairman of the Board, Arthur D. Little, Inc.—"Perspectives and Prospects in Space." Presented at Honors Convocation, American Institute of Aeronautics and Astronautics, Boston, December, 1966.

Harper & Row, Publishers, Inc.—*Self Renewal* by John W. Gardner. New York, 1964.

Harper & Row, Publishers, Inc.—Foreword to *Cyborg: Evolution of the Superman* by Manfred Clynes, D. S. Halacy, Jr. New York, 1965.

Harper & Row, Publishers, Inc.—*Introduction to World Resources* by Erich W. Zimmermann, edited by Henry L. Hunker. New York, 1964.

Industrial Research Inc., *Industrial Research*—"The Isolated Brain" by Robert J. White. Beverly Shores, Ind., April, 1968.

Information Forum on Technology and Nation, Atoms and U.S., Inc.—"Can Technology Replace Social Engineering?" by Alvin Weinberg, 2nd Quarter, No. 3. Newark, Del., 1967.

The Institute of Electrical and Electronics Engineers, Inc., *IEEE Spectrum*—"Human Enhancement Through Evolutionary Technology" by Warren M. Brodey. New York, September, 1967.

Journal of World History—"Time and Change in Twentieth Century Thought" by Corinne Lathrop Gilb, Vol. IX, No. 4. Neuchatel, 1966.

Robert Jungk—"Outline of a European Lookout Institution" (draft). Institut Für Zukunftsfragen, Vienna, 1967.

Alfred A. Knopf, Inc.—*Consciousness and Society: The Reorientation of European Social Thought 1890–1930* by H. Stuart Hughes. New York, 1958.

Mankind 2000 International—Preparatory International Secretariat. London, May, 1966.

Marine Technology Society—"Ocean Fisheries: Status and Outlook" by W. McLeod Chapman, Transactions of 2nd Annual Conference of Marine Technology Society. Washington, D.C., 1966.

McGraw-Hill Book Co., Inc.—*Understanding Media: The Extensions of Man* by Marshall McLuhan. New York, 1966.

Mentor Books—*The Age of Revolution 1789–1848* by E. J. Hobsbawm. New York, 1962.

Meridian Books, Inc., division of The World Publishing Co.—"Strategies of Inquiry: The Use of Observation" by Harold D. Lasswell, from *The Human Meaning of the Social Sciences* edited by Daniel Lerner. Cleveland, Ohio, 1959.

National Academy of Sciences, National Research Council—"Energy Resources," Publication 1000-D, Committee on Natural Resources. Washington, D.C., 1962.

Nature—"Technology, Life and Leisure" by Dennis Gabor, Vol. 200, No. 4906. London, November 9, 1963.

New York Academy of Sciences—"The Biological Significance of the Space Effort" by Ward J. Haas, from *Planetology and Space Mission Planning* edited by Robert D. Enzman and Edward M. Weyer. New York, 1966.

Oceanology International, Industrial Research Inc.—"Drugs from the Sea" by Robert E. Hillman. Beverly Shores, Ind., September/October 1967.

Oceanology International, Industrial Research Inc.—"Deep Submersibles" by Andreas B. Rechnitzer, Oceanology International 1968 Yearbook Directory. Beverly Shores, Ind., 1968.

Oxford University Press, Inc.—*Communication and Social Order* by Hugh D. Duncan. New York, 1968.

Oxford University Press, Inc.—*Essays in Sociology* by Max Weber, translated and edited by H. H. Gerth and C. W. Mills. New York, 1958.

Pergamon Press—"Technological Forecasting in Corporate Planning" by Erich Jantsch, from *Long Range Planning*, Vol. 1, No. 1. Oxford, United Kingdom, and Long Island City, N.Y. September, 1968.

Boris Pregel—*L'Energie Atomique et L'Abondance*, L'École Libre des Hautes Études. Paris, 1948.

Boris Pregel—"Peaceful Uses of Atomic Energy," *Social Research: International Quarterly of Political and Social Science.* March, 1947.

Prentice-Hall, Inc.—*The New Utopians: A Study of System Design and Social Change* by Robert Boguslaw. Englewood Cliffs, N.J., 1965.

Prentice-Hall, Inc.—*Man's Place in the Dybosphere* by Richard R. Landers. Englewood Cliffs, N.J., 1966.

Psychology Today Magazine, Communications/Research/Machines/Inc.— "The Psychology of Robots" by Henry D. Block and Herbert Ginsburg. Del Mar, Calif., April, 1968.

vii *Acknowledgements*

Rand McNally & Company—"Social Organization and the Ecosystem" by O. T. Duncan, from *Handbook of Modern Sociology* edited by Robert L. Faris. Skokie, Ill., 1964.

Reynal and Hitchcock Publishing Company and Williams and Wilkins Company—*The Next Hundred Years* by C. C. Furnas. New York and Baltimore, 1936.

Routledge & Kegan Paul Ltd. and Alfred A. Knopf, Inc.—*The Social History of Art*, Vol. 4 by Arnold Hauser. London and New York, 1951, 1958.

Saturday Review—"Prospects for Humanity" by R. Buckminster Fuller. New York, August 29, 1964.

Science, American Association for the Advancement of Science—"Peaceful Uses of the Earth's Atmosphere" by Walter Orr Roberts, Vol. 152, No. 3719. Washington, D.C., April 8, 1966.

Science Journal (incorporating *Discovery*)—"Mineral Wealth from the Oceans" by John L. Mero. London, July, 1964.

Scientific American—"Salt Water Agriculture" by Hugo Boyko. New York, March, 1967.

Scientific American—"Remote Sensing of Natural Resources" by Robert N. Colwell. New York, January, 1968.

Martin Secker & Warburg Ltd. and Alfred A. Knopf, Inc.—*Inventing the Future* by Dennis Gabor. London and New York, 1963.

Sheridan House—"The Impact of the Nuclear Age" by Boris Pregel, from *America Faces the Nuclear Age*, a Cooper Union Forum lecture, edited by Johnson E. Fairchild and David Landman. New York, 1961.

A. W. Sijthoff and Oceana Publications—*The Image of the Future*, Vol. I by Fred L. Polak. Leyden, and Dobbs Ferry, N.Y., 1961.

Department of Sociology, Southern Illinois University and the Maxwell Graduate School, Syracuse University—"Economic Development and Conflicting Values" by Peter A. Munch (manuscript).

Southern Illinois University Press—*Nine Chains to the Moon* by R. Buckminster Fuller. Copyright 1938, 1963 by R. Buckminster Fuller.

Soviet Life Magazine—An interview with Bestuzshev-Lada, Robert Jungk and Fritz Baade, No. 5 (140). Washington, D.C., May, 1968.

Spartan Books—"Simulation of Statistically Composite Systems" by Henry D. Block, from *Prospects for Simulation and Simulators of Dynamic Systems* edited by George Shapiro and Milton Rogers. New York, 1967.

C. Guy Suits, Vice President and Director of Research, General Electric Co.—Seventh Panel on Science and Technology, 89th U.S. Congress. Washington, D.C., January, 1966.

System Development Corporation—*Technology and Man's Future* by Hasan Ozbekhan, Sp. -2494. Santa Monica, Calif., May, 1966.

Think Magazine, published by IBM—"New Windows into History" by Arnold J. Toynbee. Copyright 1965 by Arnold J. Toynbee.

TRW Systems Group—"Results of Space Research 1957–1967" by E. R. Spangler, *TRW Space Log*, Vol. 7, No. 3. Redondo Beach, Calif., Fall, 1967.

University of Chicago Press—*The Human Animal* by Weston La Barre. Chicago, Ill., 1954.

University of Chicago Press—"Oration on the Dignity of Man" (1486) by Giovanni Pico della Mirandola, from *The Renaissance Philosophy of Man* edited by E. Cassener and translated by E. L. Forbes. Chicago, Ill., 1948.

U.S. Department of Labor—"Automation, Skill and Manpower Predictions" by E. R. F. W. Crossman. Seminar on Manpower Policy and Program, U.S. Department of Labor, April 15, 1965.

U.S. News & World Report—"End of the Population Explosion?" by Donald Bogue, Vol. 64. New York, March 11, 1968.

Verlag Anton Hain K.-G.—*History and Futurology* by Ossip K. Flechteim. Germany, 1966.

George Weidenfeld & Nicolson Ltd.—*The Savage Mind* by Claude Levi-Strauss. London, 1966.

Contents

I   THE SENSE OF THE FUTURE   3

II   THE FUTURE OF THE PAST

    1.   Time's Arrow   19
    2.   The Industrial Revolution   39

III   THE FUTURE OF THE PRESENT

    1.   The Dimensions of Change   57
    2.   An Ecological Overview   66
    3.   The Environ Systems   75
    4.   Man Plus   98
    5.   The New Symbiosis   123
    6.   Problems and Prospects   149

IV   THE FUTURE OF THE FUTURE

    1.   Outer Space   175
    2.   Inner Space   196
    3.   Resources of the Planet   208

V   PROPHETS OF THE FUTURE   241

VI   TOWARD A PLANETARY SOCIETY   267

    REFERENCES   301

    BIBLIOGRAPHY   311

    INDEX   318

To Magda

The future of the past is in the future

The future of the present is in the past

The future of the future is in the present

I

The Sense of
the Future

The future is an integral aspect of the human condition. Man survives, uniquely, by his capacity to act in the present on the basis of past experience considered in terms of future consequences. By assuming a future, man makes his present endurable and his past meaningful. Pasts, presents, and their alternative futures interweave in the anticipation and prediction of his future actions.

The centrality of the future in human affairs is attested by the great variety of social roles and institutions accorded to the prediction, and possible control, of future events impinging upon the individual and the society. These range, historically, through the oracular clairvoyance of the shaman, the medium, and fortuneteller for the interpretation of individual futures, to the larger social function of the priest king, the prophet, or political leader, to the more explicit professionalism of today's planners, forecasters, and long-range strategists. The ascendancy of science over religion, in our recent past, is partially based on claims for its greater predictive accuracy, derived not from inward contemplation, but from the direct observation and measurement of environmental phenomena.

Culturally, however, the idea of the future, in the sense that we now employ it, is relatively new in human experience. Most previous societies operated with quite different models—of the past, present, and future of man, of society, and of the universe.

For some, the future was largely a continuation of the past beyond a relatively unchanging and unchangeable present. Their purview of any future state was limited by their consciousness of time, by constraint within the narrow margins of survival in the present, and by the lack of adequate symbols and images to communicate radically different future states.

3

The closer realities of life were birth and death which bounded the unknown; the remote future belonged ultimately with the unknowable. Magic, art, and religion mediated with the unknown, provided symbolic currency for its propitiation, and shrouded its awesomeness in quasi-familiar and tangible forms. The future, as life-after-death of the individual, was a move into the past to join his ancestors. If a member of an elite, he then became a god or entered the service of a god; if a commoner, his future was generally less favorably augured.

Many societies, particularly in the East, operated with a cyclical model of such future changes, of recurring cycles of individual birth, death, and rebirth, whose predestined sequences moved toward the unknowable—a nirvana state of tensionless merging with the universe. The eternal return was to the source of all origins.

Our Western view of the future, which is relatively unique and recent in the historical sense, is a specific social and cultural development. It embodies within it the idea of progress—both material, in terms of the improvement of human welfare in the present or near future, and metaphysical, in terms of the perfectibility of human institutions and, to a degree, of the perfectibility of man and his society. As so stated, it is the kind of idea that emerges typically in our own period, one of whose major characteristics is an acute sense of historical time and of the relative nature of temporal, spatial, and other phenomena which were previously considered to be more absolutely fixed and determined.

Such a view of the future arises out of a complex series of value developments and assertions, and carries with it many normative assumptions about ideals and possibilities which go beyond past constraints and present inadequacies. In our immediate period these have crystallized around the idea that the future of the individual and of human society are within human control.

Thinking about the future remains, therefore, an idealistic and value-bound enterprise. It assumes a unique character, however, in a period in which the material means become available for the first time, on a scale that measures up to the idealism. The conscious degree of material control which man may now exercise in determining his individual future, and collectively that of human society, is quite unprecedented in all historical experience.

5 *The Sense of the Future*

The material control of future possibilities comes largely through the development of science and technology which have been traditionally value-free agencies. But the present range and scale of our actions and their consequences require increasing value commitments to specifically preferred and possible futures in human terms.

In general, today's modes of confronting the future, of predicting its course, and of accommodating to its possibilities are different from those of the past—from the nineteenth century and even from the early twentieth century. We have abandoned, to an extent, the preoccupation with the inevitability of progress.

Our view of the future is no longer that of a great evolutionary onrush, largely independent of man's intervention, tinged variously with doom or elation. We realize, for example, that man does not, in the end, master nature in the nineteenth century sense but collaborates within the natural world; his very existence depends upon an intricate balance of forces within which he is also an active agent.

The Malthusian and utilitarian feeling that the future was limited to those most able to prove their material strength and mastery is a viewpoint which, in its more negative and large-scale aspects, is increasingly confined to our military establishments. We grapple now with a less deterministic image of man, in which he no longer represents the unidimensional agent of economic, political, sexual, and other "organic" drives, but in which he emerges, albeit hesitantly, as a freer and more autonomous being. This new image of man reaches beyond the traditional and constraining definitions of the past and consistently eludes, in its emerging complexity, the administrative and legalistic conveniences of the present.

In essence, there is a kind of polarization taking place around the mid-twentieth century which divides the intellectual establishment. There are those who are still preoccupied with the world as conditioned by its pre-World War Two—or in some cases even pre-1900—parameters, and those who are attempting to recast and reorient their view to a world that is in many ways distinct from all previous human experience. The dichotomous nature of this debate lies further back in the Western tradition, and was perhaps expressed in its earliest clarity during the Renaissance, when the central argument was concentrated on man's relation to, and conscious control of, his own forward development. Reverberations of this philosophical debate continued increasingly down to our own time period.

At a particular point in time, soon after the Industrial Revolution, the summation of various scientific discoveries and access to large-scale technical facilities tended to invalidate one side of the debate. With the material means for the physical survival and larger maintenance of human society augmented beyond any previous expectation, the possibilities and potentialities for a more conscious forward development became available.

The first great changes came with the advent of the Industrial Age, based on engines that used energy stored in coal beds, which built cities and navies, wove textiles, and sent steam trains across the widest continents. Since then, with energy from petroleum and other sources, changes have come more swiftly. Today, radar telescopes scan the universe to record galactic explosions that occurred billions of years ago; oceanographic ships explore the undersea; electronic devices measure the earth's aura of unused energy and similar equipment traces inputs and outputs of single nerve cells; television cameras orbiting the earth send back photographs of entire sub-continents; electron microscopes photograph a virus; passenger planes fly at almost the speed of sound; and machines set type in Paris when a key is tapped in New York. These are only a few of the changes. . . .[1]

From this point on, there is a growing realization that man's future may be literally what he chooses to make it, and that the ranges of choice and the degree of conscious control which he may exercise in determining his future are unprecedented.

Prediction

As man gains more knowledge of the forces operative in, and external to, human society and of the powers available to him, he is forced to couch his questions about the future in the form of the alternative possibilities of human actions in terms of their long-range consequences. The more knowledge and power, and the larger the scale of material actions, the greater the number of alternative paths and the longer the range of possible consequences.

Predicting the future is no longer the business of utopians or lunatics; indeed the latter term transformed into space scientist becomes one of prestige rather than derogation.

It is the modern *hubris*. . . . What stands in our favor is that knowledge is cumulative. And, within the open community of science, it is self-corrective. We know more of economics than the "Political Arithmetick" of Sir William Petty who started us out with "Number, Weight and Measure." We have clearer conceptual distinctions than Herbert Spencer and his primitive efforts at establishing social differentiation. We have more complex statistical tools than Pearson or Galton. What is more important, perhaps, is that we have a better appreciation of method. For what method allows us to do is to reformulate insight into consistent explanation. . . . Prediction without explanation is insight, experience, or luck.[2]

Prediction, on any or all of the bases above, has now come to pervade many sectors of society. Governments and industries alike, committed to long-range programs of the most varied nature, find that they are increasingly forced to think not only of the next ten or twenty years ahead, but of the next fifty—or even the next hundred years.

To send a manned space vehicle to the moon requires that work on the project be started many years before; other programs requiring long-range coordination and development demand similar efforts.

But, even given the enormous complexities of time, resources, research, and productive capacities involved, planning a series of manned rockets is relatively easy in present terms. We can forecast with reasonable accuracy the types of basic research in metals and other materials which should be initiated this year, so that their bulk production may be available in three years, in time to phase in with parallel developments in lubricants for near-vacuum (which it can be predicted will be available in four years), and so on. By compiling the research trends and rates of technological development, we can attain to variously workable ten, twenty, or even fifty year predictions. Of course even such apparently straightforward forecasting is subject to swift alteration, through human serendipity.

Workable predictions can also be made about overall physical resources and their technological exploitation. Though such areas would seem to be fixed and determinable, actually what we mean by resources depends upon the prevailing culture; technologies are not immutable. However, within such possible variability we may still calculate alternative paths of use and determine their contingencies. All such major resource questions are, in varying degree, affected by factors already known or predictable in some form from today's knowledge. Even if they are not, we are still forced to proceed on such a premise.

Social Futures

When we come to social futures, the situation is very different, but the need to introduce predictable parameters and concomitant action has become increasingly urgent. We have viewed, in the past few decades alone, the often drastic and unforeseen consequences of not predicting—particularly in relation to the social effects of new technologies.

Finding out what we want should become a major object of attention . . . there is a vast difference between letting changes occur under the impact of technological advances and choosing the changes we want to bring about by our technological means.[3]

On the local and international scale, governments now attempt to predict situations productive of violence and disorder. Though limited by the short-term range of their political mandates, they are forced to take cognizance of the consequences of legislative actions which may not be wholly visible for years.

Industry, too, has become increasingly preoccupied with the markets of the 1980s or 1990s. The future of this industry or that —"In the Year 2000"—is now a standard board room or convention topic.

Choice

Dealing with specifically social futures reintroduces the subject of the potential capacity of human beings to determine their own future. This is a central point that will bear repetition. Given his present state of knowledge, social as well as scientific and technological, man now has an enormously enhanced capacity to choose his future, both collectively and individually.

The outcome of the futures chosen will depend in turn on our ability to conceptualize them in humanly desirable terms and on our willingness to engage with their prediction.

There is, in this sense, no future other than as we will it to be. If we conceive of a future state as desirable, we tend to orient ourselves toward it and to initiate the courses of action necessary to its attainment. Of course, willing a future connotes more than wishful thinking; it involves an action-oriented commitment to the future in ways that transcend past constraints and present obstacles. The latter are often more apparent than real in our current affairs, where lip service to change is the norm that conceals even the strongest investments in the status quo.

The collective aspect of choice of futures is reflected in the growing concern of our local societies with the allocation of public funds to long-range social programs. We begin to agree, for example, that investments in prenatal care, child welfare, and preschool education, which may not pay off for twenty or thirty years, are realistic societal strategies.

We attempt to control and legislate the future pollution of the waters and the air, the future state of our cities, and the allocation of other living spaces on the same basis.

We may note, also, that the longer the range and consequences of such commitments, the less they may be constrained within immediate economic measures. In terms of futures' cost effectiveness,* social costs and gains transcend more limited and obsolete criteria.

The pattern of a desired future based on even the least factual or measurable prediction commits us to consensual action. Our collective assumption is, increasingly, that the environments and forms of our society are within our positive (or negative) control.

The individual choice of futures has become more flexible. In previous eras a man, even in the so-called advanced countries, would feel impelled to prepare himself for one occupation, pro-

---

*Cost effectiveness, one of our latest planning slogans, comes paradoxically from weaponry budgeting, in which economic costs have rarely functioned as a restraining factor in any real sense.

fession, or career, committed more or less to a particular geographic locality and largely determined for him by the circumstances to which he was born. Now we have the emerging situation in which an individual may reasonably expect to change occupations, career role, and geographic location many times in his life.

The future of the individual is based, again, on whatever expectation of the future he acquires. His paths toward this or that future, though conditioned in part by physical makeup, disposition and talents, may now be viewed as more largely determined by his particular conceptual mapping. The individual life may be viewed as embracing a larger number of alternative possibilities and life-chances than ever before—in life styles, locations, careers, and social roles. That this is still not even approximately true for many disadvantaged millions around the earth does not reduce its potential promise and expectation for all.

The future of the future is therefore what we determine it to be, both individually and collectively. It is directly related to how we conceive of its possibilities, potentials, and implications. Our mental blueprints are its basic action programs—whether immediate or not depends on the individual and his society. All our actions have consequences and both action and consequence may be effected on a larger scale, with further reaching contingencies, than was ever consciously possible in human history.

The range of predictions regarding the future is now relatively enormous. The number of professionals engaged in exploring the future is, possibly, matched only by the number employed in excavating the past. Futures research—as it is now rather primly termed —is already divided among a variety of academic disciplines. The danger is no longer that the future may be neglected, but rather that it may become overprofessionalized—if not out of existence, then at least out of reach of lay participation and interest.

We need more, and more diverse, alternative futures, not fewer. The future belongs to all men. We should resist its division into a number of intellectual provinces cultivated only by their respective expert elites.

We have the means to provide almost any, and as many, kinds of futures as man may desire, but our collective futures tend to be oriented toward those models and scenarios that receive public attention and support. Much professional futures research is already overbalanced toward the technological, the economic, and the politico-military. Moreover, its alternatives are tied to the traditional premises and priorities that reside in our respective national ideologies and local value systems.

While science and technology must be allocated a prime role in the changing of past and present, the more crucial aspects of the future are now more clearly nontechnological, in the traditional sense. The "hardware" to solve many of our physical problems is available for use. The "software," or social thinking, through which we may apply our developed capacities in humanly desirable terms, is less than adequate.

The models of human society, of our institutions, and of our social capabilities and relatedness, with which we still operate, restrict much of our futures thinking within obsolete historical conditions. We can produce material goods far beyond immediate necessity and have elaborated our organizational capacities beyond those necessary for mere group survival and security, but our outdated models still generate the same stereotyped "dilemma" responses to most of our social problems. The constraining myths that bind us to obsolete forms, old fears, and insecurities may be our most dangerous deterrents. Our traditional attitudes and ideologies are inadequate guides to the future, serving mainly to perpetuate old inequities and insecurities.

Our highest futures priority lies with social invention—the reevaluation and redesign of our social forms and possibilities. We need to experiment more consciously with innovative social organization, with new modes of individual and cooperative relationships, and with decision-making. The fact is that our traditional theories of social action tend to construe innovation as deviance and social experiment as aberrance. They have, so far, been of little predictive value in assessing the qualitative thrust of social change in our societies.

At the world level, the greatest need for social inventiveness manifests itself in the breakdown and obsolescence of all the traditional modes of confronting our major problems. The agencies of change have forced us swiftly into a new global reality. But, as we emerge into the planetary society of the future, the geopolitics of the past are the most dangerously constraining myths of our present.

In the second half of the twentieth century, there is a perceptible shift in human consciousness and conceptuality which begins to alter man's overall relations both to his fellow men and to his planetary habitat. Aspects of this change in conceptuality extend inwardly, from unraveling of the micro life code at the molecular level, to the successful maintenance of men beyond the earth's atmosphere and under its oceans, to the outward monitoring of other worlds and galaxies.

A new awareness of the origins and possibilities of human life and intelligence is engendered in these explorations. In our relation to time, we now begin to probe into the future almost in like ratio to the extent that we successively locate the beginnings of life itself ever more remotely in the past.

At the daily level of experience we may note this increased awareness in more popular acceptance of a "one world" view. Even where this lacks positive action and is most often qualified in "their world" or "our world" terms, it marks a shift toward recognition of the planetary interdependence of the human community and the sustaining system of natural forces within which it exists. Such awareness is due, in no small measure, to the swift and myriad diffusion of images and messages in the global communications network. The significance of local events of any consequence for the larger community is rapidly felt and reacted to around the world.

Whereas tribal man became disoriented when separated from his local group and surroundings, and early city/local state man could barely conceive of any larger territory, we are now in a period when many men think casually in terms of the whole earth. The planet as life space is accepted as naturally as was the earlier conceptual extensions of childhood area, home town, region, or country.

Accompanying these expansions of the levels of conceptual awareness is a significant recourse to the planetary ecology as a pragmatic framework for their interrelation, with the focus on the role of man as symbiotic agent and disruptive factor.

Our major problems evidenced in present disparities between the developed and lesser developed regions of the world (food, shelter, health, and education) may be more clearly and operationally defined in terms of ecological imbalance. The urgency of their solution thereby broadens, from its present evaluative level of appeals to the humanitarian concern of the more fortunate minority, to the common self-preservation of all.

The inequities between have and have-not peoples may thus be viewed as a grave threat to the overall future maintenance of the human community. The explosive rises in population, the pressures on food lands and other resources, the scale of wastage, disorganization, and pestilence accompanying our "local" wars are also directly linked to the global revolution in human expectations. As physical and psychic events, these press ever more critically upon the resources and social energies of even the so-called advanced nations; as world problems, they are increasingly beyond the capacity of any locally organized effort to mitigate, or solve, them in anything but the shortest range.

The world, then, which the expanding network of electronic communications is fast reducing to a complex but single ecosystem, confronts the technological civilization with a profound and growing imbalance . . . the first step towards a human future is the acceptance of responsibility for meeting the emergency in our total environment by creating those generalized human conditions which will at least prevent the system from degenerating further. In the immediate term, the only way we know how to do this is by devoting the necessary physical resources to feeding the hungry; in the immediate term we must do it by inventing the necessary means to graft our technological knowledge on all branches of the human tree.[4]

Thus there are no local problems any more, such as may be left to the exigencies and dangerous predilections of local economic or political convenience. We have reached the point in human affairs at which the basic ecological requirements for sustaining the world community must take precedence over, and be superogative to, the more transient value systems and vested interests of any local society.

Where critical imbalances occur—whether biophysical, in terms of earthquakes or other natural catastrophes, or sociophysical, in terms of famine, disease, or the catastrophe of war—we need to recall that the resources of the planet can no longer be possessed by individuals, corporations, or national groups any more than these can possess the air we breathe. Exclusive ownership of a key watershed, mineral deposit, or scientific discovery is as farcical, and as dangerous, a proposition as our supposed sovereignty of a national air space in these days of earth-orbiting satellites.

The self-sufficiency and "manifest destiny" of the nation-state was a social invention, which may have been of value in the past but is of doubtful utility in the present. National pride need not be confused with national power. Individual cultural freedom and diversity may best survive when physical survival itself is no longer threatened by locally oriented expediency.

The transition toward a world-man image faces a situation analogous to that of the past emergence of national and empire man models. Formerly the local ideological issues revolved around the national control of public health, child welfare, pure food, water legislation, etc. Much the same arguments now prevail in defense of the vested interests and "rights" of individual nations to behave as if they were isolated, self-contained, and wholly autonomous physical and social entities. Though such a fiction may be a comforting security for local identity in a rapidly changing world, it is dangerously removed from reality.

We need to face up to a world that has been made into one interdependent community, less by political or ideological ideas than by scientific and technological facts.

The scale of our global systems of material production and distribution, and of communication and transportation, has now gone beyond the capacities of any single national or regional group to sustain or operate wholly. These systems require and are dependent upon the resource range of the entire planet for their material constituents, in which no nation is now self-sufficient. Each system is complexly interlocked with all others. And the whole is increasingly dependent upon the global interchange not only of raw materials and finished products, but also of the knowledge pool, comprising research and development, technical and organizational expertise, and the individuals who sustain and expand this knowledge.

Ours is possibly one of the most critical periods in human experience. Poised in the transition between one kind of world and another, we are literally on the hinge of a great transformation in the whole human condition.

The next fifty years may be the most crucial in all of man's history. We have few guides to follow and almost no usable precedents. "Many of the old moralities have suddenly become immoralities of the most devastating character."[5] All our previously local actions have now been magnified to planetary scale. The knowledge with which we might make the correct decisions is barely adequate—yet our gross errors may be perpetrated for many generations.

In such a context the depiction of ideal forms of future societies is not the only projection of the future. The nature of social ideals changes as society changes. It is true that idealized, or utopian, images retain a powerful role as the guiding visions that make the past and present meaningful and impel men toward the future. We should recognize, however, that we can now accommodate many such possible and diverse ideals and that they may coexist rather than exclude one another.

The immediate and most necessary task is the exploration and methodical investigation of all avenues and approaches to the future. These range from reevaluation of the past, to the study of human trends and needs in the present, to the projection, forecasting, and imaginative construction of a plurality of individual and social futures.

Important, but comparatively neglected, areas of futures thinking are: (1) the psychosymbolic aspects of the future—the ways in which viable images of future life styles and social forms are previsioned in the arts and communications media; (2) the study of future scientific and social implications as a fertile common ground for the various academic disciplines; (3) the communication of the sense of the future, and its participative forming and controlling, to the wider public.

The future of the future is determined not only by what may be possible or probable in economic, technological, or sociopolitical terms, but also by what man himself deems necessary, allowable and ultimately desirable, in human terms.

▌▌
The Future of the Past

1
Time's Arrow

Individual and social events occur in time. What we have discussed as the sense of the future is intimately linked with the sense of time in its individual subjective dimensions, in the social time conventions and periodicities of specific societies and cultures, and with what may be loosely termed the historical time sense.

In all these dimensions, past, present, and future have no actual fixed time locus. The future is compounded of past and present. The past is constantly re-created in the future. Past, present, and future commingle in any one conscious instant.

For various social purposes (scientific, historical, or religious), we assume various modes in which events are connected in time. In our present Western mode, time is unilinear in that the past comes before the present and the future follows upon the present. So pervasive is this mode that it is difficult for us to imagine a practical way of relating events other than in such a sequence. "Time's arrow," in Eddington's phrase, points toward the future, and history follows the course of the arrow.

Though we may comply with this convention for the major part of our present discussion, some consideration of the variability of time relations is crucial to any discussion of the future. Merely to assume that the future is an as yet unvisited time about which we can have no certain knowledge does not help us to gauge the import of present events and past historical phenomena for our future.

Even if Eddington's arrow is constant and the future emerges from the present, the future of that future is also in our present and in those successive presents that are in process of emergence. Much of the disorienting nature of change in today's society may well come from the public image of a past that has irrevocably disappeared, and a temporary present which is swiftly and universally advancing into an inexorable and unknown future.

In actuality, many of the events that effectively predispose the future are already in the recent past. Much of our recorded knowledge belongs in this category. Most of our social institutions and processes are designed not only to regulate the present, but also to transmit past values and useful experiences into future forms. The socialization and education of the young assure a measure of continunity of conceptual orientation and social attitude. The use, and misuse, of various physical technologies has already produced situations that directly affect the courses and options of future development.

Other significant events occur in the present but may be so far below our threshold of recognition that their importance is not evaluated until their cumulative effects reach critical mass at some point in the future. Then, in changing the future, they may also require changes in our view of the past. This may be seen in our current efforts to legislate the pollution of the environment; for example, where chemical pest and weed controls were used indiscriminately in the past, their long-range effects emerge only in our present and consequently lead us to reevaluate our past (and future) practices not only in this area but also in many others.

Though simplistic, such examples may serve to underline the interpenetration of social pasts, presents, and futures, and to dispel the notion that they are wholly linear and irreversible in direction.

Again, though we customarily regard the present as more directly under our control than past or future, this may be more apparent than real. The present is often only definable and describable when it is past. The significance of a past or present event may become so only in some near or remote future. In terms of plasticity, the past and the future might, perhaps, be regarded as more under our control than the tenuous present.

Our individual subjective relation to the past is paradoxical and inconsistent. There is, as in the social sense of time, the assumption that the past is unalterable—"what's done can't be undone." But memory continually reshapes our biographic past in the same manner that our selective perception and means of communication screen the present and future.

Expectation, intention, anticipation, premonition, and presentiment—all these have a forward reference in time. Our entire psychic life is permeated with the hope of things to come, which is the counterpart of nostalgia for the past. Implicit in all our actions are plans, however vague and inarticulate, for the future, and sometimes, as in saving or investment, this planning is deliberate. As we ascend the evolutionary scale, the temporal horizon becomes more and more extended. This may be illustrated by the fact that in experiments in delayed reaction, the interval of delay may be increased at higher phylogenetic levels: the rat can sustain a delay of some 4 minutes, the cat 7 hours and the chimpanzee 48 hours. In man the horizon may reach beyond his own brief existence: from infancy onward there is a growing capacity to relate what is happening at the moment to events foreshadowed in the more and more distant future.[1]

We tend to rearrange and reselect events and impressions of the past, and this realignment to a new point of view in the present alters our past and future. Any deep emotional experience, such as religious conversion, causes us to see our past selves in a new light and carries with it an implied change in the present and future; thus psychoanalysis, as secular redemption, significantly re-creates the "persona" by reordering and reinterpreting its past experience.

Entering into both individual and social time is the element of myth. Mircea Eliade suggests: "The myth relates a sacred history that is a primordial event that took place at the beginning of time."[2] It is before and out of time in the ordinary sense. Most of our myths are thus concerned with the past, with the origin of things. As sacred history, they are immutable, unchanging, and, as such, unchangeable, for what would happen if we changed our beginnings? This mythical dread of changing past time remains a recurring element—even in the most recent science fiction themes where in time travel, changing the past as little as the fractional alteration of a leaf often causes the present to cease to exist or creates a new future.

Myths, then, sacralize time and import meaning into its flow. Their ceremonial reenactment establishes social periodicities that give an endurable structure to time. Though generally considered as referring only to the past, there is in both sacred and profane ceremonies a binding of the present to the past, and to the future. Rites of passage reenact the myth of origin, but the rebirth is to an altered social status in the future. Fertility ceremonies commemorate past periodicities, but are also propitiations for future continuance.

From being "out of time," the myths of origin come to pervade all past time. This holds true even for the secular society that has manifestly replaced its mythical past with a rational historic past. The latent mythopeic tendency is to invest all past origins, past events, and long-sustained sequences of social action with this sacred quality.

We may comment here, parenthetically, that Marx and Freud, two of the major formers of our secular present, were in their separate ways preoccupied with the "sacred" quality of the past. Marx hewed to the inexorable law of history which, if understood and acted upon, would return man to his original state of communal freedom. Freud, also grounding present problems in past conflicts, stayed closer to mythic interpretations, but maintained that freedom lay in circumventing the inexorable law by reenacting and resolving past conflicts. For Marx, in many senses, freedom lay in conformity with the sacred past: for Freud, in destroying it.

As for us in other domains until recently, antiquity and continuance are the foundations of legitimacy. But the antiquity is conceived as absolute, for it goes back to the origin of the world, and continuance admits neither of orientation nor degree. . . . Mythical history thus presents the paradox of being both disjoined from and conjoined with the present. . . . Thanks to ritual, the "disjoined" past of myth is expressed, on the one hand, through biological and seasonal periodicity, and on the other, through the "conjoined" past, which unites from generation to generation the living and the dead.[3]

The traditional mode, generally, as mythicized past behavior, is not only defined by custom, but is also endowed with sanctity and strength by this more fundamental source. The mode refers back to a perfected and idealized form of the original behavior which is mythic in character.

The social uses of the perfected form are, of course, not wholly defined by its emergence from, and maintenance of, a past tradition. It may also evolve into a transcendental goal toward which behavior is referred in the present and striven for in the future—as being different from, and better than, past behavior.

In both its past-oriented and future-oriented aspects, the perfected form operates as a life-style model for ongoing social action. The traditional models are familiar: the saint, the man of honor, the soldier. In their more extremely secularized forms, such models of life-styling may also be viewed in the types of popular figures such as stars and celebrities, heroes and antiheroes, and other images who circulate within the mass media.

Even the most radical, innovative, or deviant social modes swiftly evolve a life-style model, a "tradition of the new" with which to gauge role performance, goal attainment, and deviance from the model. The more antitraditional or antihierarchical, the more hairsplitting the degrees of lapsed or nonperfection become: revisionist, square, straight, sellout, and the like.

Part of the ongoing utility of perfected forms is in their tacit dimension of unreachability—they serve to maintain conduct at a pitch. Like myths, they are somewhat outside ordinary life limits and time. Once launched as symbolic constructs, they pursue lives of their own, which may be progressively elaborated without reference to the realities that engendered them.

This autonomy of the ideal is particularly marked when we engage with utopian forms as perfected images, which are rarely revised according to the changing nature of reality, but endure as autonomous symbols. Most early utopias have been traditionally cast as forms of perfected societies. Their projection was not always into the future; it might be another place. Whether remote in the geographical sense or remote in the time sense, they often resemble the myth of an originally perfect beginning. They tend to construct a society such as it was originally meant to be, or shall be again—when God (or the god in man) wills it.

Each institution has its own miniature utopia. As Polak, one of the most perceptive writers in this area suggests:

Religion reveals a world such as this one was meant to be, and shall sometime be according to the decree of the Almighty. *Philosophy* describes the world that might have been had the creator been a philosopher or had a philosopher been the creator. *Ethics* indicates how the world ought to be if man lived in virtue and justice according to her absolute laws. *Science* reconstructs the world as it must be, provided that reality can fit herself to the truth of her schemes, formulae, definitions and obstructions of various kinds. *Technology* shows how this world can be remade or destroyed through the proper or improper use of natural forces.[4]

Social theory has also divided societies according to their orientation to the past and to their traditional perfected forms. Sacred societies are viewed as resistant to change, as being unable to accept or value the new or untraditional. Secular societies, a relatively modern development, are oriented toward change, and consciously seek out and value new and untraditional ways. By implication, sacred and secular societies are respectively oriented toward the past and the future.

The secular society emerges from the sacred by transforming religious values into rational-ethical values. The catalyst of this transformation may be compounded of a number of factors, such as the emergence of a special class interest in promoting rational-ethical values. Thus we see the evolution of the idea of history and of material progress in Western society, when new religious concepts of individual salvation through redemption and conversion in the present become fused with the development of a scientific view of society as it may be redeemed or transformed in the future.

The sacred/secular dichotomy does not, of course, dispose of the mythopoeic tendency,* which remains constant in both value orientations. Rationalism, progress, and science swiftly accumulate their own myths and their own traditionally sacred pasts. The tradition of the new comes increasingly to coexist with, rather than wholly supplant, the old.

One important aspect of the change from sacred to secular societies is the way in which their myth orientation deals with change within a society. Where they remain religious, myths satisfy the need for what Max Weber calls the "theodicy of suffering" by dis-

---

*As may be noted in the names accorded to advanced scientific and technological ventures (for example, particularly in aerospace, Atlas, Saturn, and Thor rockets: the Apollo, Mercury, and Gemini projects).

placing the cause of suffering and injustice into past transgressions or by compensating for it by promise of future joy.

One can explain suffering and injustice by referring to individual sin committed in a former life (the migration of souls), the guilt of ancestors, which is avenged down to the third and fourth generation, or the most principled—to the wickedness of all creatures per se. As compensatory promises, one can refer to hopes of the individual for a better life in the future in this world (transmigration of souls) or to hopes for successors (Messianic realm) or to a better life in the hereafter (paradise).[5]

In the secular society, this need for a "theodicy of suffering" is more broadly assuaged by myths of the future; by a "sociodicy of amelioration," which rationally accommodates the explanation of present suffering and injustice within the idea of progress toward the future material betterment of man's condition.

The latter idea, of social progress, is usually related directly to changes in our immediate past. Most contemporary discussions of progress start with science and technology as the major agencies of change. Rationalism, the scientific method, mechanization, and secularization follow in rapid order to present a picture of the abrupt and recent appearance of progress and the machine.

This is a comfortable and useful basis for eulogizing the virtues of progress and its agencies. Then, too, it serves well for inveighing against the "tyranny of progress," the unnatural evils of "the technological society," and the "dehumanization of man." But a somewhat larger purview serves to dispel the notion of the origins of the idea of progress as being closely associated with the rise of material invention or materialistic values.

For the greater part of human history, the idea of social progress was not commonly held. The social societies of Egypt, Persia, India, and the East were oriented quite differently. There was a long unchanging fixity of world view and a rigidity about the goals and purposes of such societies, which did not include any doctrine of even gradual temporal progress toward some altered social and physical conditions of the populations. Our Western view of progress and improvement in the human condition derives from two associated sources—the Greek and the Judeo-Christian traditions

—which of course emerged from, and were influenced by, earlier traditions.

The Greeks accommodated the transformation from a religio-mythical world view to an intellectual and rational vision of the city of man, which is still one of the most luminous we possess. Having reduced the god myths to the human dimension of man-gods, the Greek thinkers themselves have now been mythicized into our intellectual heroes whose sacred texts are still invoked to legitimize our major political and intellectual institutions. *The Republic* of Plato retains its viability, in some measure, as the latent blueprint for present republics and democratic states. Yet Plato and his tradition were bound close to an origin myth of an earlier perfect world; he felt that his own era was one of decay as inevitably prescribed by the cyclical nature of his view of time.

The Judaic tradition is more directly prophetic with regard to the world to come.

"In the beginning was the Word."* And the Word that comes down to us is about a single God who made a covenant with a chosen people. The ensuing ideas of contract, of specific social injunctions, of conduct based on the communication and inter-pretation of the Word are of an oddly arresting modernity.

The Word is typically conveyed by the prophet, the archetype of the charismatic leader. His words "I say unto you" and "It shall come to pass" are continuous, repetitive exhortations to the people to follow the law, lest society fail to enter into the promised earthly utopia of the covenant.

The importance of this tradition with reference to change and progress is that:

. . . for the first time the prophets placed a value on history, succeeded in transcending the vision of the cycle (the conception that all things will be repeated forever) and discovered a one way time . . . Historical facts thus become "situations" of man with respect to God, and as such they acquire a religious value that nothing had previously been able to confer upon them.[6]

*The "Logos" or "Order" is not only divine; it is the truth about a reality that is conceived to be revealed as spoken and heard, and it pertains to an ongoing social dialogue as well as sacred ritual.

Within this tradition, there were also the messianic and apocalyptic visions through which the prophets sought to prepare the people for the new society, which would come about through change in socioethical relationships consciously lived in accordance with the law.

Change for good and bad was measurable and predictable, and the bad brought immediate and personalized retribution, not only for the individual but also for all the people. Magic is displaced in favor of individual ethical responsibility as the change force in society, and religion is turned from ecstatic propitiatory ritual into a form of progressive social criticism.

In the period of the apocalyptic visions, the immanent nature of abrupt change precipitated in a profusion of images of future states contingent upon the climax of the struggle between good and evil. These apocalyptic images, generated by the tensions of the period, are paralleled in the millenarian visions that presaged the end of the Middle Ages and by those of the more recent nineteenth century social prophets such as Saint Simon, Fourier, Comte, and Marx, whose acute awareness of social disruption and change produced a spate of secular and sacred utopias.

Christ concretized the idea of the Judaic vision and sharpened its contingency upon individual social conduct within society. Man is reborn physically and his baptism is extended universally instead of being confined to the chosen. All men are chosen and become identified with *the man*—the Son of God. History, change, and progress are also reborn in this process, and made universal. The individual and social past becomes mutable. Through conversion and redemption it is recast and altered to conform with the renewed expectations of a kingdom of God on earth.

A key progressive concept here is redemption, which changes the mere possession of sacred values and beliefs into an active belief in being redeemed from and for some particular purpose.

Redemption attained specific significance only where it expressed a systematic and "rationalised" image of the world and represented a stand in the face of the world. For the meaning as well as the intended and actual psychological quality of redemption has depended upon such a worked image and such a stand. Not ideas, but material and ideal interests, directly govern this conduct. Yet very frequently the "world images" that have been created by "ideas" have, like switchmen, determined the tracks along which action has been pushed by the dynamic of interest. From what and for what one wished to be redeemed and, let us not forget, "could be" redeemed, depended upon one's image of the world.[7]

Christianity has been not only a religious but also a social movement, requiring specifically prescribed changes in institutions, roles, and social expectations. The crystallization of the idea of ameliorative material progress is present within it, even though this was more often displaced by other-worldly negation of the secular present in favor of a spiritualized life after death.

One could trace the development of the idea of progress from these early beginnings up to our own period. It is one of the core ideas that give Western society its distinctive orientation to the future and to the possibilities of redemptive development which make that future orientation different from that of other past societies.

. . . a disjuncture had been effected between past and future, and man's will and effort were what would fill the gap. Change, in short, could be the result of individual purposive action, pitted against the forces of present reality. The transfer of the power to change from God to man came with the concept of possible breaks in the formerly smooth continuity of time.[8]

Much of our present malaise and disillusionment originates in the apparent failure of this vision. The visionary ends, having attained to mastery of the material means that could fulfill the conditions of the vision, seem to be vitiated by the unredeemable and more negative predilections of human nature. Both the malaise and the apparent failure may lie more in the dichotomous treatment of ends/means relations than in any intrinsic fault within man himself.

The key that activates redemption of the vision may lie in the abandonment of the either/or dichotomies through which the sense of failure and disillusionment are engendered. Our historical experience of preindustrial, marginal survival dictated that material means were separate from, and possibly inimical to, spiritual ends —else how, in the relative fluctuating and inequable distribution and scarcity of the former could the latter be nourished and kept alive? This sustaining myth is well documented in the voluntary poverty of the religious mystic, the asceticism of the philosopher, and the material renunciation by the artist. The association of material means with the corruptibility of physical power also ensured a sufficient opposition to the unrestrained acceptance of might as right, which preserved in varying degree the inviolability of the power-deprived and materially poor individual against both the temptations and the dictates of material power and wealth.

Even in our vastly changed condition, we still cling to the comforting myth that the "evils" of a technological society may abide more in such moral dichotomies than in any contemporary reality. It is also more widely noticeable that those who most vigorously proselytize the old virtues of nonmaterial values and spiritual priorities do so from a base of material security.

Any serious study of the future implies an equally rigorous hindsight operation on the past. Rather than approach this in terms of traditional historical modes, we need to review the past as a vast collection of incompletely recorded social and cultural experiments conducted under many different degrees of local controls and environmental determinants. The records of that past are our experimental data for charting the future.

Traditionally the value of the past was to supply stability and continuity to the present, but its more critical relevance lies in identifying within our past historical conditioning those attitudinal constraints that endanger and obscure our future possibilities. The need is not to cut ourselves off from the past so that we can achieve the future, but to review past potentials and disabilities in the light of those changed conditions that give us a greater range of choices and options.

Given a more pragmatic and secular approach to our sacred pasts, we may find that the laws of history are inexorable only when and where we deem them to be so. As laws, they belong more in the realm of self-fulfilling prophecies; their inferences return circularly upon the premises from which they were inferred.

One might even say that this reevaluation of the past is of greater priority than the elaboration of more futures. This is particularly true in relation to evidence in the sociopolitical theories, which constitute the latent assumptions and take-off points for all social futures. From such theories, we derive our images of man, his institutions, and the possible forms of his societies. Yet, patently, many of these theoretical assumptions were formulated in the preindustrial phase or under the transitional stress to the industrial period.

The social sciences, upon which our current models of society are based, have their most critical formulation and academic definition during the periods of revolutionary change at the end of the eighteenth, through the nineteenth, and early twentieth centuries. Born of the widespread social disorder and abrupt change attending the demise of an old society, the grand systems of Comte, Spencer, Marx, and others reflect an underlying pessimism and troubled uncertainty about the future condition of man. In concert with the next generation of social thinkers, such as Durkheim, Freud, Weber and Pareto, the theories of these earlier economists and philosophers reflected and possibly perpetuated the anxieties and uncertainties of their origins.

The dream of the eighteenth century enlightenment, òf man as a self-conscious, freely choosing, and rational being was largely abandoned for one which

. . . agreed that the basic characteristic of human experience was the limited nature of its freedom. Men were masters of their fate . . . only for limited periods and in strictly limited segments of their activity. . . . Some such conviction of the inevitable limitations on human freedom—whether by physical circumstance or through emotional conditioning—has become the unstated major premise of contemporary social science.[9]

Our present image of man as an oversocialized performer of various roles, motivated by institutional conditioning and unable to escape from old fears and insecurities, is still largely derived from these unsupported premises. This has been perpetuated by an academic disinclination to question the sacred theories of the past in favor of their piecemeal methodological verification in the present.

Within our present context, some brief review of these origins may be of value by way of comment.

The French Revolution is, in many senses, the beginning of our contemporary present, a dividing line after which all our major social movements and ideas are colored by its rhetoric or polarized within its major issues. With respect to symbolic import, not one revolution but several are involved. Of these the American Revolution might be characterized as primarily political, the Romantic Revolution as psychosocial, and the Industrial Revolution—the most pervasive of all—as basically socioeconomic and technological. The reverberations of these movements continued up through the nineteenth century to the Russian Revolution in the early twentieth century. Much of our current social unrest, the revolutions of rising expectation, "wars of liberation" and the like, are still preoccupied with similar problems and issues.

The labels by which we categorize these major upheavals are for semantic convenience. The movements themselves are but part of a more general transition that had been building up since the Renaissance, when man broke free from the manifold restrictions of the older classical world. Again, even this is only a watershed; to seek for perfected and unequivocal origins is, at best, an academic and somewhat utopian gesture.

The French Revolution remains the symbolic, ideal type of social upheaval. But its first proclamations reflect middle class liberal demands, now less than revolutionary in their modesty, containing guarantees for civil liberties, for private enterprise and property, and (significantly) for the retention of social distinctions on grounds of common utility. Our image of the revolution is based rather more speciously on the later period of the war government, and on the "terror" resulting from the pressures of counterrevolution and external intervention.

Conservatives have created a lasting image of the Terror, though by Twentieth Century standards, and indeed by conservative repression of social revolution such as the massacres after the Paris Commune of 1871, its mass killings were relatively modest; 1700 official executions in fourteen months. . . . But for the solid middle class Frenchmen who stood behind the Terror, it was neither pathological nor apocalyptic, but first and foremost the only effective way of preserving their country.[10]

It is these latter developments, and those generally of the next years of rapidly changing regimes, that further build the image of social chaos and disorganization, of war, and of individual, family and property insecurity—as inevitably incident upon revolutionary political change. This image gradually diffuses to include any radical social, economic, or political change, particularly those involving direct mass action by the lower class. The "specter" has continued to haunt not only Europe, but also the world.

The Romantic Revolution, though sharing certain common features with contemporary radical movements toward economic and political change, runs counter to the eighteenth century enlightenment ideas of rationalism, conscious progress, and future-oriented change. Its philosophical mentors (Hegel, Schopenhauer, Nietzsche) tend to view history as a framework of iron laws within which great men, and the clash of individual wills and passions, are the unwitting instruments of progress.

Whereas the eighteenth century philosophies, with their high tide of reason, negated the past and turned man's view toward a rationally malleable future, romanticism glorified the past and, when it was not wholly antireason, was distrustful of its premises. Citing reason as classical in tendency, inclining toward order, control, and external consistency, we may characterize romanticism as anticlassical because of its claims for natural disorder, tolerance of inconsistency, and internal orientation.

Aesthetically, whereas classical reason resolves internal ambivalence or conflict in controlled expressions of order according to various laws of harmony, proportion, and the like, romantic unreason externalizes its ambivalence in stylistic disorder. The former mode assumes that internal problems may be solved by ordering and changing the external environs. The latter suggests that only the internal problems are real; therefore their spontaneous expression is in itself the solution to the problem, and art is not for order's sake, but for its own sake. So, extremely expressed, both philosophies are absolute modes: one, the Light Absolute of the conscious act, of mind, of reason; the other, the Dark Absolute of the unconscious, of the emotions, of what D. H. Lawrence calls "the dark forest of the soul." In the balance, however, reason or reflective rationalism is the more inclusive mode, capable of accepting the irrational and idiosyncratic as also characteristic of the human condition.

Romanticism tends to evolve a technical rationalism which allows for the employment of rational means to ends that, in the larger sense, may be wholly irrational. In various forms, it provided a general balm for the wounded spirit of the middle classes whom reason had abandoned in the defeat of the French Revolution, through its passing into the hands of "the rabble." This was particularly the case outside of France where, though the need for change was recognized, there was also the need to avoid the explicit radicalism of the French model.* The yearning for political power through revolutionizing society was sublimated in the revolutionizing of culture. To avoid the ideological dilemmas of the present and the commitment of reason to the future, Romanticism sought for its ideal social order in antiquity. History and culture become the opiates of the bourgeoisie—as Marx might have said. The demand for political freedom was largely shifted onto the plane of cultural freedom—an ideal of unfettered art and culture, which accorded well with the laissez-faire of economic individualism.

But this replacement of the political by the cultural revolution, in certain ways also made for theoretical justification of more personal expression in manners, and life style. The Romantic attitude expressly elaborated the personal style and the staging of the expressive act which, no longer simply the display of reason in conduct, became "living" itself. Eccentricity, dandyism, and rugged individualism were the surface manifestations of a deeper concern with the quality of the personal and individual life. The Romantics' emphasis upon the differentiation of personal life style led to the proliferation of a great many coexistent period styles, in repertoires and decor for the staging of social acts. Every age and geographical region was ransacked for artifacts and atmosphere to supply

---

*For example, in Germany and England. In the former, social change became directed toward national unification and identity in accord with a reawakened interest in the glories of the past; in the latter, buffered by a mercantile empire, it was implemented by a gradualism that took its form from the traditions of an enlightened colonial paternalism which led eventually to the concept of the ameliorative welfare state.

the multiplicity of role changes, which the Romantics' expression seemed to need and encourage. Its fascination with the past may, in this way, be somewhat defended as a celebration of individual freedom in the present, even though such freedom was generally and tacitly restricted to that of the higher orders.

The revival of medievalism* is not the least interesting aspect of nineteenth century romanticism. The rehabilitation of the Gothic, particularly in England, and the return to the pre-Raphaelite dream of Ruskin, Morris and others accorded well with the advocacy of a return to the simplicities and the natural order of monastic utopians such as Fourier. The uncertainties of the present were assuaged by the renewed enthusiasm of an uncomplicated faith in old stabilities, in the security of a vanished era that, in the sense that the Romantics viewed it, never existed.

The creative fervor, the "revolution for life," supersedes the image of the man of reason with that of the artist as the driven agent of the soul. Heedless of political power and the temptations of material wealth, the new hero brings with him the key to Boheme —a timeless, wistful and slightly immodest kingdom to which even the bank clerk, the functionary, and the tired businessman could retire for evenings of leisure and concupiscence.

Behind this revolt against politically tainted reason there was perhaps a subtler fear, that of the machine. Having finally stormed the Bastille of classical culture, and now busily engaged in refurbishing it appropriately in medievally handmade decor (or in less costly Biedermeier), the intellectual sector of the middle class also saw that its hard-won gains were now threatened by the mass production of cultural value objects by the machine. Even "the rabble" could have ready-made culture now, without the self-denial and moral investment that true appreciation and taste required, though their unimproved preference was for machine-debased forms.

---

*It is particularly evident also, for example, in the work of Auguste Comte, the founding father of sociology, whose great theoretical system culminates in *The Utopia of the Virgin Mother*, in which the future of man is viewed as best served by the severity and regularity of a medieval religious state. It is not generally recognized how deeply conservative and past-oriented such early social scientists were and the extent to which their theoretical biases still permeate social thought today.

Significantly accompanying the Romantic Revival in the nine-teenth century, therefore, is the "Werkbund" to elevate the aesthetic taste of the lower classes. Indeed, the whole of what we term the "modern movement" in architecture, design, and town planning arose out of an aesthetic reaction against both the products of the machine and the so-called dehumanization of man's labor through the machine. One of the founders of modern architecture, Henry van de Velde,* went so far as to redesign and have hand-made every item of furnishing in the houses he built.

The beginning unease and distrust of science and the industrial machine were brilliantly mythologized earlier by Mary Shelley in her *Frankenstein, or the Modern Prometheus*, and later on, by Robert Louis Stevenson in *Dr. Jekyll and Mr. Hyde.*

These motifs continue to haunt the intellectual to this day.† Their Pygmalion inversion is also part of what we may term the alienation myth: Man became severed from society by his machines and by his own creations, which take on an autonomous life of their own. By imputing life or value to his created image, he incurs the wrath of God, who then destroys both.

The apotheosis of the romantic dream may be found in the *fin de siècle* artists. Here the rejection of modern life leads to what would now be termed deliberately deviant and alienated modes. One of the bibles of Romanticism and of the cult of decadence is Huysmans' *Against the Grain*. Poets like Baudelaire, Rimbaud, and

---

*Ironically enough, Van de Velde and the Grand Duke of Saxe-Weimar were also the main agencies in sponsoring the creation of the Bauhaus, the German design and architectural school of the 1920s and 1930s, whose stylistic influence still endures in the machine-design quality of many of our consumer goods, furniture, typography, book and poster design, etc. The now classical image of a technological art thus proceeds from the old master of the Art Nouveau style and a feudal patron.

†John W. Gardner, *Self Renewal* (New York: Harper & Row, 1964). "He sat in an air conditioned studio. Behind him was a high-fidelity phonograph and record library that brought him the choicest music of three centuries. On the desk before him was the microfilm of an ancient Egyptian papyrus that he had obtained by a routine request through his university library. He described a ten day trip he had just taken to London, Paris and Cairo to confer on recent archaeological discoveries. When I asked him what he was working on at the moment, the professor said: 'An essay for a literary journal on the undiluted evils of modern technology.'"

Verlaine in France, and the Yellow Book* school of Wilde and Beardsley in England, represent the extreme. Edgar Allan Poe might be described in our contemporary jargon as typically deviant and alienated, both in his life and in the gothic necrophilia of his work. It is no historical aberration that around this time Gauguin runs off to the South Seas and Rimbaud abandons poetry for a trader's life in Ethiopia. Even earlier Melville, whose Captain Ahab and Ishmael are classically alienated heroes, had written *Typee*, with its vision of primitive and paradisiacal society.

With few exceptions, such as St. Simon and Marx, we find this estrangement from modern society recurring again and again in the social and cultural thought that ushered in our own period. It is particularly marked in the social sciences:

The fate of our times is characterised by rationalisation, intellectualisation and above all, by the disenchantment of the world.

Max Weber's later phrase, above, sums up the feeling of malaise and nostalgia that Durkheim also expresses in his studies of suicide and anomie. Following the conservative bent of Comte, social thought continues to seek some return to earlier cohesive forms and simplicities. Modern man may find solace only through allegiance to the larger solidarities; the way toward individual security and collective normalcy, the restoration of norms, binding customs, and social health lies with emphasis on the group, with conformity. The reduction of individual anxiety and alienation may be achieved by adjustment, to whatever degree of alienation may be inherent in the particular group, community, or society.

This emphasis has remained with us up to the present. The social institutions and directions that have been accorded prior academic interest and official support have been those identified with stability and integration rather than those associated with change and creative innovation.

*In a manner reminiscent of the Frankenstein and Mr. Hyde, this "little yellow book," which Oscar Wilde's character Lord Henry Wotton gives to Dorian Gray, starts the latter off in his career of dissolution, in which only his painted portrait reflects his age, decay, and alienation. This theme also occurs in many earlier forms, particularly in that of the Golem, who is significantly brought to life or programed by an amulet of words placed in a hole in his forehead.

The seductive implications of this view were observable, at various removes, in the appeal of national socialism to large sections of the European middle class in the period between the World Wars One and Two, as it is in currently renewed nationalistic fervors and "manifest destinies," and even to an extent in the new "tribalism" advocated by many leaders of the youth. Its roots lie deep in the culture shock induced by the abruptness of social and technological changes in our recent past and the increased pace of such changes in the present.

In many important senses, those who provide the intellectual visions and sociopolitical models that guide and influence Western society have been unable to accommodate to changes in the forms of society, which they could not wholly account for in terms of past traditions to which they belong by class, education, and professional commitment. Their acute awareness of the disruptive nature of accelerated change is not seemingly accompanied by any realization that such rates of change may be sustained and be flexibly accommodated within new social modes rather than through the return to some earlier, more stable form.

They have, in consequence, been more preoccupied with combating old specters than in confronting emergent realities, and are more easily recruited to maintenance of the status quo than in devising new ways through which society may circumvent its present problems. Even the currently fashionable spate of "future" studies by those more recently, and more resolutely, committed to the past is, in many cases, yet another way of avoiding the consideration of change in the present.

In the period that we have been discussing, the fear and rejection of industrial society was largely confined to the intellectuals. The nineteenth-century middle class, though generally flirting with Romanticism as an alternative to other radical modes of change, subscribed to an optimistic view of the inevitability of material progress through science and technology embodied in the machine. The working class, apart from earlier groups such as the Luddite machine breakers, sought to improve their lot through direct political and economic action that would secure them a more equitable share of the products of their industrial labors.

As we approach our own period, we find that the distrust of, and estrangement from, industrial society has lingered most strongly in literary and humanist thought. The literary masterworks of the early twentieth century—*Ulysses, The Wasteland,* etc.— are sensitive testaments to the breakdown of values and the "chaos of the present." Whereas such works were insightful in recording the continuing disintegration of an old culture, now their attitudes rather than their creative spirit have been perpetuated and institutionalized within the traditional establishment to provide a set of stereotyped responses which continue to hamper the emergence of new cultural forms.

The visual artist, on the other hand, reacting more swiftly and intuitively to changes in his immediate environ, and being less hampered by academic specialization and professional commitment, has been more attuned to new forms and technological potentials of our period. If Dadaism, Surrealism, Constructivism, and their later variants have sensitized the contemporary vision to the metamorphosis of cultural values, often through a savage and corrosive irony, they have also provided a usable mythology of the machine and an insight into its creative potentialities.

The Romantic attitude of the nineteenth century has evolved into many peculiarly contemporary forms. Thus the Romantic of today has often fallen in love with "the mechanical bride" and her key-punched IBM progeny. The latent fear of individually fallible reason, per se, is displaced by an absolute trust in the security and value neutrality of instrumented process or in a systems mystique whose scientific laws are taken as both moral force and infallible truth. The kingdom of Boheme, largely evacuated by the artist, has been invaded and developed into a sanctuary by the young, whose romantic unreason often proceeds from more reasonable and humane premises than that of their reasonable elders.

2
The Industrial Revolution

Without subscribing to any unideterminism, it may be suggested that the more pervasive aspects of change in our recent past, and those that are still transformative of our present society, are scientific and technological. The most significant material changes have occurred through the direct and large-scale application of mechanical, and latterly electromechanical, energies to the production of the goods of physical survival.

The steps toward a specifically industrial technology in Europe had their origins in the conceptual revolution of the early 1600s, but progressive technical improvements in tools and instruments lie further back. Concepts were sharpened by the elaboration of the consciously scientific method of observing, measuring, and predicting the laws and principles that underlie the behavior of natural phenomena. At first, the changes visibly wrought in society by new discoveries in the sciences were relatively slow. They gained rapid momentum only when such principles began to be applied to industrial technologies in the late eighteenth and early nineteenth centuries.

Though the social and intellectual bases of society were affected by new scientific ideas, the full effects of the scientific revolution are not parallel with those of the early phases of the industrial revolution; they occur later in the nineteenth century. The emergence of the *professional* scientist is more closely identified with those specific discoveries that form the springboard of modern science—the extension of experimental and measurable ranges into the invisible, subsensorial world of atomic and radiation phenomena.

The favored benchmark for the development of modern technology as industrial revolution occurs somewhat independently of later specific scientific developments produced within, and for, industry. The lineage is much more that of a craft-technology tradition which has pursued its course through technical inventions conceived in terms of immediate practical ends. The introduction of the breast harness and stirrup, of the windmill and blast furnace as energy converters, and even Watt's epochal modification of the Newcomen steam engine predate discovery of the scientific principles of energy conversion.

Though we normally associate the beginnings of industrial society with such inventions and with the system of breaking down productive work into repetitive units in the factory system, these aspects predate the Industrial Revolution. They belong more with the intensification and routinization of the craft and cottage industries, which were incident upon the increased mercantile and colonial expansion of the seventeenth and eighteenth centuries. A number of the key inventions leading to the factory system were made in the eighteenth century:

1734—Paul and Wyatt's roll spinning apparatus
1764—Hargreaves' spinning jenny
1769—Arkwright's water frame
1779—Crompton's mule
1785—Cartwright's power loom[1]

The mass production of standard components, then assembled through specialized division of labor into further complex units, was already present in embryo form in the slave factories of Greece and Rome. Its specifically modern features in the first phases of the Industrial Revolution came from increased precision of component and machine tolerances and from the improvement of the steam engine as an energy source. The first machine tool is generally considered to be Wilkinson's boring mill of 1775, used to make accurate metal cylinders for Watt's improved steam engine. The boring mill was swiftly followed by the invention of the family of machine-tool types that carry out many of the basic industrial farming operations today—drilling, turning, punching, reaming, milling, grinding, and form cutting.

Machine tools are the key to early industrialization of mass production. They are the generalized *tools to make tools*, which are used to manufacture the prime movers and the mass production machinery itself. Mass production is made possible by specialized machines that produce standard components. It is through the development of machine tools that early industrialization really accomplishes its accelerated growth.

On the lathe, man can make ten more lathes, instead of consumer products, and then ten men can go to work, each making ten more lathes and each can be a better lathe than the one before.[2]

Industrial mass production has similar early beginnings, generally associated with Whitney's "American System" of 1798, used for the manufacture of muskets with interchangeable parts, and with North's manufacture of pistols by the same methods. One of the first large-scale uses of the copying lathe, in 1818, was in the turning of gun stocks by Blanchard. The mass production of clothing (rather than the handcraft processing of machine-made textiles, which was the general system) also started around this period and was further accelerated by U.S. Civil War uniform needs. It is interesting to note the traditional allocation of advanced technologies to military needs—a trend that continues to the present day.

Many of the features that have been considered as enduring characteristics of the scientific and technological industrial process are actually the end phases and adaptations of the older craft production tradition, such as the human factory system, the sweatshop assembly of manufactured components, the routinization of work, and the concentration of populations and production centers in close association with raw materials and energy sources.

This is an important qualification when we begin to consider the supposedly inherent evils of industrialization. One of the distinguishing features of the successive, and specifically industrial, revolutions is the large-scale application of mechanized energies to the production of the physical necessities of life. Rather than man and his society being further enslaved by the machine process, he is potentially freed from his previous bondage as a muscle machine and from survival dependence on wholly material and economically determined relations.

In the later developments of the scientific industrial process, even the term "mass production" requires qualification, since automated general purpose tools may be programed to turn out product runs with different conformation and qualities. Similarly, as the range and quality of products increases and they become more available, the mass consumption market tends to break down into an expanding range of individual and group preferences for differentiated products.

The term "industrial society" is therefore in many ways a misnomer. As the phenomenon of scientific* industrialization develops, it is less directly constraining upon the form of society than were the craft-agricultural herding and hunting phases that preceded it. Rather than becoming a more visibly identifiable determinant of the societal and physical environ, its processes shift over into relatively invisible metabolic functions. This is particularly the case as it evolves successively through later chemical, electromechanical, and electronic phases. At the same time, the major institutions and social forms shift also from emphases on materially productive activities and economically determined relations toward a wider range of human concerns.

As the period at which man takes off from an agriculturally based margin-survival type of society to types based on possible machine-produced abundance, the scientific and technological revolution is one of the major turning points in human affairs. This viewpoint, which still emphasizes a high level of productivity as a criterion for the possible increase of human well-being and freedom, has been much criticized in recent years. This is especially true of those Western countries that have enjoyed a relatively high standard of living for some decades, in which the increase in gross national product has become a fetishistic measure for societal well-being. Yet, it should be remembered that until the material means for living, beyond mere physical survival, are available to the majority of men, it becomes a somewhat academic plaint to worry about our locally corrupting affluence. Freedom and psychophysical well-being, though not guaranteed by increased material productivity, are at least made more attainable for more men. For

*A criterion of difference from craft to scientific and technological industrialism would be the institutionalization of innovation in the latter. Whereas craft evolution is more determined by traditional precedent, the scientific structure has change and innovation built in as the working premise.

the majority of the world's people, these conditions (increased life expectancy, minimal material security, and access to the knowledge and products of our civilization) are not even yet approximated.

The industrial revolution is also at the point where there occurs the specific and critical interdependency of the various world regions, through the need for globally available materials and markets, improved communications, and intraglobal transportation. This is another major characteristic of the industrial process that tends to be ignored: "the peculiar interrelatedness [from this time on] which makes it possible for certain countries to talk in terms of national economic growth.[3]

Industrialization is, by its nature, a global phenomenon that cannot be wholly sustained locally.* The more advanced the technology, the more pronounced its trend toward global service; telephones, airlines, and satellite TV are inherently global, minimally requiring such interlinkage and the widest availability of use for their most efficient operation.

The problems of early industrialization were of the same order and source as those which constrain our societies even today. Historically conditioned to slow change, minimal and competitive survival, and the innate scarcity of preindustrial society, man is still not oriented toward the qualitative and quantitative changes inherent in industrialization and the fundamental changes in value, in survival advantage, and in material wealth which this entails.

The early land-use laws, enclosure practices, and the like, which drove the people from country life into the factory towns, also meant in many cases a rise in living standards and life expectations. Though much romanticized by those who did not have to endure it, the golden age of the peasant was hardly even gilt; even his age expectancy was rather low. Agricultural workers often fled to the factories to escape the low living standards, the famine-ridden and minimal expectations of rural life. Even before the

---

*Henry Ford was one of the earliest to appreciate this aspect of the industrial process when he extended his local assembly line to include the "mobile inventory" flow of raw materials and components from widely separated remote centers, in a timed sequence of transport and processing operations from around the world, to converge at their local United States processing centers.

factory, women and children worked in the fields from dawn to dusk; the tenant farmer and the serf were no less bound and disciplined by their relation to the land than to early machine-minding.

These considerations in no way compensate for the genuine degradation and inhumanity of many early industrial conditions. They were compounded by the evils of revolutionary change to yield a social-humanitarian view of modern industrial society, which still persists in many of its important aspects. The case has been well documented: the effects on socially cohesive institutions, the disintegration of the family, the routinization and loss of meaning of work itself, the degradation of the spirit through alienation and anomie, the psychic decay, the faceless anonymity of the city—all culminating in an indictment of the mass society and the decline of civilized life as inevitably contingent upon the large-scale development of science and technology.

Which part of this picture is myth and which is reality has become difficult to pinpoint. Though supportive of humanitarian concern and providing a focus for ameliorative social study and legislation, the mythical aspects of this compound image may well hinder its more pragmatic evaluation and distract attention from more radically innovative social directions. It is the legacy of past attitudes and obsolete social forms which may be more productive of such pathologies than any factors intrinsic to the industrial process.

. . . the human tolls of industrialization are not built into the process itself. They are the result of an image of man in social change which delineates him as a passive agent mechanically responding to immutable forces, or as the pawn in a political chess game, or as the expendable material in an economic vision. The questions we must ask of the process of industrialization cannot be phrased apart from the ineluctable fact that man makes himself or he is not made at all.[4]

The dilemma here, as we have already hinted, lies with the social definition of the image of man and the degree to which that image is overdetermined and overconstrained by a conservative vision of the possible forms and directions of human society.

A central issue is the nature of individual freedom and its relation to the social, economic, and political controls within society. Yet freedom and liberty are, in essence, the liberty to choose, the freedom to make choices. It is interesting to observe that the most characteristic and successful advances made under these slogans occurred at that point in the past when it first became feasible to assume that such rights and freedoms could be applicable to all people—when the first large-scale industrial revolution got under way in the Western world. Though earlier social, political, and utopian movements may have established the vision and promise of such freedom, it could not be redeemed without the availability of the material means that have been evolved largely within the past century.

The problem is that most of sociopolitical and economic definitions of man, of his rights, freedoms, and relations to society, were defined in preindustrial terms.* Since then, the dialogue has been acutely polarized: on the one hand, by those who advocate the extremes of an economic and technological determinism, and obedience to the laws of historical materialism; and on the other, by those who advocate return to an equally determined folk solidarity, of artificial consensus, within which the individual enterprise of certain preferred groups would operate without constraint in the "national interest."

Until recent times, all human societies were largely based on margin-survival agricultural and craft economies whose stored surpluses were rarely sufficient to maintain more than a small elite in relative long-term security. The long historical conditioning to such socioeconomic realities, which effectively limited any widening of the range of possible life strategies for the majority of people, produced our present outlook on work, economy, and the function of social institutions in the West—and equally, but differently, in the East.

Our developed version, and its attendant image of man, is gen-

---

*The use of the term "preindustrial" here is not meant to denigrate the value of traditional views of the rights of man, but to suggest that fundamental changes in our condition require that they be more vigilantly preserved and expanded, to avoid encroachment upon them by agencies, techniques, and means of control and coercion that did not exist when these views were formulated.

erally cloaked under terms like the "survival of the fittest" or the exigencies of the "Protestant ethic," or lauded in the Toynbeean sense as the competitive striving that alone produces great civilizations. Both the virtues and evils of this latent viewpoint were largely born of the necessity, derived from the pressures of fundamentally marginal survival, to gain as much power (or life advantage) as possible, and to adhere to the norms and mores of local group institutions for survival. Life in preindustrial society was largely framed in either/or terms—either work, as societal rules prescribe, or starve; either conform or be variously censured, ostracized, or killed; either marry or burn, and so on.

With the introduction of large-scale industrialized production requiring less time and human energy investment, we are able to abandon many of our previous either/or choice parameters as constraints upon the forms of society and individual life modes. When we can produce far beyond marginal survival necessity, a vast range of goods and life conditions becomes freely available. The human condition is eventually characterized by a nonexclusive multiplicity of both/and choice possibilities. Ways of living are no longer constrained by economic necessity. As the available modes of earning a living are initially increased, the socially imposed necessity for the direct earning of living becomes progressively eroded.

But we venture too far from our consideration of the immediate past. The first phases of industrialization were marked by an intensification of economic measures as the sole criterion of social gains.

Probably the most rational—but hardly the most humane—image of Man created by any culture is the Economic Man, always in pursuit of wealth, profit and economic advancement. Once an ideal, or perhaps just an idea, the image has in our Western Civilization been brought to real life and has, in some highly admired instances, reached near perfection. But whether the Economic Man "really" exists in the flesh or not is beside the point. His image is always with us, and his ethos has permeated our lives to the extent that, where Progress and Economic Advancement is concerned, it is taken for granted that other values must yield. Whether in business, or in politics, it all works out to a balance sheet of success, of investment and return so neat and rational that few are inclined to question its validity as a measure of all things.[5]

This image of economic man still dominates most of our control institutions and constrains our possible solutions to large-scale social problems within its bounds. To a great extent, it is already a built-in and unexamined premise for many of the refined methodological approaches to futures forecasting, and it operates as the latent criterion for evaluating the forward dispositions of energies and technologies for societal use.

Many of the latest modes of social and value accounting with their terminology of "cost effectiveness," "risk benefit," "program budgeting," etc., often reveal an underlying anxiety about scarcity, necessitating strict terms of economic priority for fear there will not be enough to go around for everything.

But neither the image nor the economic anxieties fit the types of the machine energies, materials interconvertibility, and organizational capacities that are now at our disposal. Most of these developed capabilities bear little relation to the kinds of visible and tangible agrarian values that were largely operative in human society since its beginnings.

The preindustrial producer of those resources upon which human survival was predicated could count his piles of grain and tally the number of his horses, chickens, cows, etc., which were available. He could reckon for the numbers of people who could be maintained through the visible accounting of such tangible assets. We have still not yet evolved ways of socially or economically accounting for the kinds of power, energy, and material value that accrue, for example, through the use of small transistors, or the tiny components of microminiaturized circuits, or the many other means with which we tap into the subvisible areas of the electromagnetic spectrum.

The inability of even the more rigorously scientific futures thinkers to avoid obsolete economic and social models lies, again, in the dichotomy that occurred in the recent past between scientific reality and the socially conventional wisdom.

Apart from the visibly disruptive impact of industrial changes, the transformation of science itself was a further and even more disturbing feature of the recent past. Having long supplied the general intellectual community with a lodestone of reasonable, tangible, and observable order, science slipped into an invisible world of relative intangibility and indeterminacy. From the visible threshold of directly observable, sensory manipulation of environmental phenomena, science passed over into the remotely instrumented world of electrical, roentgen, and radio waves, to subvisible causes of disease by micro-organisms and viruses, and to new scientific theories of the origins of the universe and of man.

From being a relatively contained, fixed, determinate, and rationally understandable world to the generally educated person, the whole order of nature began to shift its outlines, blur its determinacy, and become infused with other agencies that were neither visibly apparent nor logically apparent before. Alice not only voyaged in Wonderland, but also went through the Looking Glass.

Some parts of this new world view could be assimilated within the old classical order; other parts were only understandable and acceptable to those trained in the new secular faith, science itself. We may speculate here as to how far this apparent fragmenting of the outer natural world accounts for the intellectual retreat to the inward-seeking consistency of the Romantics' revival.

Despite this disconcerting shift, science continued as both methodological exemplar for other areas of human enquiry and, even more important, as supportive mystique. With science as guiding mentor, progress was not only assured but, through the discovery of evolution, became a "scientific principle," and hence a fundamental law of history.

The difference between Romanticism and Comtean Positivism has been attributed to the latter's emphasis on, and use of, a natural science model. One might equally contend that in its social science connotation, Positivism was and is a Romantics' position. Like the shift in the Romantics' attitude to change, from the political to the cultural plane, the early Positivists shift from changing society through political and economic action to a belief in the inexorable law of a scientific progress. This was supposed to take care of the macroscale social changes in due course; the Positivist could then deal with the personal-ethical dimensions that prepare for the changes wrought by science. In the latter-day Positivist, this leave-it-to-science attitude becomes more internalized, and the science mystique provides the means/ends relation hitherto reserved for religion. There develops a professional ethical neutrality to change that satisfies the need for a supportive, but evasive, faith in the inevitability of scientific law as a guarantee of progress.

As nature vanishes in science from all but the instrumented evidence of an ever more complex body of techniques, the invocation of science and scientific methodology takes on religiomagical significance. In the nineteenth century, this obeisance to technical virtuosity not only occurred in science, but was also diffused through many other areas of professional scholarship and even into the performing arts; thus the voluminous detail and methodological rigor of German historical and economic studies are somewhat paralleled by the rise of the professional virtuoso performer —violinist, singer, concert pianist, and the like. The technical expertise of means becomes autonomously valued for its own sake; performance becomes the standard for evaluating the professional role, not its relation to any larger goal.

This process was part of a more generalized trend. The nineteenth century was not only the period that brought the middle class into political and economic power, but also that in which the middle class intelligentsia became professionalized and were greatly expanded in members of the division of professional labors.* Specialized training of experts in the new universities became the norm, and professional codes and occupational licensing became restrictive relative to such training. Increasing professionalization was accompanied by more definite ideas about status and class affiliations. Large sectors of the professional intelligentsia, particularly those practicing a calling requiring technical expertise (doctors, lawyers, engineers, scientists), became more strongly class-oriented, either by origin or occupational demands.

The rules of occupational morality and justice, however, are as imperative as the others. They force the individual to think in view of

*The coffee house and salon intellectuals of the eighteenth century, who participated more radically in societal change, were still relatively "free lance" and unspecialized.

ends, which are not strictly his own, to make concessions, to consent to compromises, to take into account interests higher than his own. . . . Accordingly from the nature of the chosen task permanent duties arise. We are involved in a complex of obligations from which we have no right to free ourselves. There is, above all, an organ upon which we are tending to depend more and more; this is the state.[6]

Where ends are decided by others, the exercise of expert knowledge is divorced from responsibility for its end uses. The rules of the professional role then exclude any consideration of larger moral values that may be extraneous to its performance.

The concept of a pure science emerges and becomes the model, not only for the physical sciences, but also for the social sciences. The latter, more newly fledged, covet the status of professional expertise and value the neutrality that this model conveys.*

The strength of this development of professional occupational loyalty, status, and class obligations has important consequences for the kinds of enquiry, the models of society, and the intellectual attitudes toward the use of knowledge and change that are further evolved.

Much as society has gained from the strengthening of professional ethics in specific human service occupations such as medicine, and the law, it has lost, perhaps, in corresponding measure the more general ethical commitment of professional intellectuals to those matters of larger social morality which are not specified within their separate professional codes. This has been strikingly demonstrated in recent years.

Something of the mythic quality of this syndrome was referred to earlier in relation to Stevenson's *Dr. Jekyll and Mr. Hyde*. This schizoid ambivalence to the consequences of the uses of knowledge and the direction of change by those who are its major originators continues up to the present day.

Somehow the R & D explosion spearheaded by the military has permitted the scientific community to live with something near to a per-

---

*We may note also that this definition of professional role in terms of technical "value free" performance according to rules also became the standard for the rapidly growing formal bureaucracies in the period under discussion.

sonality split; to be a principal agent of change during the work hours in the laboratory and yet not feel committed to the consequences of such change as it enters our daily life. The state of "pureness" of intentions and "non-involvement" in consequences will no longer be possible in a society fully permeated by science. The scientific community gradually becomes aware of this change and is undergoing the painful experience of what seems to them, on the face of it, a betrayal of the very principles that made science possible and made it great.[7]

The paradox within such attitudes toward the conscious direction and evaluation of change is that our present generation now faces the future with globally developed capacities that free man, for the first time, from many of the age-old fears of material scarcity, insecurity, and competitive survival, which have paralyzed his initiative and frustrated his more innovative directions.

The obstacles and limitations to the fullest use of our resources and knowledge are now nonmaterial. They reside mainly in the obsolete economic, fiscal, and political structures that are the quasi-sacred legacies of our recent past.

The central issue within "the future of the past" is the need to reexamine the kinds of a priori assumptions and conceptual models with which we operate in the present, and upon which we are endeavoring to preview the future. Need we assume, for example, that our present major social institutions—the economy, the polity, the corporate, military, and scientific establishments—will retain their centrality as the major legitimizing and goal-setting agencies of change in our societies? The church and the monarchy were so regarded until quite recently.

The same question might be addressed to our prevailing ideologies, whose almost interchangeable polar extremes have been cited. The poverty of their approaches to our most dangerous world crises is repeatedly evident. Proclaiming "the end of ideology" as a solution, however, may be as pointless an exercise as suggesting the demise of theology. Both ideas and gods have modes of resurrection which elude their most well-meaning obituarists. We need to question, rather, the assumption that our alternative ideological preferences need be restricted to the either/or choices seemingly available to us—or, indeed, that we need assume any explicit and exclusive alternatives. The same kind of choice was recently mandatory, in much the same terms, with regard to theological preferences. It is no longer so narrow nor so binding.

This is not to suggest that some such form of ideological agnosticism would enable us to "leave questions of global morality to higher powers," as one distinguished statesman recently suggested. The way out is not to substitute value neutrality for positive assertion and expanded definition of human values.

The way forward through the present ideological impasse may be to reconsider Dennis Gabor's phrase, "inventing the future."[8] Just as we have invented the physical capabilities that now provide material paths to many alternative futures, so we now have to apply ourselves consciously toward the invention of those social forms, institutional arrangements, and even ideologies that will enable us to utilize our developed capacities more directly and expeditiously toward the service of the present and future.

To invent the future, we need, in certain senses, to *reinventory* the past. As interpenetrative of both present and future, the past requires as much vigilance and evaluation in regarding the future as does any problematic aspect of the present. Such reevaluation of the past may seem to suggest that history should be rewritten in some Orwellian fashion. Far from it. The task, rather, is to disentangle ourselves and our societies from those linearly deterministic theories of history that have come, almost, to replace history itself. As Flechteim states:

. . . the relation of the three time dimensions is crucial. . . . Isolated from the past and the future, the present tends to contract. He who lives in it alone—the man of pure and unreflected action—loses his sense of perspective. Similarly, the man who slights the future, may easily become the prisoner of dead traditions. . . . Lastly, a man who lives only in the future may become the hopeless victim of eschatological or utopian illusions. . . . We may thus characterise Futurology as an attempt to avoid the pitfalls of all three alienated ways of life by integrating all three dimensions. The point of departure would be the present, a present experienced not as an intersection, but rather as a significant section of time in which human life and action can gain true meaning. History devoured by time, is and always will be, full of dead relics. In this sense, the past is never wholly mastered.

The future, on the other hand, appears to be fully available. Hence, it would be wrong to insist on its non-existence. What matters is its growth, its rootedness in past and present, its potential being.[9]

Our past history is not only a huge and largely unexplored museum of the diverse manifestations of the human spirit. It is also the continually expanding laboratory record of a vast number of social, political, ecological, and other types of experiments conducted, and endured, under a great variety of control conditions. Its future, in this sense will never be completely written.

III
The Future of the Present

1
The Dimensions of Change

The twentieth century is entered through two great historical divides, which may be conveniently, and significantly, set by the World Wars One and Two. The major social and cultural characteristics of the nineteenth century world are still those of the first decade of the twentieth. By 1918, many of the traditional forms of the previous era lived only in the nostalgia of the prewar years, and those that survived were further shaken by the Marxian time bomb of the Russian Revolution. Today the years between the wars seem rather the haunted period of the end of an age—than the first third of a new and much heralded century.

The symbolic transition into the realities of the twentieth century world occurred at the end of the World War Two, with the use of the atomic bomb in 1945. The transition was to a world that has been changed not only physically by the war itself, but more profoundly and psychically by an Auschwitz and a Hiroshima. In this world, the ideas and ideals of the recent past—of reason, progress, and the future perfectibility of man and his society—seem oddly tenuous; they have lost their ebullience and inevitability.

A new and more sober assessment of the human condition has emerged, in which optimism regarding man's aspirations and potentialities is tempered by the implications of his more negative predilections. The quality of humanity itself is no longer a God-given constant, but a self-definition, requiring conscious vigilance and affirmation. The expansion of the physical world view by Sputnik, in 1957, strengthened the emergence of this new consciousness by circumscribing the finite limits of man's global habitat and the fragile balance of forces that sustain life within those limits.

SHRINKING OF OUR PLANET BY MAN'S INCREASED TRAVEL
AND COMMUNICATION SPEEDS AROUND THE GLOBE

YEAR	500,000 BC	20,000 BC	300 BC	500 BC	1,500 AD	1900 AD	1925	1950	1965
Required time to travel around the globe	A few hundred thousand years	A few thousand years	A few hundred years	A few tens of years	A few years	A few months	A few weeks	A few days	A few hours
Means of transportation	Human on foot (over, ice bridges)	On foot and by canoe	Canoe with small sail or paddles or relays of runners	Large sail boats with oars, pack animals, and horse chariots	Big sailing ships (with compass), horse teams, and coaches	Steam boats and railroads (Suez and Panama Canals)	Steamships, transcontinental railways, autos, and airplanes	Steamships, railways, auto jet craft	Atomic steamship, high speed railway, auto, and rocket jet aircraft
Distance per day (land)	15 miles	15–20 miles	20 miles	15–25 miles	20–25 miles	Rail 300–900 miles	400–900 miles	Rail 500–1,500	Rail 1000–2000
Distance per day (sea or air)	20 by sea	40 by sea	135 miles by sea	250 miles by sea	250 miles by sea	3,000–6000 air	6000–9500 air	The Globe	408,000 air
Potential state size	None	A small valley in the vicinity of a small lake	Small part of a continent	Large area of a continent	Great parts of a continent with trans-oceanic colonies	Large parts of a continent with transoceanic colonies	Full continents & Transoceanic Commonweaths	The Globe	The globe and more
Communications	Word of mouth, drums, smoke, relay runners, and hand printed manuscripts prior to 1441 A.D.	① The Gutenberg 1441 printing press	② The rapid print Web 1863 newspaper press	③ The Bell 1876 telephone	④ The Marconi 1895 telegraph	⑤ First commercial 1920 radio broadcast	⑥ National 1950 Television	⑦ Transcontinental T. V. 1965 with the introduction of Early Bird satellite

THE RELATIVE SIZE OF THE WORLD AS TRAVEL TIME DECREASES

1850–1930

Steam locomotives averaged 65 m. p. h. while steamships averaged 36 m. p. h.

1950's Propeller aircraft averaged 300–400 m. p. h.

1960's Jet passenger aircraft averaged 500–700 m. p. h.

15,00 AD –1840 AD

The best average speed of horse drawn coaches on land and sailing ships at sea was approximately 10 m. p. h.

Rome was the only metropolis of over 1,000,000 people from this date forward until 1800 AD.

Man on foot = 3 mph

5,000 years (300BC–1800AD) in which towns slowly evolved into cities, and then into metropolises.

5,000 years of villages & towns and then

Bubonic plague wiped out 1/4 of Europe's population

Rome's population declined by 30,000

For the first time in history it began to be safe for men to live in large cities because of advances in medicine and sanitation. Life was made more secure and comfortable by the Industrial Revolution & mechanized farming

Coach — Carevel=5 mph
Steam locomotive/Horse
Automobile
First flight across the Atlantic
Jet
XB-70
Jet super sonic

This toned area represents population growth

Figure 1.

Adapted from: International Industrial Development Center Study, Stanford Research Institute; *Science and the Future of Mankind.* Hugo Boyko, editor, World Academy of Art and Science, Vol. I, pub. by Dr. W. Junk, The Hague, 1961; *Change/Challenge/Response*, Office of Regional Development, Albany, N.Y., 1964.

Donne's poetic metaphor, "No man is an island entire of itself," is now writ large on the surface of the planet. The most abrupt and significant aspect of the twentieth century transition has been from a plurality of remote and relatively autonomous national societies to a complexly interdependent world community.

In a few generations, man's world has shrunk from a vast expanse, whose area was still incompletely known and whose peoples were relatively distant from one another, to a continuous neighborhood. No man is more than a few hours journey from all other men, and communications between men may be almost instantaneous. Man-made satellites circle this neighborhood many times in one day, and the repercussions of major events affecting any part of the human family are swiftly felt throughout the whole world.

Science and technology have not only created a new reality, but also permit the coexistence, and possible choice, of many different realities. Our decisions regarding individual and collective dispositions of time, space, and styles of life are no longer constrained within locally defined and marginal resources. Questions regarding the human condition need no longer be phrased in terms of what we *can* do, but in terms of what we *choose* to do. The choices carry more alternatives and more positive and negative implications than ever before.

Change and choice have become our bywords and, seemingly, our only constants. In just over thirty years, we shall reach the year 2000, which has long functioned as a utopian symbol; yet, only sixty years ago, the Wright brothers had not left the ground; then, thirty years later, the world was excited by Lindbergh's solo flight. Today, only nine years since the first unmanned satellite, news of a three-man earth orbital flight can be almost edged off the front page by a local election, and the average man may casually board a 600-mph jet plane to pay a family visit.

It is also evident that this change rate, possibly the most rapid in human history, is barely under way. The most recent and dramatic advances, such as space flight, have come from consciously applied scientific research and development, approximately half of whose investment has been in the past two decades.

The pace and notion of change itself have become almost autonomous and no more than routinely perceived; change is now normal. There is danger as well as security in such an attitude. Like severe traumatic shock, the "culture shock" of change may numb our perceptions of its full import and obscure the implications of its forward consequences. The phenomenon of change has many complex elements. Some of these are more amenable to our control than others, but all require more critical scrutiny.

Increased Frequency. The new relations and narrowing intervals between scientific discovery, technological development, and large-scale usage have already introduced many unknown environmental effects.

Range and Scale. Relative to frequency, the long-range and large-scale effects of various types of changes in environment, in social relations, food, health, etc., have received serious attention in many fields of inquiry only in recent years.

Expanded Impact and Awareness. Through increase in the speed of transportation and communication, the agencies of change (ideas, artifacts, techniques, images and attitudes) are diffused more rapidly and penetrate more swiftly into many areas of living.

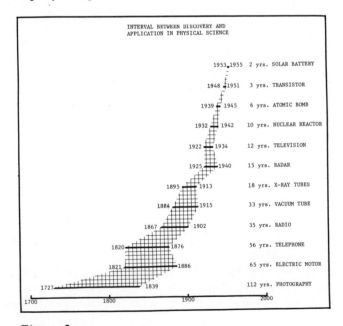

Figure 2.
Technology and Social Change, Eli Ginzberg, Columbia University Press, 1964; National Security Seminar, 1965; Industrial College of the Armed Forces.

There is no less time for critical assessment and for individual or social adaptation. At one extreme, change becomes the preferred norm; at the other, as associated with disruption and uncertainty, resistance to change becomes the mode.

Differential Rates. As we appraise change acceptance in the various industries, from aerospace, to defense, to communications, to air and surface transport, and to housing, in that sequence, we find increased lags in acceptance and use of innovative discoveries and their ancillary developments. In this same approach we may also rank social institutions and organizations in terms of their flexible and critical response to change.

Our understanding of the new dimensions of change and of their immediate and long-range implications has not kept pace with the changes themselves. Repeated emergency-pressured attention to the long-standing social consequences of various technologies is evidence of inadequacy in our conceptual mapping of change relations and in the indicators we use to monitor such changes.

As emphasized earlier, the main difficulty stems from our historical perspectives. Accustomed to slow and sporadic change and the visible linearity of linked cause and effect, we are still captive in much of our thinking to the concept of stability as the obverse of change. In our earlier mechanical models of relative motion, bodies persisted in a state of rest until affected by other bodies. Our now latent assumption is that we alternate between stability and change, instead of assuming that since change and motion are constants, we may have stability *in* change.

Our past historical periods of apparent stability only appeared so because the rates and cumulative effects of ongoing changes were not so directly perceptible.

In keeping with our theme that the future of certain trends in the present may be often examined more perspectively in their past, Wilkinson makes the following suggestion:

Some interesting discoveries about the general nature of innovation might be made if the methods of the Department of Defense's Operation Hindsight were adapted to the investigation of certain social phenomena. Operation Hindsight is a retrospective study of successful management in Research and Development, especially for weapons systems, about twenty of which have been analyzed. It is difficult to break it down into its constituent parts. The team then attempts to identify the who, when, where, how, and what of the system. If we were to apply this method to something beyond the cost-effectiveness of weaponry—say, to discover just how and why our cities became slums, or just how our environment became so polluted—the methods of Operation Hindsight could have a wider meaning than they now have. Undoubtedly the results would make a thundering indictment of certain sacrosanct aspects of our national life, including individuals, which is probably why the technique will not be used until it is too late.[1]

Where change is violent, abrupt, and of human origin, we tend to call it revolutionary; where it proceeds slowly, without apparent human intervention, we term it evolutionary. There is the additional connotation that in the former there is a return to some previously known or projected state of order, while the latter evolves toward some irreversible new order. The distinction seems arbitrary and semantic. Natural evolutionary change has been as violent as any man-made change, and our more important human revolutions—in conceptual thought, for instance—have occurred over long time spans without any conscious impetus toward violence. Evolution is permanent revolution. What we term "revolutionary changes" occur when the natural adaptation of obsolete forms becomes critically overprolonged, that is, when conscious intervention and re-forming involves abrupt discontinuity and instability.

In the mid-twentieth century situation, two aspects of change are crucial. One is the explosive growth in man's capacity to interfere on a large scale with natural environmental processes. The other is the lag in conceptual orientation toward these capacities and toward the social processes through which man accommodates change. In both cases, the conceptual understanding of the occurrence of changes, their potential consequences, and their relation to physical and social processes have now become a prior survival imperative.

Our present concern with the future is an expression of that imperative. To the extent that futures research is concerned with "the application of systematic and appropriate knowledge to human affairs for the purpose of creating intelligent action and change,"[2] it is also concerned with the conscious control and guidance of social and technological change in relation to human society.

To remind ourselves that the future of the present is in the past is an oblique way of emphasizing the need for a more comprehensive understanding of past change and past-change agencies as a guidance to present and future change.

The abruptness and discontinuity of our present transition is paralleled only by that occurring, most recently, in the nineteenth century. Though we have characterized this period as an age of revolutions, it was in its turn only the cresting of many waves of reverberative change that had built up in the immediately preceding centuries. The Renaissance, the Reformation, the French and Industrial Revolutions, etc., are only symbolic benchmarks for successive adjustments in the relation of man to his social and physical environment. The effects of these adjustments have now reached world scale.

Our present revolutionary waves differ not only in their quantitative aspects from those of the recent past, but also in their *qualitative* characteristics. Whereas in the nineteenth century we might have dealt conventionally with relatively separate revolutionary strands within their local geographical context, our present revolutions are now global in their spatial and quantitative aspects. Their quality is no longer that of isolable sequences of events whose interrelations were more separated in time, in numbers of people, and in the social and physical processes affected.

Our present series of revolutionary transitions are more specifically characterized by their simultaneity—the swift interpenetration, increased feedback, and interdependence of one group of changes upon another.

Global in scale, potentially affecting the physical balance of all life on the planet itself, and reaching into every aspect of individual human life and society, our ongoing change patterns now constitute an *ecological revolution*.

Since the term "ecology" has generally been used in a more restricted sense to define the more highly specialized study of animal and plant communities, and thus implies a certain natural determinism and conservation regarding such ecosystems, we should qualify its use here. Our present usage suggests that we may extend the physical and biological concepts of ecology to include the social behaviors of man. But it also goes beyond what is normally called social ecology, that is, the study of local demographic factors and of the economic, social, and physical interrelations of regional agrarian or urban complexes.

In most thinking about man's role within his environment, there is a tendency to treat the individual as a relatively depersonalized unit whose functions are limited by, and within, the larger aggregate. Our present approach suggests that it is individual human responses, personal and group decisions, that play an important and almost wholly neglected role in determining how man relates to ecological processes.

The conceptual extension is towards a *planetary ecology* which assumes that its prior concern is with the maintenance of the planetary society. In using this approach, however, we tend to go beyond the "systems" approach of the natural and social ecologists. We deemphasize the control of natural laws and the closed determinism of a more rigorous systems analysis of the forces operable in ecological processes, and we concentrate instead on human communication and response.

The concern is not with the conservation or equilibrium maintenance of some ideal steady state, in terms of arresting or controlling various human developments other than those which may be dangerous to the maintenance of the overall ecological matrix (as in the case of atomic and biological warfare). We have no way of determining what such an ideal state would be for man, nor perhaps will ever have, other than for certain specified activities and then with reservations.

The approach, therefore, is merely one that suggests a more inclusive accommodation with the understanding of past and present change, and even more importantly, with their future implications, by considering the planet and its society as an ecological whole.

The tendency within such approaches is that once the whole is viewed as a system, meaning becomes detached from the human action and is imputed to operations of the system. But man and his evolving needs, desires, and expectations must be regarded as superogative to any system. Otherwise, there is a tendency to modify that definition of man to fit the system, or to assume as irrelevant and marginal those human individual and idiosyncratic needs that are difficult to accommodate within the system.

We should therefore keep in mind here the following cogent remarks:

Social Acts are now described as events that order themselves through a "tendency to self-maintenance." Social systems are likened to solar systems and social roles are said to "bring out" possibilities of behavior which fit the needs and tolerances of the particular "patterned structure." In this model of society, attitudes "gear" and "mesh" because "patterned structure" and "integrative patterns . . . bring it about that all statuses of the society intermesh like a series of interlocking wheels." Communication of expressive symbols is not studied as an enactment of social order, but as a process of cathexis in which meanings are "attached" to objects and persons.[3]

Our approach here is only a conceptual recognition that the natural world is not solely modified by physical forces; beyond a certain period in human development on earth, this modification also emanates increasingly from human acts within the environment. It recognizes also that such acts are not confined to physical exploitation and transformations of the earth to achieve various economic purposes, but include those that are less amenable to direct perception and measure and which comprise our social and cultural symbolic systems.

Our individual and collective actions have now moved to a scale and degree of possible negative or positive capability, which suggests that we must also move, concomitantly, to assume conscious responsibility for the overall stewardship of this planet.

2
An Ecological
Overview

Life on earth has been possible during the past billions of years only through the relatively stable interrelationships of the variables of climate, the composition of the atmosphere, the oceans, the life-sustaining qualities of the land surface, the natural reservoirs, and natural cycles.

Within the thinly spread biofilm of air, earth, and water space around the planet, all living organisms exist in various systems of delicately balanced symbiotic relations. The close tolerances of many of these relationships have become known to us, generally through their disruption, only in recent times.

For at least 2,000,000 years, men have been reproducing and multiplying on a little automated space ship called earth, in an automated universe in which the entire process is so successfully predesigned that men did not even know that they were so naive as to think they had invented their own success as they lived egocentrically on a seemingly static earth.[1]

Apart from the comparatively local disturbances of natural cycles occasioned through hunting, herding, and primitive agricultural practices, until quite recently man did not have the developed capacities to interfere seriously with the major life-sustaining processes of the planet. He could live and find food only under conditions restricted by his technological development. The earth surface available to him, with breathable air, water and arable land, was less than one-eighth of the earth area; the remainder—the seas, mountain peaks, and glacial and desert areas—was mainly inaccessible to human habitation or large-scale use.

Though the evidence of ancient disruption of natural balance is still with us in the form of man-made deserts, deforested lands, etc., these were essentially local in their scope and consequences. It is only in the more recent and brief historical period that man has developed sufficient power to be actually, and even more potentially, dangerous to the overall ecosystem.

His acquisition of specifically technological means of gaining control over local aspects of the environ through fire, implements, weapons and other means is accompanied by the swift increase and geographical spread of human populations. From approximately 20 millions in 300 B.C., population increased to 500 millions by the seventeenth century; in the short interval since then, there has been a fivefold multiplication, to 2,500 million people. This explosive increase coincides with the introduction of mechanical energies in machine production, to mechanized agriculture and the use of chemical fertilizers, improved sanitation, general health measures, and higher life expectancy.

As each earlier invention increased the amount of energy and survival advantage available to man, so it adjusted the ecological balance to favor the increase of his progeny. The latest growth change in human population since the onset of the industrial revolutions is, within all previous contexts, an extremely abnormal one; "It represents in fact, one of the greatest biological upheavals known in geological, as well as in human history."[2] In the longer range, of course, this expansion may be viewed as the natural evolutionary development of a unique species.

The first fifty years of this new phase, of adaptation and species extension through intensive industrialization, seemed to confirm the notion that man could indeed conquer nature, could free himself from the biological laws governing development of other species. But as the series of technological revolutions has multiplied in frequency and power amplification, this view has been somewhat tempered by the equivalent increase of knowledge about the overall effects on the planetary habitat.

Though it has been obvious for some time that we cannot simply extrapolate human development in terms of natural laws, and that Malthusian and other limits may not strictly apply, there are still many central questions of evolutionary adaptation through man's capacity to externalize his intellectual and physical means in symbolic and technological systems. He is, in this sense, more directly in control of his own future evolvement, but the extent of that control over the environ and over his own uncontrolled activities within the environ depends on his capacity to apply himself *consciously* to an adaptive process that has been largely unconscious.

Through his intelligence, man has enlarged his ecological niche to include the whole planet. His activities are no longer constrained to horizontal deployments around its surface, but extend increasingly into and beyond the atmosphere and beneath the oceans. These activities include the transformation of vast amounts of the material resources of the planet to his purposes.

The mechanical revolution . . . brought into use strata of the earth previously beyond the reach of man. The subsurface was made to yield its wealth both of fossil fuels, the sources of inanimate energy itself, and of the metals required for the application and control of this new energy. Moreover, man pushed his frontiers upward as well. The air became a source of nitrogen; sunshine itself could be more fully used; radioactivity was discovered; and the energy of moving water came to be exploited in different ways and, hence, more fully. Generalizing, one might say that man pushed the exploitation of land vertically, both downward and upward. Land thus ceased to be identical with surface, with a thin layer of soil or surface minerals. It was no longer two dimensional; it spread out into the third dimension, to say nothing of the fourth dimension of the physicist.[3]

The scale of these activities and the expansion and proliferation of man-made systems now approach magnitudes in which they directly affect larger and larger areas, sectors, and relationships of the overall planetary system.

Man and the Biosphere

The volume of air, water, and soil surrounding the earth, within which conditions are supportive of life, is variously termed the bio- or ecosphere, biofilm, or envelope. It extends vertically to a height of approximately 6 miles and downwards to the greatest known depths of the oceans, and to a few thousand feet below the earth's surface.

The life space is a unitary system of processes contained within

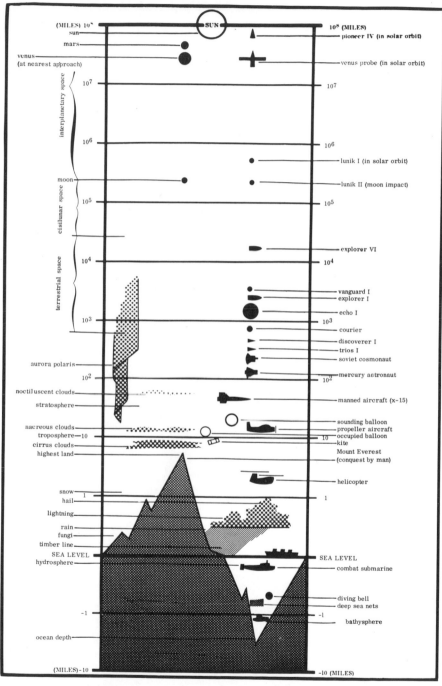

(MILES) 10⁸   **SUN**   **10⁸ (MILES)**

sun —
    — pioneer IV (in solar orbit)

mars —

venus —
(at nearest approach)
    — venus probe (in solar orbit)

interplanetary space

10⁷   10⁷

10⁶   10⁶

    — lunik I (in solar orbit)

moon —
    — lunik II (moon impact)

cislunar space

10⁵   10⁵

    — explorer VI

terrestrial space

10⁴   10⁴

    — vanguard I
    — explorer I
    — echo I

10³   10³

    — courier
    — discoverer I
    — trios I
    — soviet cosmonaut

aurora polaris —
    — mercury astronaut

10²   10²

noctiluscent clouds —

stratosphere —
    — manned aircraft (x-15)

nacreous clouds —
    — sounding balloon
    — propeller aircraft
troposphere — 10   10 — occupied balloon
cirrus clouds —
    — kite
highest land —
    Mount Everest
    (conquest by man)

    — helicopter

snow — 1   1
hail —

lightning —

rain —
fungi —
timber line —
SEA LEVEL   SEA LEVEL
hydrosphere —
    — combat submarine

    — diving bell
−1   −1 — deep sea nets
    — bathysphere

ocean depth —

(MILES) −10   **−10 (MILES)**

3.   Vertical Mobility

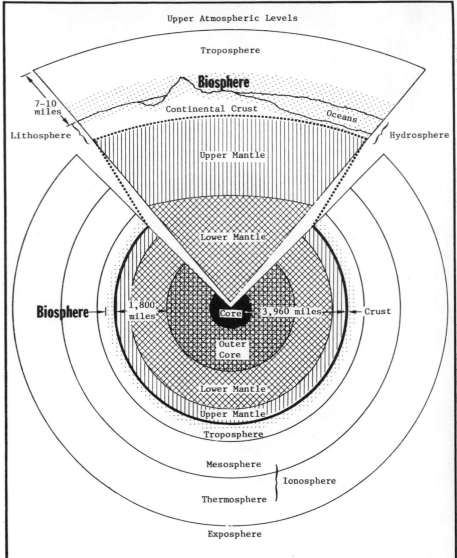

The biosphere is that thin film of air, earth and water around the globe within which most living organisms are found. Within this 'life space' are all the energy patterns and processes of interaction which sustain our major activities. Though extending vertically about seven miles into the air and for thousands of feet below the earth and oceans its most densely populated region is just above and below sea level.

Figure 4.

these three layers of the atmosphere, the hydrosphere, and the geo-
or lithosphere. In turn, these layers are conditioned by the energy
radiations that provide motive power for the system. The major
source of energy is from the sun, but there are also the kinetic and
potential energies from the earth's gravitational system and the
geothermal energy from the interior of the earth mass.

The atmospheric filtering of external radiation and the gravitational, pressure, and temperature constants provide a median environment for organic life. This environment is of a sufficiently
steady state for long evolutionary change and of sufficient range
to allow a great variety of species.

The planetary surface is relatively meager; about one-third of
its 197 million square miles is dry land and the remainder is water.
In human terms, we live at the bottom of an ocean of air, on a
small island surrounded by an ocean of water. Within this life
zone, most living forms are held close to the surface of the earth,
but the evolutionary process has been specifically characterized
by the enlargement of occupancy of the vertical and horizontal
ranges of the biosphere. Our own most singular, and recent, exploit
of life space extension has been to broach its limits by orbiting
animals, plants, and men outside the earth's atmosphere.

Despite the close dimensions of the life zone and the relatively
narrow tolerances endurable by living organisms, there are countless varieties of habitats within which forms of life pursue their
cycles of individual growth and decay.

Man, of middle size in range and one of the least specialized
of complex living forms, has almost evolved beyond the stage
where he is constrained within any specific habitat or ecological
niche parameters. These may be distinctly characterized for most
other organisms by differences in medium, of earth, air, and
water; in physiochemical factors of salinity, acidity, etc.; in temperature, pressure, and light availability. At one end of the scale
we may distinguish such ecological habitats as climatic zones,
ranging through the tropical, subtropical, temperate, subarctic,
and arctic. At the other end we have organisms under several atmospheric pressures in the ocean depths, and those whose niche
is on or within the tissues of another life form.

The fundamental relation between all organisms and their environ (as including other organisms) is the maintenance of life through various types of energy exchanges. The basic life materials are the chemical elements; thus, 99 percent of the human organism is composed of hydrogen, oxygen, carbon, nitrogen, calcium, and phosphorus, with various other trace elements in fractional amounts; water comprises 60 percent of its mass.

All such materials are, of course, energy—at varying levels of relatively temporal organization. We could therefore refer to all materials as energy whose mass and structural characteristics have a given stable configuration in the particular material state. Energy and materials are in constant and complexly regenerative flows between, and within, organisms and the environ.

The overall energy flux into and out of the biosphere and its larger containing earth system, from radiation received from the sun and that radiated outwardly from the earth, is roughly in balance. This allows us to consider the biosphere, theoretically, as a locally closed system within which no energy may be lost or gained overall. The energy flow within the biosphere, as a closed local system, should ultimately be reduced through its various exchange

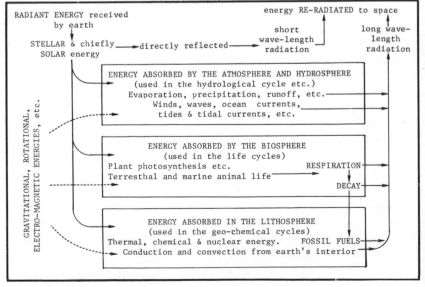

Figure 5.
Energy Resources, M. K. Hubbert, National Academy of Sciences, 1962.

losses to an evenly dissipated end state of *entropy* or minimal energy flux.

This state of minimal order, of the final running down of the system, may be characterized partially by the process of organic decay. In this stage, the arrest of material growth and the slowing down of external and internal flows is finally resolved in the disintegration of the complex organic structure into its elementary constituents.

Entropy is also used, in terms of information, as a measure of uncertainty or disorder of knowledge. But to the extent that information increases order and predictability in the system and reverses the tendency toward running down, it is antientropic. As the agency or principle of complex ordering in the environ, its role has not yet been fully or clearly defined in relation to energy and material organization. It is significant, however, that while the amount of available energy and material elements in the ecosystem remains relatively constant, the amount of order increases. The bioevolutionary direction is toward increased complexity of order; information increases and accumulates.

The information extracted from the environment by one organism does not in equal measure reduce the amount of information available to any other organism, nor does what is learned by one diminish the amount that can be learned by another. A genetic population in expanding its numbers increases, if anything—its per capita information supply, even if per capita supplies of materials and energy be reduced. . . . Evolution viewed as a "learning process" entails the incorporation of more information into population systems: 'In the long view there has been an increase in the complexity of genetic instructions [Medawar, 1961]'. . . . Social organisms in sharing information increase the amount by increasing the distribution rather than inversely.[4]

Man's function in the ecosystem may then be viewed as

1. Entropic—in using energies to reduce complex material resources to simpler structures, i.e., where he acts as an unconscious biological agency as in food processing, reducing and extinguishing other organic populations, disordering towards malfunction of "natural" systems, in air, water, earth, pollution, etc.

2. Antientropic—where he uses energies more consciously to

modify and transform his environ towards higher levels of complexity. Through the application of organized information/knowledge in his artificial systems he increasingly reprocesses, reorders and redistributes energy and materials in more, rather than less, complex forms.

The balance between man's entropic (disordering) propensities and his antientropic (ordering) propensities is, in this sense, a central point of our present discussions.* We can only surmise, in terms of our brief historical record, that this balance is already tipped, through evolutionary development, toward the antientropic processes as more favorable to the survival of the species.

The concept may also be extended beyond life on earth, toward the imminent engagement of man with extraterrestrial systems. Some of these, such as the moon, are of a different and apparently less complex order and of lower energy level. What may be the evolutionary effect of introducing antientropic bias into such entropically oriented systems? The question enlarges philosophically to the consideration of all life forms, including the nonhuman, as an antientropic process or principle. Our more immediately pressing consideration is, however, human life and society within the present confines of the biosphere.

The basic biological functions that we share with other organisms furnish only some of the parameters of our overall ecosystem requirements. Our further needs are complicated by the high degree of social development of the human species. Social patterns are more determinant of biological events than we generally concede.

We may schematize our ecosystem relations by labeling certain areas of the environ system and the human systems, at the same time bearing in mind that this is an extremely limited conceptual convenience. Such schematic models, in which divisions or "boxes" are set out in linearly connected fashion, can in no way approximate the dynamic complexity of our simplest relationships in which every aspect of every activity is interconnected.

*The hinge of this proposition rests, of course, with a specifically anthropocentric view of order.

3
The Environ Systems

Atmospheric

Though the shell of atmosphere surrounding the earth extends thousands of miles above the surface, the sector most immediately concerned in the human biosphere is the tropospheric layer. This constitutes about 70 percent of the air mass and is confined in a narrow layer about 6 miles in depth. Within this layer move the global and local wind systems, which ventilate the ecosystem, carry water vapor and other gaseous and solid exchanges around the earth's surface, and play a major role in the climatic system. This shifting air mass is a vast cycling reservoir for the various energies and materials that are taken up into its systematic flows. The passage of an air parcel around the earth in mid-latitudes requires about one month; a complete interchange of all circulating air masses between latitudes and hemispheres is calculated to take about two years.

The composition of the atmosphere close to the earth's surface is mainly nitrogen, oxygen, and argon in approximately 75, 23 and 1 percent by volume. Other constituents amounting to less than a tenth of 1 percent are hydrogen, neon, helium, krypton, xenon, radon, tritium, and others. We are generally not aware of the extent to which the atmospheric environ is freely mined of its elements in our various agricultural and industrial technologies. They are, of course, replaced by other parts of the organic and inorganic cycle. But we do not have, as yet, accurate monitoring of the vastly enlarged scale at which this or that key constituent may be in the process of extraction in excess of renewal by the ecosystem.

All available waters in the biosphere come from condensation of water vapor circulated in the atmospheric system as rain, snow, hail, dew, etc. The distribution of this evaporation/precipitation/exchange cycle is global, and it links the terrestrial, atmospheric, and marine environs in a massive interchange, not only of water but also of various other material elements injected into the different sectors of the cycle.

In addition to gases and water vapor, the atmospheric air masses carry around the earth quantities of dust, bacterial spores, decomposition and combustion particles, and soil removed by wind erosion and evaporation. We have referred to the pollution of the atmosphere and water as a global, not local, problem; dust particle masses and other materials may be carried almost 3000 miles by a wind of only 10 miles per hour before they are deposited on the earth's surface. Dust and sand storms are a common enough phenomenon; during the dust bowl storms of 1934 in the United States, it was calculated that about 700 million tons of topsoil materials were eventually blown out to sea.

The "greenhouse" effect of the atmospheric layers is so called because of the way in which these layers admit the major portion of incoming short-wave solar radiation, but trap the outgoing long-wave radiation that moves upwards from the earth surface, thus retarding the dissipation of energies from the biosphere and stabilizing the temperature at the earth's surface. Particular attention has been given in recent years to the way in which the increase of atmospheric carbon dioxide, due to the use of fossil fuels, may further accentuate this heat-trapping greenhouse effect. Suggestions have been made that this direct, but originally unwitting, interference with one of the largest of the ecosystem's maintenance patterns could eventually raise average temperatures a sufficient degree to cause gross climate changes, high enough to reduce the polar and other ice cap areas. Whether accurate or not, such calculations do enable us to pose more precisely oriented questions regarding the long-range consequences of our technological directions.

Terrestrial

Terrestrial surroundings, treated here as land environ, occupy only about a third of the earth's surface and are the primary ecological habitat of man, from which he extracts most of his food and other energies and upon which he conducts most of his activities.

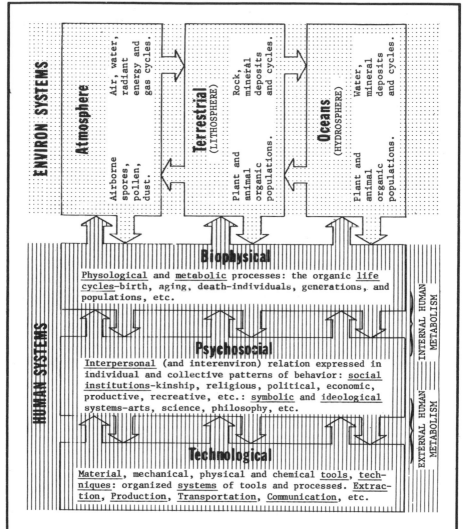

We need to extend the physical and biological concepts of ecology to include the social behaviors of man--as critical factors in the maintenance of his dynamic ecological balance. Nature is not only modified by human action as manifested in science and technology--through physical transformations of the earth to economic purpose--but also by those factors, less amenable to direct perception and measure, which are political-ethical systems, education, needs for social contiguity and communication, art, religion, etc. Such 'socio-cultural' factors have played and will increasingly continue to play a considerable role in man's forward evolutionary trending and its effects on the overall ecology of the earth.

Figure 6.

The greater portion of the material resources contained within the land surface have been built up over long periods of geological time. In particular, the great metal and mineral deposits upon which human society is dependent for its extended technological systems, have taken millions of years to accumulate in the earth surface. As a side glance at our present use rate of these nonrenewable resources, the following rough figures are instructive.[1]

Geographical Time Required To Produce 1 Ton Metals or Minerals	Millions of Years	Man's Removal Rate Millions of Tons Per Year
Petroleum	250	600
Coal	1,000	2,000
Iron	2,000	200
Lead	4,000	4

Metals, of course, though not renewable in the strictest sense, are cycled through successive use/scrap processes. The fossil fuel extractions are of a more seriously depletive nature.

The dry land usable by man, which also sustains large animal populations, is less than a quarter of the usable land space; the

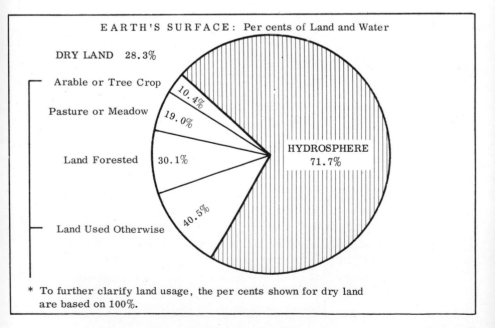

EARTH'S SURFACE: Per cents of Land and Water

DRY LAND   28.3%

Arable or Tree Crop   10.4%

Pasture or Meadow   19.0%

Land Forested   30.1%

Land Used Otherwise   40.5%

HYDROSPHERE   71.7%

* To further clarify land usage, the per cents shown for dry land are based on 100%.

Figure 7.

remainder is desert, jungle, ice caps, or mountain peaks. The usable agricultural area provides food through direct use of edible crops or through other animal food converters. In terms of traditional food-yield uses, this area is confined to a thin depth of topsoil in which most of the plant nutrients are present in a relatively critical distribution balance. This is a renewable resource base, dependent on the various geochemical and climatic cycles; in recent historical time, however, the rapid growth of population, its aggregation in great densities, and the pressure upon the food soils has led to misuse and relatively permanent loss of great areas of this vital soil base. One of our most critical present limitations remains biological and terrestrial; human society is still almost wholly dependent on the plant and animal food yield from a relatively fixed area of arable land.

Recent calculations[2] suggest that the present maintenance of three billion humans in the biosphere requires a plant yield sufficient to accommodate 14.5 billion other consumers. These others, the animal populations, are an essential element in maintaining the humans by acting as intermediate processors for many plant products indigestible by man. Pigs, for example, consume as much food as 1,600 million people, when measured on a global scale; the world horse population has a protein intake corresponding to that of 650 million humans—almost the population of China.

Marine

Oceans cover more than 70 percent of the planetary surface. In terms of planetary space, food, and other material resources, this is comparable to having several more environments at human disposal. The comparatively shallow areas of the continental shelves alone are about half the area of the earth's lowlands, where most of humanity lives.

Our knowledge of the oceans is rudimentary. As man's most hostile environ for centuries, only the surface has been traveled upon. Not until recently have the depths been at all investigated. Barely 1 percent of all sea organisms have been studied, and the cyclic migrations of its larger creatures have been little charted.

Also pertinent is the fact that about four-fifths of the planet's animal life and the bulk of its vegetation are under water, yet comparatively little of these are used as food. The ecological recycling of such resources in the oceans is much more frequent than on land. Fish and other organic populations have higher growth rates; ocean crops have less variable weather problems for possible cultivation and harvesting than has the land.

The other material resource potentials of the oceans have hardly been tapped. Vast deposits of pure metal ores have recently been located on the ocean bed, and the waters themselves are a rich source of extractable materials.

The use of ocean waters for direct irrigation of the land has also been considerably pioneered in recent years. As specifically applicable to the sandy desert soils, such research is of extreme importance in the critical area of world food production.

Arid and semi-arid regions cover a third of the land's surface . . . many of (these) sandy regions could be made productive with salt water irrigation . . . any advance in making sandy soils productive adds to the resources available for the production of food. And any such addition can be a factor in the effort to keep the production of food abreast of the growth of population.[3]

Desalination, the production of fresh water from sea water, also forms part of the growing use of the oceans. The most promising developments are those combining nuclear-power and fresh-water generation plants in the same productive units. Such units in present use around the world have a desalting capacity of about 50 million gallons per day, an increase of 100 percent over the past two years.

In view of these great potentials, it is hoped that planned use of the oceans may in time reduce the spoilage that has already occurred in many areas, particularly of the key coastal shelves. Indiscriminate sewage and industrial wastes have already ruined future developments of considerable areas for some time to come. This process is further increased by the discharge of fuel oils from sea tankers, which have contaminated beaches for years and have taken heavy toll of sea birds and other ocean organisms. Also, overfishing and hunting have led not only to greatly reduced catches in many previously well-populated fishing zones, but also to the near extinction of certain ocean species.

The ecologically designed use of the oceans could provide man with an enormous expansion of his environs, which would also help to solve many of his most pressing terrestrial problems of food, scarce and depletable land resources, and increasing water requirements of agriculture and industry. The recreational potential and challenge of exploring the oceans may also become a new and perhaps illimitable frontier.

The Major Cycles*

We have referred previously to the complex interchange patterns of air, water, and other constituents of the biosphere. Between the discussions of the environ and the human system, it may be appropriate to introduce some brief notes on what are generally termed the "biogeochemical" cycles. These are the basic material elements exchanges in the ecosystem.

Of the inventory of chemical elements in the universe, between thirty and forty are known to be essential to life forms. Some— carbon, hydrogen, oxygen, and nitrogen—are required in large quantities, and others in minute or trace quantities. All are in more or less constant circulation within the biosphere. Though local shortages may occur, as in the loss of critical soil components, all elements are potentially inexhaustible as recirculating in the eco-cycles or in reserve in the great reservoirs of the oceans, air, and earth crust.

Man is only one of the species of organic life in the biosphere and, as do all forms, exists only in interrelation with all others. The precise degree of interdependence may seem remote and tenuous between a briefly viable colony of micro-organisms in a large area of virgin jungle on one side of the globe and a community of human beings on the other; nonetheless, it is real. Plants, animals, men, and their environs are bound together in a complex web of relations. Animals depend on plants and other animals for

*For example, the photosynthesis and energy cycles, the food chains, and those of specific elements such as nitrogen and phosphorus.

food; man depends on both. The plants draw nutrient elements from the soil, and these are in part returned from various stages in the food chain.

The soil-plant-animal-soil cycle is only one aspect of the larger cycling of essential elements in the system. The soils themselves become exhausted of various elements through repeated plant and animal populations, and it has long been man's practice to fortify the natural cycling of essential soil elements with natural or chemical fertilizer elements. One of the greatest revolutions in human society, the agricultural revolution, was brought about through increased understanding of the fundamental growth patterns of plants and their relation to the natural cycles of energy and materials in the ecosystem. The second and more recent wave of industrial revolution was also predicated on increased understanding, and gainful advantage, of the energy-cycling principles.

The major cycles in the biosphere are therefore of key importance to our environ considerations. Almost all our major societal undertakings are affected by, or—more importantly—affect the natural cycling of energies and materials in the system. In some cases, the cycling patterns are so large that their compensating mechanisms have sufficient latitude to correct any maladjustment when assisted by human intervention. Others require careful attention to avoid serious disequilibrium of, and locally occurring disparities in, the essential elements with which they are concerned.

THE HUMAN SYSTEM

Man is a wholly integral process. As in dealing with the environ, we should again emphasize the wholly denotative convenience of labeling different parts of what is an essentially integrated and dynamic whole. The use of the word "system" should also be qualified in this application. We need, particularly, to avoid mechanical systems models here.

When we deal with human activities, the complexity tends to force us to resort to simplistic schema. Though these may function well as limited conceptual supports and will reduce the complexity into some neat disciplinary format, we usually end up with models such as economic man, behavioral man, political man, and technological man. These concepts, abstracted for convenience, tend to become *reified*, that is, to assume an autonomous reality in themselves for which they are unfitted. This is particularly dangerous when we attempt to solve human problems in such reified terms. We often assume that many large-scale problems may be solved within the artificial divisions set up for intellectual convenience.

No social problem of small or large scale—and all human problems are axiomatically social—can be solved within the terms of any single field or discipline. A wholly technological solution, however logical and seemingly efficient, may fail by overlooking some elementary sociocultural requirements. Solutions conceived solely in economic or even in biological terms, as in the case of population and food, may fail through lack of adequate technological considerations. The point seems an obviously simple one, but examples could be cited at length of our present failures to solve human problems because of inadequately conceived solutions.

The divisions used here—*biophysical, psychosocial, technological*—are adopted for present convenience. They overlap considerably, and are in no way suggested as an exhaustive classification of the major aspects of human activities in the biosphere.

Biophysical

From the strict viewpoint of biological and physical apparatus, there are few characteristics that make man a unique life form. There is no need to elaborate here on the specific anatomical and physiological features that describe his species position—a mammalian primate of medium size, with certain kinds of individual variability, brain size, psychophysical capacities, temperature and pressure tolerance, and other functional processes.

One aspect of his recent biophysical development that has most implications for the future is the degree to which man now augments his basic organism through chemical, technical, and other means. Various biophysical modifications through sophisticated technical means are already routine. Artificial organs and extensions of organs are now operating, as well as electronically controlled artificial limbs and natural organ transplants.

The artificial limb prosthetic attachment is one of the most interesting examples; although produced in response to human defect through birth or amputation, it is capable of much wider application. The problems of delicacy of control and requisite power of manipulative and holding action have now been largely solved. Key difficulties had been power source and directive control operation; these were recently solved by two Soviet scientists who amplified bioelectrical muscle currents in limb stumps to trigger microminiature servomechanisms for hand movements, versatile enough to unscrew a light bulb, bend each artificial finger joint, and lift up to 9 pounds.

The use of electric energy drawn directly from the body itself to power various internal and external devices directly, or to use for remote control of other mechanisms outside the body, has far-reaching possibilities. Apart from self-powering artificial organs, heart pacemakers, and the like, it could also be used for transmitting signals for operating other controls at a distance, or acting internally as receiver-activator of metabolic control signals for remote medical centers.

With new valves for damaged hearts, synthetic tubes, clips, organs, and assists and metabolic amplifiers of various kinds, the biophysical organism may now enter a new era of synthetic regeneration. This field is more than simply spare-parts medicine; it has evolved swiftly into bioengineering.

Surgery is essentially an engineering discipline . . . the integration of electronic circuits into the human body as functioning and permanent parts . . . is going to become very important within the next ten years.[4]

The most striking extension of all has been the general increase in human life expectancy and improved physiological function throughout the lengthened life span, in the advanced regions of the world. This capacity to prolong life, however, already has attendant problems in population control. We may anticipate further problems when prolongation is expanded toward genetic control of biophysical characteristics before and after birth, and also when, by many present and emergent means, we increase our capacity to modify the emotional, mental, and physical aspects of the human organism. Coupled with these developments is the possibility of creating new types of living systems based on quite different biochemical configurations.

These advancements in biophysical control are specific aspects of the general advance in man's knowledge of himself as a biological organism. The interaction of biological, medical, and engineering sciences which this entails is also under way in other areas such as water supply, water disposal, air pollution, food preservation, and public health.

We may sense, again, the growing ecosystems' approach as beginning to operate at both the micro and macro extremities of human environ control, within the human body itself and outwardly to encompass the entire planetary body.

Psychosocial

Even man's given biophysical organic structure is modified through his social and psychological development. This is the central aspect of man, which defines in most senses his humanity.

Man is human by virtue of his social existence; he lives in, by,

HISTORICAL LIFE EXPECTANCY

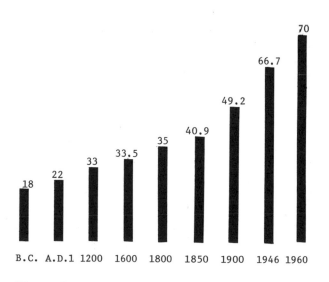

Figure 8.
Metropolitan Life Insurance Co.

and for his communication with others. This is not to devalue the individual, but to underline that his human nature is socially produced. By using the term "social," or "society," we do not limit the meaning merely to "belonging" to the local society, but within it encompass the larger awareness of the continuity of human experience. Meanings and values for one individual are inseparable from those of others.

Man is made human by his earliest experiences of human communication. He *learns* to be a human being. When acutely deprived of such early socialization, the organism exists, but its mental or even physical development is so impaired that basic survival is endangered.

Symbols are our human reality. Human action is grounded in symbolic interpretation; both verbal and nonverbal symbolic languages order our perception and control the meaning and communication of what we perceive.

. . . the qualities and characteristics that constitute the visual sensations of which we are conscious . . . are not inherent in the so-called external "things" at which we are looking. The origin of our sensations is the prior experiences and the characteristics and qualities of our sensations are our unique personal social history. . . .[5]

This symbolic bias is one of the main keys to the understanding of human action. No matter how objective we may strive to be, the formulation of objectivity is itself a peculiarly human symbolic process. Objective truths are most clearly expressed in highly abstracted symbol systems—as in mathematics, the expression of the physical elements and their periodicities, and the electromagnetic spectrum. These symbolic constructs are the highest ordering principles that we know, and though we refer to their "discovery" in nature, they have been apprehended only as conceptually created and shared symbols. Science, in this sense, is another form of art, defined primarily as a symbol-ordering and verification activity.

The biological evolution of man is marked by the development of his nervous system and its associated organs for monitoring and controlling the environment to his purpose. It is suggested that though man stopped evolving about 150 thousand years ago, and is now a social animal, evolving only through his extensions, many of his apparently irrational behaviors are explicable as instinctual responses that were biologically meaningful in early development but which are no longer appropriate to his changed condition.

Fears and insecurities, expressed in certain traits such as dominance, territoriality, and crowd and flight responses, which had survival value in the past, often appear to act negatively in a more socially secure present. Their measurable physiological reactions are acute and often stressful. Taken as part of the total human system, they are, however, powerful sources of social energy when appropriately channeled. Language and other symbolic responses are, for example, now interposed between physical stimuli and action response.

We may, more accurately, characterize the key evolutionary stage of man not as tool making or using, but as communication through symbolic languages. But language itself "may be termed the first industrial tool, as it involves a plurality of men, and is a prior requirement for the integrated efforts of many men."[6] Tool use by man is a cumulative and progressive activity unlike that of the tool-using animals. Language as a prime tool extends our control over the environ as demonstrably as any physical artifact; by naming and ordering, we control as effectively. Organized information is now our major tool resource.

Man's ecological expansion has been particularly characterized by the role in which accumulated knowledge about the environ is preserved and passed on through succeeding generations. This would form part of the major evolutionary step in adaptability of the organism. Such generational transmission of sociocultural experience of that which makes man human was possible only through the evolved family unit, within which a relatively fragile organism with an unusually long period of defenselessness and dependency on others could be effectively nurtured until able to survive as an individual. The period of nurture is also that of socialization, of forming the human personality.

The function of transmitting social and cultural experience and of regulating social interaction also led to the complex growth of other human institutions—to human society as we know it. There is little to suggest that human society evolved instinctually in the strict biological sense. Rather, when we refer to the evolution of society, this may, perhaps, be more accurately meant in the sense of more consciously adaptive development. Animals have forms of society, but these lack the evolutionary capacity that has allowed human society to be more plastic and variable in its responses to particular environ situations. Change has been of key importance in this process, and allows for the interaction of individual change agents within the society as influencing and modifying the overall societal orientation.

Social evolution has been likened to a cybernetic process, one that is oriented to its goals by "feedback." Increased and more highly organized information about the environ and the society, as an integral ongoing process, is fed back in due proportion so as to guide forward development. The analogy is often the wrong way round. We liken human beings to machine systems, when we might just as easily characterize the latter as being more human in their evolution as they approach the complexity of man. Considering the role of individual agents in monitoring the signals and in suggesting and predicting the changes of course required, we may refer to "psychosocial evolution" as more clearly defining this process.

All human action is, in this sense, social action. Contemporary social theory generally analyzes human behavior as occurring, therefore, in a system of socially interactive relationships; even when the specific interaction is with a physical resource, its form and purpose are socially determined. Further division of the psychosocial environ system would account for *individual* action, the *society* as an aggregate or collectivity of such actions, and the *culture* as an overall continuum within which individual and societal actions take place.

The personality system of the individual may be viewed as motivated toward action by his needs and desires, in terms of various goals, commitments, and socialized patterns of behavior. Different needs, desires, situations, and purposes elicit different roles or learned patterns of symbolic responses. The individual person, however, is always more than the sum of his various roles and responses!

Human acts are not only reactions but also procreations. If we remove from the human act all that was possibly determined by the value of "input" variables still something will be left. This something did not enter into the system from outside; it is the (personal) creation of the human being. This something distinguishes any human being from any machine and is responsible for the fact that human behavior is only partly predictable.[7]

The social system, or structured order of social actions, consists of the basic human institutions (family, kinship, religious, political, economic) and their related organizations.

These should not, however, be viewed as static forms, but as temporal configurations undergoing various rates of change according to their dynamic content of idiosyncratic individual actions.

The culture system contains the heritage of customs habits, belief systems, and the like, in various ideologies, values, and standards. These are all expressed in various symbolic modes—in more tangible form in the religions, mythologies, philosophies, etc. We might even include technology as a cultural artifact form expressly concerned with the control of the physical environ through tools. Such tools are, themselves, also symbolic artifacts, increasingly dependent upon environ information input refined through symbolic language processes.

Culture, used in the more generally inclusive sense to describe the whole system, may be termed *the* ecological context that encloses and screens all human activity within (and without) the biosphere.

The social behaviors of man are now the most critical factors in the maintenance of the ecosystem. Not only our behavior modifies the environ by human action as manifested in science and technology; all social institutions also play their part in orienting the directions, goals, and purposes that guide such modifications.

As discussed earlier, it is only recently that we have acquired the social awareness that we may, from this time forward, exercise a more consciously direct control of our forward development. We generally forget the extent to which past historical societies were unaware of this, believing that such control lay more with capricious agencies external to man. In this sense, we do invent the future as a consciously orienting strategy for our forward survival.

In terms of environ control, the tribal village, the city-state, and latterly the nation-state, were inventive adaptations toward our present ecological dominance. At our present level of planetary interdependency, the nation-state form, for example, may be as dangerously obsolete as the self-governing autonomous tribal and city principalities that preceded it. The growth of transnational social organizations seems to indicate this.

The essential organizations that maintain the human ecosystem are no longer national in any real sense—world health, communications, transportation, and the like are by agreement vital to all, and decisions relative to their governance may not be abrogated by any local agency. The continued growth of such world organizations may no longer, however, be left to emergency-pressured need, but must become the object of conscious innovative action.

In general, biological survival has been evolutionarily successful through the bias toward integrative function; the manner, for instance, in which the specialized organic functions are integrally directed toward the overall end purposes of the organism. Man is one of the least specialized biological organisms. Extreme specialization in evolution is usually accompanied by lack of adaptability; the organism tends toward extinction or remains low in the species hierarchy. The trend toward increased specialization may now be dangerous because of the lack of integration of our overall environ activities, as evidenced in air and water pollution, etc. The extremely swift and relatively uncontrolled growth of technological systems has not been accompanied by a corresponding extension of our integrative systems.

Fortunately, this negative trend seems to be in the process of reversal where very large-scale undertakings, as in the space programs, have forced a return to consideration of human activities as whole systems. The accompanying increase in global monitoring of the earth system through satellites, and the swift diffusion and interchanges in the world communications network, engender further awareness of the essential unity of the planetary community.

We may note here, in conclusion, that the psychosocial extension of man throughout the biosphere has been characterized as adding a "noosphere" layer.* This idea of organized human thought now covering the globe as a functional part of the overall ecological system is, to an extent, physically demonstrable in our present global communications networks, and in the enormously accelerated growth of human knowledge with its parallel increase in the numbers of messages, meetings, journals, etc., ceaselessly circulating around the earth.

Our basic critical impasse in global terms is still, however, our inability to use our collective knowledge. The block is to be found most often in the persistence of obsolete social forms and attitudes. This brings us back to earlier comments on the role of social invention as a prime need. To circumvent traditional, but now inadequate, modes of social action, we need to experiment with new forms of social organization, to refashion the psychosocial environ as vigorously as we have transformed the physical environ in the past century.

Technological

Life is maintained by securing energy and materials from the environment. This is a rather simplistic statement, but one that accounts for much human activity in past historical periods. Evidence of human culture is found at the lowest levels of early human development, but its more durable and widespread forms are associated with access to more energies than could be provided solely by unaided physical effort.

Chipped flints and similar artifacts are usually mentioned as the first tools used by man. But before these he must have had the prime tool of some form of language which enabled men to work together to perform tasks, or convert energies that would be impossible for an isolated man.

The symbolic gesture or sign is therefore a first technological extension, and the second would be fire. It is difficult to see how

*First described by W. I. Vernadsky in *La Biosphere* (1929); more recently discussed by Teilhard de Chardin in his various works; notably, *The Phenomenon of Man* (The Cloister Library, Harper & Row, New York, 1961).

the knowledge of fire could be transmitted without language. Fire is a way of gaining access to stored solar energy, of extending the internal oxidation of the body to metabolism, to provide an external source of heat and predigest food; it also provides one of our most durable symbols in the process.

The earliest men seem to have subsisted by hunting and food gathering, simply tapping locally available, naturally cyclic, energy supplies. Such techniques would seldom provide the energy surpluses necessary to give sufficient leisure for large-scale cultural pursuits except in particularly favorable habitats. Higher sustained yields and surpluses appear to have come first from the deliberate cultivation of selected plants and the herding and domestication of animals. This would allow for more permanent settlement, storage of food energies, and the leisure with which to experiment and devise survival strategies. In significant association with settlements is usually found evidence of the recording of seasonal and other periodicities to allow future planning. The agricultural revolution, therefore, marks a major transition.

It is not the origins of technology that concern us here, but rather the fact that the system of artifacts, which this now connotes, has developed in an organic, evolutionary manner. This idea has been presented by many contemporary thinkers, but the following quotation from La Barre conveys it in succinct form:

Since man's machines evolve now, not anatomical man, he has long since gone outside his own individual skin in his functional relatedness to the world. The real evolutionary unit now is not man's mere body; it is "all mankind's-brains-together-with-all-the-extrabodily-materials-that-come-under-the-manipulation-of-their hands." Man's physical ego is expanded to encompass everything within reach of his manipulating hands, within sight of his searching eyes, and within the scope of his restless brain. An airplane is part of a larger kinaesthetic and functional self . . . and airplanes are biologically cheap (as evolutionary devices). Without being, through specialization, a biological amputee, he attaches all sorts of prosthetic devices to his limbs. This evolution-by-prosthesis is uniquely human and uniquely freed from the slowness of reproduction and of evolutionary variations into blind alleys from which there is no retreat.[8]

This extension of organic capacities is also evident in the invis-

STAGES OF TECHNOLOGY

①

FIRST Technological revolution. The discovery and use of the wheel	SECOND Technological Revolution. The discovery of methods for smelting ores and for making alloys and forged tools and weapons	THIRD The Industrial Revolution	FOURTH Chemicals & Chemical Engineering	FIFTH Electrical Transmission & Telecommunications	SIXTH Transportation	SEVENTH
Tusk, horn, and bone hand tools / All purpose stone & wood fist axes / Special purpose stone & wood hand tools	Metal handtools with energy supplied by man and animals — Bronze — Iron Age	end of Franco-Prussian war	World War I	World War II		controlled atomic fusion

AUTOMATION
MECHANIZATION
DIVERSIFICATION
DOMESTICATION
ADAPTATION

STAGE V — DEVELOPED SOCIETIES Industrial Economies of Abundance
STAGE IV
STAGE III — UNDERDEVELOPED SOCIETIES Agriculturally Based Marginal Economies
STAGE II
STAGE I

10^6 5×10^5 5×10^4 10^4 5×10^3 5×10^3 2,000 AD 965 BC — AD 10 11 12 13 14 15 16 17 18 19 1965 — 1,965 Years Before Present —

②

THE LINE OF HIGH ADVANTAGE MOBILE ENVIRON CONTROL DEVELOPMENT WHICH GOES FROM SHIP, TO AIRPLANE, TO ROCKET, TO MANNED SPACE VEHICLE

	Sailing Ships							Clippers	Steam Ships		Airplanes		Saturn V Rocket
MODE											Propeller	Jet	
TIME PERIOD	2,500 BC	500 BC	1,000 AD	1400	1500	1600	1700	1800	1900	1940	1940	1950	1965
AVERAGE TONNAGE	150	250	30	300	100-500		1,000	2,100	2,500	4,500	3,500	12,000	3,000 Tons
HORSE POWER	80	120	30-90	150-250	....	500	750	1,000	1,200	1,400	3,500	12,000	200,000 lbs.thrust
AVERAGE SPEED	8 knots	8 knots	12 knots	10 knots	12 knots	11 knots	12 knots	17-22 knots	16 knots	20 knots	300 m.p.h.	600 m.p.h.	25,000 m.p.h.

③

DOMINANT AGES	MODERN CRAFT 1,000 - 1784	MACHINE AGE 1785 - 1869	POWER AGE 1870 - 1952	ATOMIC AGE 1953 -
POWER	Human and Animal Muscle Wind and Water	Multiple Horse Teams and Steam Engines	Gasoline Engines and Electric Motors	Atomic Energy and Fossil Fuel Burning Equipment Used to Produce Electric Power and Heat - Fuel Cells
TOOLS	Hand Wrought Iron and Wooden	Machine Wrought Iron and Steel	Multiple Machine Tools and Automatic Machines	Cybernated Factories with Computer Closed Feedback Control Loops
WORK SKILLS	All-Around Skilled Craftsmen and Unskilled Manual Workers	Subdivided Manufacturing Processes Replace Skilled Craftsmen With Semiskilled Machine Operators	Human Feeder or Tender Replaced by Skilled Inspector - Mechanic	Highly Trained Engineer - Designers and-Skilled Maintenance Technician Systems Specialist and Programmer
MATERIALS	Wood, Iron and Bronze	Steel and Copper	Alloyed Steels, Light Alloys, and Aluminum	Plastics and Super Alloys (32 New Metals Used, Notably Magnesium and Titanium)
TRANSPORTATION	Walking, Use of Animals by Dirt Road or Via Waterways by Sailboat	Horse and Buggy, Steam Trains Via Steel Rails, and Steam Ships Via Ocean Ways	Automobile Via Paved Highways, Diesel Trains and Ships, and Airplane Via World Airways	Rocket and Jet Vertical Take Off Aircraft, Atomic Ships, Ground Effect Craft, Helicopters
COMMUNICATION	Word of Mouth, Drum, Smoke Signals, Messenger and Newspaper	Mail by Train and Ship, Mechanically Printed Newspaper, Telegraph, and Telephone	A.M. and F.M. Radio, Movies, Television, Magnetic Tape, Trans-Ocean Telephone, and Microfilm	Video - Phone, Data Phone, Telstar & Syncom, World Wide Communication Satellites, 'Graphic' Computers

Figure 9.

(1) *Science and Engineering and the Future of Man*, W. Taylor Thom, Jr.; *Science and the Future of Mankind*, W.A.A.S., 1963; (2) "The Process of Man's Occupancy of the Earth," Hans Carol, Dept. Geography, York University, Ontario, 1964. (3) *Technology and Social Change*, Allen and others, Appleton-Century-Crofts, Inc., 1957.

ible tools of number, symbol, and image, which have had so powerful an effect in transforming the human condition.

Where hand tool, lathe, grinder, and other mechanisms extend physical capacities, our communications networks of radio, telephone, television, and interlinked computer processing are extensions of the human senses and nervous system. Through his instruments man can now "see" in the infrared, ultraviolet, and other radiation frequencies; he can "hear" radio and other waves, and he can "feel" more delicately through electronic devices than with his most sensitive touch.

As man has extended his immediate physical control over the environment, he has also extended, through these latter means, his range of psychic mobility in space and time. As more of the present is increasingly presented for his simultaneous viewing of widely separated events, and he extends his vision into the past through refined archaeological techniques, he begins to navigate his way forward into the future.

Much of the large-scale development of our complex industrial tools has taken place in the past two hundred years. The brevity of this period probably accounts for the widespread feeling that technologies are out of control, that their scale and consequences now threaten human existence.

Jacques Ellul, in his concern with the negative aspects of technology, suggests that, "its evolution . . . is progressing almost without decisive intervention by man."[9] There is a larger and perhaps unintentional truth in this observation. Technology may be as natural a part of human evolution as the differentiation of finger and thumb, and in this sense has been until now almost as free from man's possible control. We do not yet fully understand or accept the organic evolutionary quality of technological growth. The idea is, in itself, somewhat alien to our comprehension.

Man has always assumed that an evolving technology would be of the mythological robotic variety, formed in his own image. This is why it is difficult for us to observe the evolutionary phases of the airplane from single person/single engine with multiple wing surfaces to propellerless jets of enormous size, speed, and possible 400-passenger carrying capacity, almost in one generation; or to accept easily the evolution of the family of "extended eyes" from bulky, tripod, wet-plate still-cameras to microminiaturized television cameras spinning around the globe outside the earth's atmosphere. For the time being, we can only "humanize" technologies and hope to exert more conscious control over their development by extending to them a more inclusive and ecological approach rather than treating them as recent and alien intrusions into our society.

As created, renewed, and ultimately directed by human life, technology is as organic as a snail shell, the carapace of a turtle, a spiderweb, or the airborne dandelion seed. In many respects, it is now more ubiquitous as a functional component of the ecosystem than any organic life form other than man himself. The amounts of energy converted by machines, the materials extracted from the earth, processed, recombined, and redistributed in the technological metabolism, and the gross effects of such increased metabolic rates on the ecosystem, are now greater than the effects of many global populations of other organic species. Guidance and control of our technological and other recent systems can be realized only through greater understanding of their growth. So far, there has been little effort to understand; more attention has been given to unheeding exploitation or equally unreflective rejection.

To speak of the organic nature of technology as we have done is not simply to pose some technological determinism as accounting for all human development and change. One could as easily suggest poetry as the determinant, and with as much validity. Rather, the purpose is to reemphasize the integral nature of human activities, whether labeled technological, religious, economic, cultural, or whatever.

Given the nature of the organism and its enclosing environ, and some notion of the history of its development within that environ, we may observe certain periodicities and orders of growth. So far, our understanding of the larger patterns of the human ecological transformations has been limited by our tendency to compartmentalize our knowledge of the process. The periodicities and orders of one discipline are usually separated from and unrelated to those of another. The greater dangers in our phase of development may well lie in extremes of academic specialization, which turn men into technically expert instruments, rather than in making the technologies themselves the instruments of man.

The most recent and spectacular area of technological evolution has been that of *cybernetics*, a word significantly and symbolically derived from the Greek for "steersman." It is noteworthy that this development, as with many other so-called breakthroughs, originated in the fusion and generalization of a number of separate specialities rather than in one area of academic discipline.

Although defined as the mechanization of sensory thought and other psychophysical processes, cybernetics is actually an extension of the control principles of the human nervous system into electromechanical devices. Without elaborating on its technological ramifications here, we may underline its importance in ecological terms. Just as the mechanical and chemical energy converters of the first series of industrial revolutions freed human muscle from routine tasks, so the computer revolution potentially frees man from comparable routing of intellectual tasks such as monitoring, supervising, and controlling many simultaneous and complex technical processes. Also, and importantly, it makes possible the swift expansion of our global production, distribution, and logistical support services so that we can satisfy the urgent material needs of large numbers of human beings still on the edge of survival.

In reducing the direct link between work and physical maintenance by automation/cybernation, many of the basic premises for our major social and economic institutions are becoming obsolescent. These have been largely born of a past when it was necessary to persuade, coerce, or otherwise sanction the majority of men into spending the greater part of their lives producing the basic products for human physical survival. From this time forward, we may potentially produce, in abundance, all such material life-sustaining requirements without need to extract or demand human life-labor in equitable return. Instead of spending most of his years maintaining himself, man is potentially freed to address himself to the larger purposes and enormous range of activities implicit in the larger human enterprise.

The cybernetic revolution has occurred largely within the past two decades. It is important to remember this and to recognize its evolutionary significance in the light of our discussion above.

The specific focus of our discussions centers around our capacity to control the enormous scale of our present global undertakings in a more positive and naturally advantageous manner and to avoid the dislocations and dangerous side effects of our technological and other growth patterns.

It is of key relevance, therefore, that this new change agency of cybernetics should be also specifically developed for control and decision-making in handling large-scale systems with many complex and variable factors. At the point, then, where man's affairs reach the scale of potential disruption of the global ecosystem, he invents precisely those conceptual and physical technologies that may enable him to deal with the magnitude of a complex planetary society.

4

Man Plus

In his first historical phase, man spread out horizontally into every corner of the planet; in the present, he has become vertically mobile, out into space and down to the bottom of the oceans. We have characterized his technological development as the overlay of another evolutionary form on the natural genetic process. As there is little other comparative evidence, we do not know whether this overlay pattern of human extensions evolving for man may or may not be equally natural. The impulse toward such development occurs within man; hence, even if seemingly supernatural, it is human. What we refer to as specifically human in the social and civilized sense is that amalgam of physiologically instinctual and unconscious processes with the consciously reflective and intellectual capacities which transforms them into recognizably human actions. The quality and sensibility of the human condition seems to reside particularly in this arrested balance between man and animal.

Perhaps only in the interplay between these aspects of himself does man define and reaffirm himself as a human being:

Thou constrained by no limits, in accordance with thine own free will in whose hands we have placed thee, shall ordain for thyself the limits of thy nature. We have set thee at the world's center [so] thou mayest from thence more easily observe whatever is in the world. We have made thee neither of heaven nor of earth, neither mortal nor immortal, so that with freedom of choice and with honor, as though the maker and molder of thyself, thou mayest fashion thyself in whatever shape thou shalt prefer. Thou shalt have the power to degenerate unto the lower forms of life which are brutish. Thou shalt have the power, out of thy soul's judgment to be reborn into the higher forms, which are divine.[1]

As expressed by Pico della Mirandola in the fifteenth century, this half-divine image of man endowed with free will, choice, and the control of his own destiny, yet ever poised between lower and higher commitments, is still relevant today. We may speculate that man retains this human quality or allows its more paced development only by externalizing his various physical and intellectual capacities into autonomously evolving systems.

The earliest uses of symbolic communication and tools mark a turning point when man became an active agent in his own development, when his species survival was no longer dependent on natural evolutionary processes. But his consciousness of this active participation did not occur until quite recently, and then in a groping manner, during the Renaissance. The idea of his possible control over his own future development crystallized even more recently.

The early simple tools, which physically extended the limb and amplified the hitting and leverage power of the arm and hand, have now become complex assemblies of tools that amplify manyfold the combined limbs and energies of many men. The automated factory is not only a series of augmented hands but also of extra eyes, brains, and other sensing and control capacities.

We can trace this extension in many ways. From the skin as protective enclosure, we progress to clothes, houses, cars, planes, space capsules, and submarines as mobile coverings that give increasingly greater protection against environmental extremes. From the eye, we extend vision, and therefore survival advantage, through the microscope and telescope, the photo and television camera, and on to sophisticated systems that record, amplify, and relate complex visual and aural patterns of great magnitude.

Parallel with man's extension into horizontal and vertical (outer and inner) space, is his extension of sensing and control into the invisible space of radiation phenomena. Through instrumented eyes, ears, and touch he can explore and control in widening areas of the electromagnetic spectrum, beyond his normal vision, and sense into the infrared, ultraviolet, radio, x-ray, and other wave frequencies.

As the information gathered from his increased monitoring of

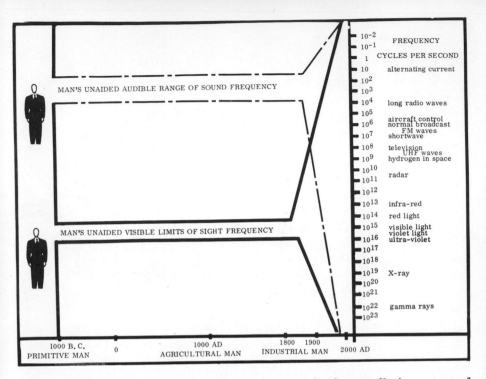

	FREQUENCY
10^{-2}	
10^{-1}	CYCLES PER SECOND
1	
10	alternating current
10^{2}	
10^{3}	
10^{4}	long radio waves
10^{5}	
10^{6}	aircraft control
	normal broadcast
10^{7}	FM waves
	shortwave
10^{8}	television
	UHF waves
10^{9}	hydrogen in space
10^{10}	radar
10^{11}	
10^{12}	
10^{13}	infra-red
10^{14}	red light
10^{15}	visible light
	violet light
10^{16}	ultra-violet
10^{17}	
10^{18}	
10^{19}	X-ray
10^{20}	
10^{21}	
10^{22}	gamma rays
10^{23}	

MAN'S UNAIDED AUDIBLE RANGE OF SOUND FREQUENCY

MAN'S UNAIDED VISIBLE LIMITS OF SIGHT FREQUENCY

| 1000 B.C. | 0 | 1000 AD | 1800 1900 | 2000 AD |
| PRIMITIVE MAN | | AGRICULTURAL MAN | INDUSTRIAL MAN | |

10a. Sensory Extension. The most abrupt and fundamentally important of the transitions which lead up to our present world developed in the sciences in the late 19th century and became first evident in the technology of World War I. Experimental science began to extend its measurable range into the invisible subsensorial world of atomic, molecular, and "radiation" phenomena.

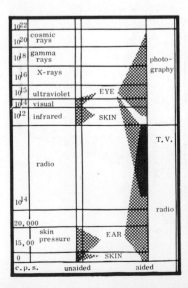

10b. The visual pattern recognition capacity o the eye lens and correlated brain function has been progressively extended and amplified through the simple magnifying lens to the microscope and tele scope, through the camera lucida and obscura t the photographic and television camera, an toward sophisticated systems which record, am plify, and relate complex visual and aural patter of great magnitude.

This development also encompasses the way in which man has widened his "sensorial" mon toring of the electromagnetic spectrum throug instrumentation. He can now "see" into the infr red, ultra-violet, and X ray frequencies, "hea in the radio frequencies, and, may more delicate "feel" through electronic metering than with most sensitive skin area.

11. Picturephone that transmits a visual image as well as sound.
Bell Telephone Lab.

2. Instrument dials punches cards to business machines any-
here and receives replies and instructions.
ell Telephone Lab.

the environment exceeds the storage capacity of the individual brain, man externalizes his memory by using symbols, books, photographs; he off-loads his memory burden into routine processing and computation by the computer, which serves him by extending information processing, storage, and access and retrieval systems. When his physically mobile speeds increase, but his natural reflex actions are too slow for adequate survival response, he invents servomechanisms and cybernetic linkages that have a much faster and controlling reaction time. These externalized controls also enable him to deal with more complex patterns of information and with the more coordinated operation of his other extended systems. The amplification of human function is not confined to physical instruments. Ideas and concepts also shape the environment through language, signs, symbols, and images. The invention of the zero may have had as comparable an impact on planetary affairs as the atom bomb.

Just as ships and airplanes have extended man's physical mobility, so the arts and other communication modes have enormously expanded his *psychic* exploration in space and time. The long historical absorption with basic physical survival has often downgraded these modes of human expansion to peripheral concern. In the phase that lies beyond the preoccupation with basic material survival needs, we may expect that these and many other nonphysical modes will become a more centralized and conscious focus for human activity.

In many senses, however, our present differentiation between activities will disappear. Though we speak of physical and nonphysical agencies or modes, all are based on psychosymbolic communication processes. An airplane designed from a series of symbolic notations regarding environ behaviors is no more physical than a poem.

Social process may also be viewed as a strand of human extension in the growth and variety of its institutions. The inventive development of cities, states, families of national groupings (as advantageous to survival) is paralleled by the more conscious invention of systems organization for large-scale, long-range planning of exploration of new areas such as aerospace. Innovative modes of organizing complex man-to-man as well as man-to-machine relations are as crucial as any technical invention.

The most striking extension of all has been the general increase in human life expectancy. The control of disease, advances in surgery, and other scientific achievements are specific aspects of a general advance in man's knowledge of himself.

The direct modification and augmentation of the human organism has become a strong focus of interest in recent years. Present applications (and specifications) range from the relatively simple biomechanical assistance or replacement of physiological functions, to transplantation of organs, and even to more radical suggestions of extended immortality through maintenance of the brain independently of the body. Drug-induced mind expansion, one of the oldest forms of extending human experience, has become a new quasi-religious cult. Other directions include the refinement of remotely controlled electromechanical manipulators, of body harnesses that give increased strength, and of robotic copies of man himself to work under conditions too extreme for human endurance.

To a certain extent, man has already undergone considerable modification. Humans around the world live at high altitudes where others can hardly breathe; many maintain normal skin temperatures in subzero cold, thrive on dangerously ill-balanced diets, and otherwise adapt to abnormal environmental conditions. To these modifications may be added man's conscious innovations: a number of biomedical modifications are by now routine: for example, artificial organs and extensions of organs, electronically controlled limbs, and live organ transplants.

Transplants have been most recently and dramatically headlined in the news through the increase in heart replacements. But blood transfusions, bone-marrow implants, and bone and skin grafts have been common for some time. More than 1200 kidney transplants have been recorded since 1954 in 19 countries, and half of the patients have lived for several years or longer. The spleen, pancreas, and duodenum have also been successfully transplanted. Theoretically, almost any organ or part of one body can be implanted in another, and when the immune response factor of resistance to foreign implants is overcome (without other deleterious effects), this could become a more widespread technique. Present-time restrictions on keeping organs alive between donors are gradually being lengthened, and the possibility of organ and tissue banks may become an adjunct to present blood banks.

The difficulty, however, of obtaining a sufficient number of such organs, for other than highly selective emergency use, seems to indicate that this may not be the most promising direction. There may be also psychological and ethical problems for patients who use "secondhand" organs from unknown persons. The more viable approach may be through artificial organs. These have several advantages: supply can meet demand, storage is easier, and the immune response is negligible when inert materials are implanted. It is estimated that approximately a quarter of a million people already have various implanted spare parts such as tubes, clips, and valves made from silicone plastics.

Implantable artificial hearts are in development; artificial kidney machines for operation outside the body have been used since the 1940s to sustain the lives of people with kidney damage; artificial lungs have also been used for some time. Of less dramatic news value than live transplants, and for more general use than entire artificial organs, are the electronic and electromechanical augmenters of various types. About 3,000 lives in the United States alone depend on tiny mercury batteries that deliver regular pacemaking pulses to the heart.

In many ways, this type of machine augmentation is of the same order as the electronic hearing aid. The miniaturization of such devices, and of their power sources, presages a family of similar inventions which, even though they may not always directly prolong life, can make living easier and restore normalcy to damaged functions. One may envisage such aids used more routinely to amplify normal functions also.

Longevity and even immortality has been a persistent human search. Noting that medicine had increased life expectancy by about twenty years in the last half-century, Dr. Michael De Bakey, one of the artificial heart pioneers, suggests that, "There is no reason why a person can't live to be 100 or 150 years . . . by the end of the century we may think of a person as being old—we won't think of old age as such." The possibility of controlling the aging process had already been tackled in small organs isolated from animals, as long ago as Dr. Alexis Carrel's famous experiments in the 1930s. More recent experiments with rats and mice indicate that the aging process in larger organisms may be delayed considerably.

Another form of potential immortality derives from the work of Dr. Robert J. White, who has isolated the live brains of monkeys from their bodies in order to study more closely the neurological functions. As he states:

The mammalian brain is the most magnificent achievement of biological evolution. Before it, all human accomplishments—space travel, sophisticated computer design, synthesis of DNA—are humbled. Yet it can be sustained as a viable, isolated entity using mechanical equipment no more complex than that of a child's electric toy.[2]

Obviously, with regard to human brains, as White adds, there are moral and social factors operating which will require a considerable period to be able to accommodate this possibility.

This latter step, which goes beyond our earlier repair and augmentation of function approach, suggests the evolution of new

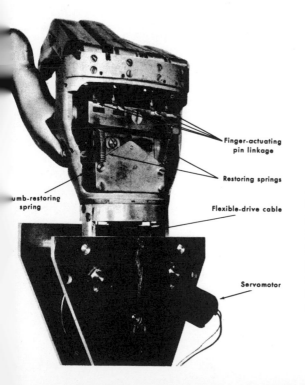

Finger-actuating pin linkage

Restoring springs

Thumb-restoring spring

Flexible-drive cable

Servomotor

13. Pressure sensitive hand, designed by Prof. Rajko Tomovíc of Belgrade, that can be used as a prosthetic device, activated by a newly learned pattern of muscle control or—more alarmingly—by remote electronic control.
Design News, August 19, 1964.

forms of men who are combinations of living and nonliving, but active, components: a living brain in a machine body, for instance, or the Wellsian idea of cultivated giant brains that operate through a variety of remotely extended systems. Such concepts already exist, metaphorically, in the close-working relationships of men and machines today.

Their alien quality may be somewhat dispelled by recalling the earlier symbiotic relations of man with plants and animals. The Greek centaur figure is a similar metaphoric device, as were the various totemic and mythopoeic animal/man and plant/man gods of the Egyptians, of the Maya, and the northwestern American Indians. Our fear of man/machine totems seems almost as old as Frankenstein myths. To the degree that man automates and routinizes himself rather than his machines, it is justifiable. But refusal to examine and understand the intrinsic nature of such evolving relationships increases rather than diminishes the possibility.

The changes in our advanced systems today do not preclude the more extensive development of what Manfred Clynes calls the "cyborg"—a term describing the organic fusion of the human organism with active cybernetic components (that is, cybernetic organisms):

The difference is merely that instead of using external or *attached* prosthetic devices, the man-made devices are now to be incorporated into the regulatory feedback chains—the homeostatic mechanisms that keep us viable for such an astonishingly long time.[3]

Rather than assume a permanent irreversible prosthesis of this type, Clynes and Halacy emphasize the human control and reversibility of such incorporated mechanisms. The danger, of course, of men controlled by other men is not so reversible. This is well within the bounds of practicability, as has been demonstrated by remote electronic control of animals through implanted brain-stimuli components.

The area of increasing interpenetration of man and machine has been particularly explored by Richard R. Landers, who suggests that our present transition marks the end of the predominantly man/nature relations of the biosphere and the beginning of a dy-

14. Space Workbench. Astral explorers may soon work from space vehicles resembling this self-propelled, "two fisted" platform which is shown in mock-up form.
The Bendix Corporation.

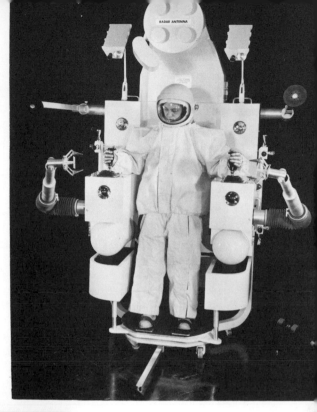

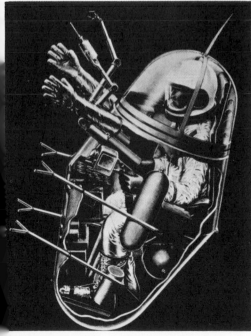

15. Cutaway view showing man in REMORA. Astronaut working in un-inflated suit with variety of manipulator arms, and the gauntlets for delicate operations.
Bell Aircraft Corporation, Report No. D 7052–953001.

bosphere, characterized by "artificially created things which behave in a life-like manner." Though Landers agrees with the thesis of Jacques Ellul, in *The Technological Society*, that machine technique has come to be "the intervention into the very substance not only of the inorganic but also of the organic,"[4] he does enter a caveat about the inevitability of man's loss of control through such machine pervasiveness.

The challenge of being dehumanised by a machine is very much similar to being "dehumanised" by a sabre-toothed tiger. If we do not accept and meet our challenges we will be annihilated just as the caveman was who did not meet his.[5]

The problem with this polar dialogue may be one of the redefinition of the machine so that it will no longer be considered as merely an aggregate of inanimate electromechanical components, but as an entity beginning to move into a biotechnical or biological phase. The machine components of tomorrow may be grown rather than built, much as a number of their electronic components are already cultivated, (for example, crystal growth) with no identifiable machine-working characteristics.

This biological phase of machine development is well defined as *bionics*—a combination of biology and cybernetics. Particularly since the discovery that the common bat's natural ultrasonic radar is far superior to any of the man-made technical varieties, scientists have become extremely interested in the study and duplication of all those biological processes connected with the reception, transmission, and processing of environ information.

The problem of the creation of reliable, small-dimensioned and effective technical devices using the principles of appropriate biological systems lies at the basis of a new scientific school—bionics—the study of biological processes, for the solution of engineering problems for the creation of fundamentally new technical devices. The growth of this new school became possible due to achievements in the field of microminiature apparatus and computer technology.[6]

This quote, from an early Soviet paper, is used only as an indicator of the age of the field and its widespread development in the past two decades. The central concept is, of course, even older

16. Blood flow simulator designed by Prof. R. Skalak.
Columbia University.

than Da Vinci's models of natural machines, but is now sharpened by available capacities.

If we interweave the strands of development discussed above, it appears that, with new surgical capacities, metabolic amplifiers, and assists of various kinds, the human body itself is now entering an era of synthetic regeneration. In the balance, it seems that the more radical directions may smooth out into a more unified over-all approach to the maintenance of man as an integral organism rather than transforming him irreversibly into a new form. Though the approach to this field in medicine is called bioengineering, Richard Skalak, of Columbia University, points out that this is no more than the interaction of biological, medical, and engineering sciences already under way in other areas such as water supply, waste disposal, air pollution, food preservation, and public health.

We may sense this growing ecological approach as beginning to operate at both the microextremities of human environ control —within the human body itself—and the macroscopic centralization of the entire planetary body.

Electromechanical circuitry within man is only part of the present trend toward massive augmentation of individual human capacities through engineering. M. W. Thring, of London University, lists the two main directions as *robotic* and *telearchic*. He distinguishes robots from telearchic machines as those that do not require a human operator to carry out their tasks but which rely on previous programing. Describing the use of robots and tele-archic remote manipulators in developing systems during the next ten years for application in the home, industry, mining, and ocean and aerospace areas, he underlines many of the points we have commented on.

Industrial robots are already at work in many forms. Two recognizably robotic machines, programable to carry out a range of generalized tasks, are marketed in the United States—the Unimate and the Versatran.[7] Both operate in much the same way. The former has a single arm to which various manipulatory devices can be attached to perform different tasks. For each series of job tasks, the robot is guided by a technician through a sample job as its memory unit records each sequence of movements. After being programed in this way, it can run through the operation on its own, repetitively. Differing from ordinary automated tools, such robots can be moved from one job to another, and need only be taught the new operation.

Present demerits of these robots are: their capacity limited to rote learning; their inability to make the kind of global generalized, rather than linear, decisions that human decision-making involves; and their lack of discriminatory pattern sensing, which is part of the human capacity. Grey Walter and Ashby, in England, and other scientists in the United States, have, however, constructed small robotic prototypes whose survival processes parallel human intelligence in sensing, probing, and reacting through trial and error to environment stimuli.

As H. Block and H. Ginsberg of Cornell University suggest:

A robot of the future may be capable of recognizing instantly whether it previously had seen a certain pattern, and if it did, of then recalling the sequence of patterns that followed it. The pattern may consist not only of imputs from various sensors, but also of signals generated inside the machine. In theory such a system has been shown to be possible.[8]

17. Battery-run implantable cardiac pacemakers.
A. Kantrowitz, Maimonides Hospital, N.Y.

18a. & b. Unimate robots are presently at work in a large cross section of industries including automobile manufacturing, die casting, forging, and plastic molding.
Machinery.

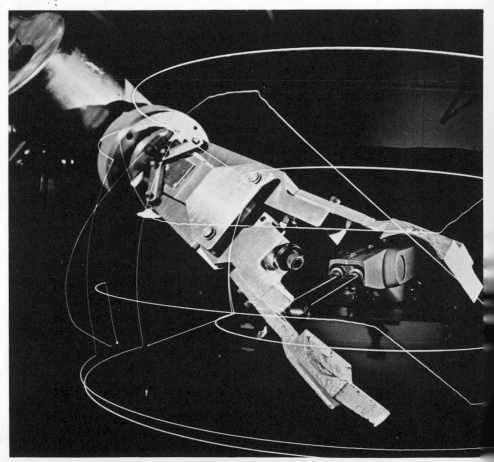

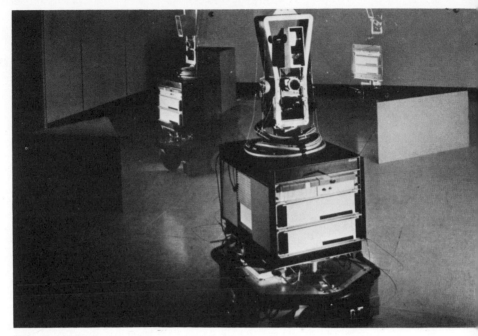

19. Mobile Automation.
Stanford Research Laboratory.

20. Computor Linked Hand Eye Machine.
Massachusetts Institute of Technology.

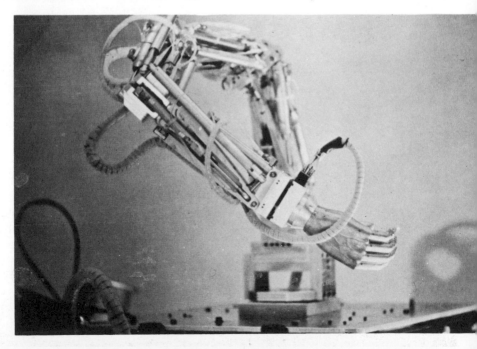

Apart from the new robot/human social relationships that will be required, there is also the old question of robots as self-reproducing automata. In discussing the work of Turing, Von Neumann, Penrose and others, Block defines one simple form of self-reproducing machine as follows:

Suppose we have at the outset a soup of primitive parts. When we stir the soup, nothing happens. The primitive parts are still floating around in a disorganised manner. Now we take the machine (which is a "specific complex of primitive parts unlikely to occur by chance") and drop it into the soup. Then stir awhile and look again. If we now find not only the original "machine" but also other "machines" exactly like it, then I think it would be reasonable to say that we had a self-reproducing machine.[9]

Such issues, of intelligent adaptive and self-reproducing machines, lead us to consider more broadly the problems of human control and direction of technologies generally. Thring, whom we have mentioned earlier, suggests that it is time for us to draw up more comprehensive codes governing some of the principles of

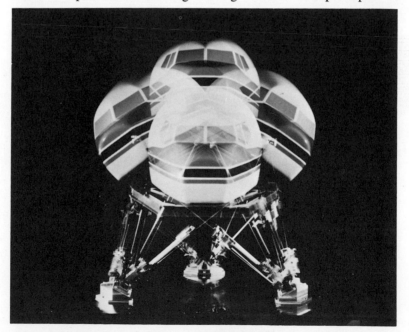

21. VAMP—Visual system and flight simulator mounted on six-degree of freedom motion system.—*Link Group Trainer.*
General Precision Systems Inc., Link Group.

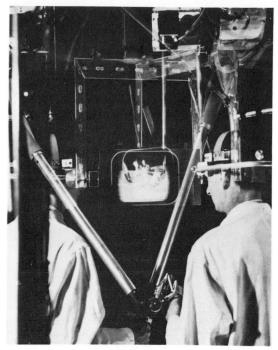

22a. & b.   Multi-exposure of slave and master stations of manipulator shows a television camera watching a pair of "mechanical
hands" (master-slave manipulators) as they perform a demonstra-
tion experiment at Argonne National Laboratory by remote control.
Argonne National Laboratory.

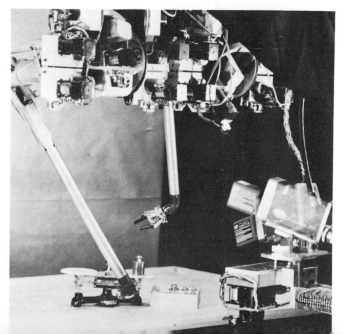

22c. Concept of a Climbing or Walking Slave-Robot Incorporating Master-Slave Legs as well as Master-Slave Arms.

22d. An Early Concept of a Master Station Incorporating a Pair of Electric Master-Slave Arms and a Head-Mounted Master Control for Master-Slave Television.

Manipulator Systems Development at ANL, Ray Goertz, Argonne National Laboratory, Argonne, Illinois; Proceedings of the 12th Conference on Remote Technology, ANS, Nov. 1964.

man/machine interaction and use. In his "Moral Spectrum of Machines," he states that, "we should put the machines that the engineer can develop on a moral spectrum based on the extent to which the machines help or hinder human beings to realize their potentialities and thus to lead satisfactory lives. Machines primarily developed to kill, maim or hurt . . . or harm human health through by-product noise or effluents must come at the bottom of the scale.[10]

This forms part of a growing dialogue about the professional commitment of scientists and technologists. The single or combined decisions of many individual professionals now materially affect directly or indirectly the welfare, and often the very lives, of millions of people around the world. In considering the future of various forms of technological and social innovation, the question of individual responsibility and participative control might be considerably aided by a formula of attestation such as the Hippocratic Oath adopted in medical practice. This would not only assist in governing the forward conduct of various enterprises but would also afford professional immunity from coercion by local narrow interests. The various political authorities have no problem in calling upon the individual's sense of responsibility in the national interest of his fellow citizens at a moment's notice, yet the innovation of a higher responsibility to the maintenance of the planetary community is still considered impractical and idealistic, just as the former was only a century or so ago.

The range of illustrations in our present text, selected on the basis of the most advanced technological capacities, shows the great imbalance in military priorities. An interesting comparative series could be made of the equivalent world problems to which such technology might be applied.

A further area example of military tool developments, which have much positive potential effects, is the "Hardiman" and "Walking Truck" concepts.[11] The Hardiman mechanism is the latest in a series of physical power assists based on an external metal skeleton with electromechanical "muscles" that give the wearer giant strength. Seemingly cumbersome now, one can easily extrapolate this development (by way of ultralight, high-strength alloys) to a harness no heavier than an overcoat. The next step, obviously,

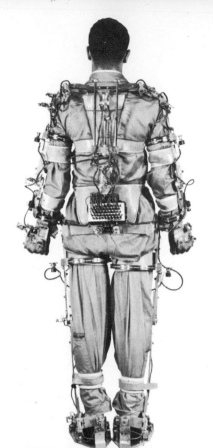

23.   An exoskeletal harness in which motor impulses from nerves and muscles are picked up and fed to artificial muscles, greatly increasing man's mechanical performance.
Cornell Aeronautical Lab., Inc.

24.   A four-legged "walking truck." Astride six-foot legs, the vehicle will be able to transport a quarter-ton load over extremely rugged terrain impassable to wheeled or tracked vehicles, at speeds up to five miles per hour. By manipulating controls attached to his arms, legs and torso, the operator will be able to maneuver the machine in any direction.
General Electric Research and Development Center.

would be to implant the exoskeleton to create an anatomically modified superman.

In the expansion of human consciousness through the use of LSD and other hallucinogenic agents, the groping toward memory control, the reshaping of behavioral patterns through reinforcement schedules, and similar psychological techniques, we have again a parallel analogy with man's vertical extension into outer and inner space. The same extraordinary intellectual forces with which he is presently engaged in remolding his planet are now being turned in upon himself.

The results of this inward exploration may be infinitely more powerful than any physically extended voyage to Mars or to the bottom of the Challenger Deep. The territory is virtually unexplored, and for centuries we have endeavored to exorcise the demons and control the energies that have emanated from its depths. Our present inward probings and mappings may now illumine those aspects of human nature—the fears, belligerence, and self-destructiveness—that have been a numbing constraint on all futures dialogues.

Bioengineering, as we have already cited, is not confined to man, but is already being employed in mass production terms for the manufacture of large microbial culture populations for industrial work in medicine, fermentation, energy conversion, and the like. On its more negative side, there is also the ongoing development of new microbial and viral agents for warfare. As a result of recent discoveries relative to the genetic coding of living organisms, we shall see all these directions expand greatly in the next half-century. With this expansion will come problems of decision and control, which will make those produced by the old-fashioned hard technologies seem like child's play!

Man has always been able to induce the death of others by some agency; life-inducing power has been more or less a happenstance affair. His recently acquired capabilities of prolonging life already create population problems. These, again, may seem mild when he expands prolongation to precise genetic control of human characteristics before and after birth, and acquires the ability to modify, by many present and emergent means, the emotional, mental, and physical aspects of the human organism.

Coupled with this is the possibility of creating new types of living systems based on quite different biochemical configurations.

Reconstituting men long dead, once a favorite story plot in horror films, is predicted by one zoologist as possibly routine within a century: "Once the genetic code is determined . . . hundreds of thousands of duplicates [of a past genius, for example] can be created."[12] Medicine is already preoccupied with the ethical and legal problems of the point of death ambiguity, in the use of current life prolongation and resuscitation techniques. At another part of the spectrum, a group of persons have formed a "Life Extension Society" (freeze: wait: reanimate) to freeze cryogenically and store living persons (for example, those with presently incurable diseases) to await future medical advances.

The concept of bioengineering, or bioelectrochemical engineering, as it might be called, is evidence of the cross-disciplinary fusing that now confronts all academically defined fields. The boundaries have suddenly vanished as new knowledge of itself has created new disciplinary configurations or areas in which there are no longer any discernibly separate disciplines. The task of adjusting our educational institutions to this new order will require social inventiveness of no mean scale. Accompanying the "mixmaster" aspect of the various sciences is a corresponding difficulty in labeling their attendant technologies. One scientist, defining the four which he suggested might have the greatest implications for future society, recently suggested computer technology, management or systems science, social engineering, and bioengineering. These seem relatively separate and subject to categorization, but closer examination reveals that they have a great many features in common.

Cybernetics does furnish one nodal link for the four technologies suggested above, and for many others, and both in its conceptual theory and identifiable technological penetrations has been one of the major change accelerators. Considered under the heading of "Man Plus," it may be placed as an extension of the human nervous system and intelligence. Significantly, basic principles originated during the World War Two period: (1) in developing self-correcting guidance and control, feedback, and mechanisms for antiaircraft guns; (2) in the operations research methods of applying logicomathematical techniques, network theory, and similar systems to problems of military logistics. From the fusion of both areas, plus ancillary developments in electronics, came the computer and the systems theories based on complex multivariable planning needs.

In general, much of our present computer usage simply regards the machine as a superfast and efficient clerical assistant. However, the real trend is (1) toward a closer individual/computer rapport so that the computer will become a generalized intelligence amplifier, and (2) toward specific types of computer systems that assume the routine operations and maintenance of all the basic physical metabolism of human society.

In new man/computer relations, the previous interfaces of special languages, programs, programers, and highly specialized instructional routines are already being stripped away. Man is back in the driving seat without the need for such devices, which tended to import their own constraints and logics into the dialogue. Now the machine instructs the user and indicates the possibilities for closer interaction. There is no need to read the manual; the user may consult the machine directly with the question, "I want to do something, instruct me!" This mode of working may now be carried on at a distance with remotely linked viewing and operating consoles, and at the present developmental rates, the system will obviously reach the portable, possibly "clip on" stage before long. Microcontrol components are, as we have seen, now available in many forms, and computer memories become progressively smaller in volume and larger in bulk storage capacities. There would be, of course, no need to carry such memory units if, more feasibly, call-up linkages to many types of central libraries were incorporated in the system.

These developments reinstate man in a more central, and more directly creative, role in many areas of scientific social, and cultural exploration. He will be able to talk to his machine assists during the exploratory process, view compiled materials in many forms at any stage, and draw upon any specialized information he may require. These, and other developing capacities, already indicate significant readjustment in our so-called higher education, much of which has been concerned with the production of highly specialized "walking" information storage units.

We conclude this brief excursion into the augmentation of human performance through new forms of man/machine relations with a statement from a scientist involved in advanced research in this area:

Our interest in evolutionary machines of all kinds, large and small, is based on a concern for what has been happening to the human users of the machine, what is now happening to them, and what is likely to happen. We see evolutionary machines of all kinds, large and small, as a prerequisite for what we shall call human *enhancement*.[13]

Implicit, then, within both the individual and societal relations to cybernetics is the emergence of a new symbiotic partnership. Where other types of machines have been merely mechanical extensions augmenting human manual dexterity and muscle power, the new biotechnical or bionic forms amplify the perception, control, and understanding of human intelligence.

5
The New Symbiosis

At the global level, as in man's natural symbiotic relations with plants and animals, his relationship to cybernetic systems has been subtly changing toward a more closely woven organic interdependency resembling his other ecological ties.

The point reached recently when such systems were combined with the remote sensing, monitoring, and control capacities of the orbiting satellite marks the extension of this symbiosis to include the entire planetary ecology.

The most pervasive aspect on earth has been the automation of production, services, and information flow in the advanced economies. Man's social role and position in society becomes less and less determined by the part he plays in the direct production of material wealth goods, the organizing of routine information, or the performance of some standard physical service. Such physical maintenance and social janitorial functions are being off-loaded into cybernetic system functions; product wealth may be more easily generated with less imput of human energy, intervention, and routine decision making.

This aspect of automation is easier to grasp, and as it becomes discernible, it proceeds slowly to assume its proper niche. The rate of integration of automated procedures into productive use is presently masked by inadequate economic criteria and indicators, but is reflected in the following figures[1]:

	No. of Computers, 1966	Growth Rate	No. of Computers, 1970
United States	27,000	10–13%	45,000
Western Europe	6,000	20–22	18,000
Japan	1,900	20	4,575
Canada	900	23–25	3,000
Australia	280	35	1,000
Latin America	200	7	440

123

In the United States alone the Federal Government uses 2,600 computers and spends over $2 billion annually to acquire and operate this equipment.

The extent to which automated systems have now assumed the operation of the *invisible metabolies* of advanced societies is more far reaching. Apart from completely automated factories and continentally linked automatic inventory, dispatch, and other control operations, the whole energy conversion, transmission, and distribution system of vast areas are increasingly under automated control. Over 80 percent of electrical capacity in the United States is, for example, controlled presently by such systems. The intercontinental telephone linking service is an increasingly automated system in terms of its myriad switching and individualized calling stations.

The processes of control, everywhere they are encountered, that is, in living organisms, social organisms, and, the psyche, lead in their development to automation. Automation creates that simplification without which further development would be impossible. Their control of the activity of the inner organs is completely automated and does not require attracting the attention. In the learning process we con-

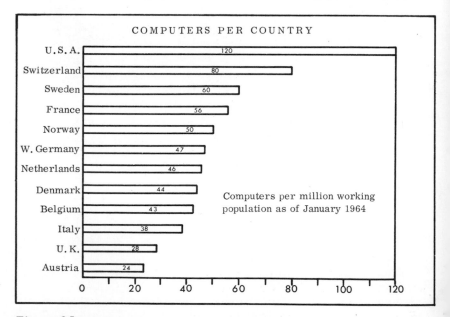

Figure 25.

"Computer Comeback," David Fishlock, *New Scientist*, England, Jan. 1964.

stantly encounter the phenomenon of automation. Even when learning to walk a system of automatic control arises in our consciousness. Habits, without which the successful execution of any kind of complex activity would not be possible, represent the working out of automatic responses.[2]

The extension of automated control measures to larger sectors of the production and distribution sectors, and to the imput/output relations of the various component industries, is being developed in many countries. It is also directly perceptible in the overall planetary economy, in the systems linkage and operational interdependence of world airlines, and in the energy and communications networks.

This type of large-scale control systems design requires prior large-scale simulation. Such simulation is much the same as our thought processes when we are confronted with problems of decision-making under various degrees of uncertainty. We review and organize information on the problem, assign different contingencies to various possible actions, and choose the optimal strategic com-

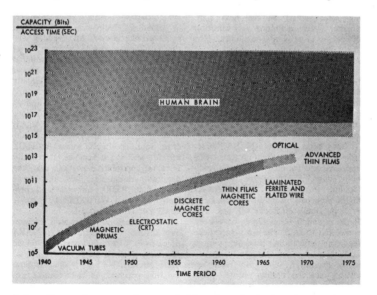

26.   One of the major activities in NASA's electronics program is development of new computer memories for future generations of spacecraft. Chart above shows how new technologies may permit capacities approaching that of the human brain.

Aerospace Technology, November 20, 1967.

bination of actions. These mental simulations, or models, plus the results of action based upon them, become memory/experience components in future decision-making. By organic automation, or habit, they are incorporated as patterns in our nervous systems.

The use of the computer in the simulation of processes with large numbers of interacting variables is now commonplace. Simulation of physical systems is relatively simple compared to that of social systems or the interactions of nations, but advances are also being made in these latter areas. In large-scale economic, business, and politico-military simulations, actions that might take weeks or months to occur in real time may be run through in a few days.

Prerequisites for such simulation, for increasing the predictive capacity of the organism in its environment are adequate information and communications. It is interesting, therefore, to observe the exponential growth of information accumulation and the parallel expansion of information and communication systems to the global level.

The phenomenal growth of knowledge in the past few years has been due in considerable measure to capacities to process information through the computer and ancillary instrumentation, and to the way in which this has fed back into the primary sector of knowledge discovery and communication. In this area, however, many of the computer's more fervent disciples still use the machine capacity more to accumulate new facts than to use its more evident capability of structuring those facts into new knowledge configurations.

We still confuse somewhat the accumulation of new facts with new knowledge. The extension of knowledge in science, for instance, has not been through the simple addition of new facts but rather through the intuitive grasp of ways in which a great mass of factual information may be simply and elegantly structured into new conceptual wholes. The process is not toward greater complexity, but toward simpler and more inclusive concepts. The computer enables one to assemble more facts, to handle more of the apparently disconnected variables, and to review and analyze them in more possible combinations and with greater speed than with the unassisted brain.

It is essentially these capacities of immense memory and recall,

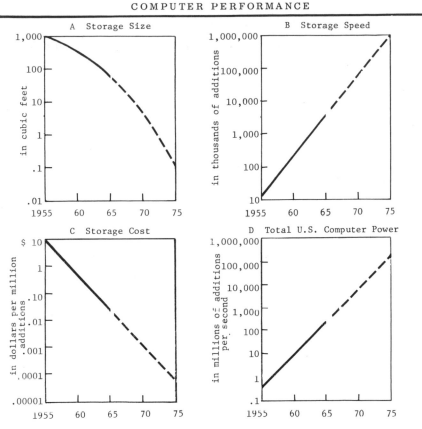

Computer Weight, Volume, Power Costs: In 1953 a computer weighed approximately 5000 lbs., occupied 300–400 cu. ft. and required 40 kw. of power.
Today's computer weighs approximately 50 lbs., is a thousand times smaller
and uses 265% less power than the 1953 model.

(A) Storage Size: From 1955–65 the storage size of central processing computer unit (cpu) has decreased by a factor of ten. During the next decade,
fully integrated circuits may reduce its size by a factor of about 1000.

(B) Storage Speed: From 1955–65 internal speeds have increased by a factor
of 200 and by 1975 such speeds are expected to again increase by this amount.

(C) Storage Cost: During the first decade of the computer the cost of performing one million operations decreased from $10.00 to about 5¢. By 1975
it is estimated that this decrease will amount to an additional factor of
about 300.

(D) Computer Power: The total installed computer power in the United States
during 1955 had a capacity of about one-half million additions per second.
By 1965 this capacity increased to 200 million per second and if growth
rates are sustained through 1975 the increase in capability will be about
400-fold.

Caption: adapted from W. H. Ware, "Future Computer Technology and Its Impact," D. D. AD 631–941. Office of Technical Services, U. S. Department of
Commerce.

*igure 27.
Computer Aspects of Technological Change, Automation and Economic Progress,"
Armer, Rand Corporation, November, 1965.

massive and incredibly fast detail processing, and reliability in repetitive operations that are salient in cybernetic applications to large-scale control systems. At the world level, the most advanced development of such systems is, of course, in support of military prediction, planning, and control procedures. If we consider that ICBMs can be launched to strike anywhere in the world in less than 30 minutes, the factors of speed in information handling of incoming data and outgoing corrections of hour by hour posture are enormous. Add to this the given figures of operational air forces of 15,000 aircraft, 1,000 missiles, and a quarter-million personnel, and we have a global operation of considerable size.

The facilities developed measure up to the requirement. Operational data referring to the location and state of these components and to global weather conditions, intelligence, materials inventory, transport, and location are constantly being fed into such centers, and within seconds can be flashed on screens for simultaneous viewing at their complex relationships. Aircraft in flight can be contacted swiftly anywhere in the world, and direct telephone contact can be made immediately through one handset with more than 70 subordinate centers spread halfway around the globe.[3]

Though negatively oriented toward diminishing man's chances of survival, such worldwide systems are working examples of Marshall McLuhan's statement: "Today, after more than a century of electric technology, we have extended our central nervous system itself in a global embrace, abolishing both time and space as far as our planet is concerned."

The most extraordinary development of this bionic extension of man's sensing, monitoring, and control has been the less visibly spectacular growth of orbiting-satellite capabilities. These are, in a very real sense, the ecological tools of the future through which global adjustments to the more harmonious use of the planetary ecology will be achieved.

More than 600 Earth satellites have been orbited since October 4, 1957, when Sputnik I first circled the globe. Almost every one of these satellites has carried a cargo of scientific instruments, even though military or engineering objects have sometimes been foremost. . . . Over 100 new satellites are launched each year and old ones constantly criss-cross the skies above us. Against this backdrop, it is difficult to

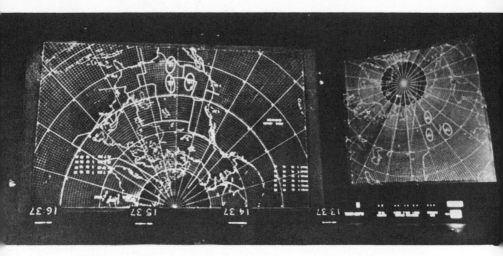

28a. The NORAD control centers have Ling-Temco-Vought Iconorama systems where all important data are projected on large screens.
U.S.A.F.

28b. Mission Control Center. General view of Tracking Map and consoles located in Mission Control Center, Recovery Room, Cape Kennedy, Fla.
Goddard Space Flight Center.

project one's thoughts back to that spare handful of years when the satellite idea received only ridicule.[4]

Already the accumulation of data about the larger configurations of our planet from satellite observation have expanded the concept of the earth from a small local body to one whose magnetosphere and other radiation envelopes trail far out into space to interact with other planetary bodies. This exploration has also revealed a vast solar wind in space, a continuous stream of plasma emitted by the sun at speeds of several hundred miles per second.

Satellite geodesy and meteorology are also revealing more clearly the true shape of the earth as a whole, and the atmospheric forces that govern the local weather conditions in various regions. The World Weather Watch, initiated in 1965 as part of the U.N. International Cooperation Year, seeks the combination of such satellite-reported data with global weather observation at various atmospheric levels; a fast, worldwide, high capacity communication system; and a large-size computer facility containing an adequate numerical model of the atmosphere.

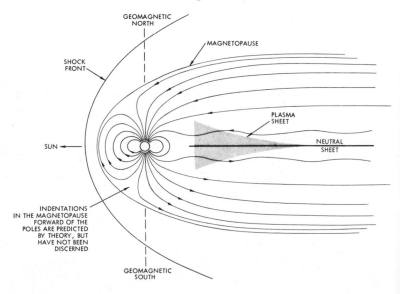

29.   Configuration of the magnetosphere when geomagnetic dipole is perpendicular to earth-sun line.
TWR Systems Inc., Calif. U.S.A. "SPACE LOG," Summer, 1967, Vol. 7, No. 2, P. 53.

With the World Weather Watch data, an adequate computer and global mathematical model, a vast array of experiments on weather and climate modification can be performed by numerical computation rather than in nature . . . full effect and potential hazard can be determined without risk to life or property. For example, a dam can be "built" across the Bering Strait for an infinitesimal fraction of its real life cost, and we can evaluate its effect on the Kamchatka or Canada wheat growing season . . . we can model a megalopolis and its atmospheric cesspool, examine the extent to which it acts as an inadvertent weather modifier, then "clean up" the atmosphere and see the difference. We can do this without taxes, political strife, vast engineering expense—in a computer.[5]

Through the geodetic use of satellite tracking, it will be possible to measure the rates of continental drift, monitor gross changes in the polar ice caps and regional glaciers, and probe the tidal, gravitational, and other mass movements of the earth.

In addition to such large-scale gross measures of planetary changes, conventional photography from both aircraft and satellites has shown the enormous potential of global overview for mapping the resources of the planet. The use of spacecraft for resource-sensing purposes goes beyond the usual resource connotation. "It is much broader than just the valuable minerals and other sought after deposits. It covers all the conditions on the Earth's surface which are of economic and cultural interest to humanity."[6]

With multispectral sensing now being employed, using a great range of sensors from visual resolution to infrared, ultraviolet, radar, and other wave frequencies, many different conditions and discrete phenomena on earth can be mapped swiftly over very large areas of the surface. This is based on the fact that every feature on (and to an extent, measurably below) this surface emits or reflects energy at distinctive wavelengths within the electromagnetic frequency spectrum. For example, with infrared sensing, unhealthy vegetation or plants at different stages of growth have different tones, owing to variable loss in reflectance; such mapping is not only quantitative in the broad survey sense, but also qualitatively sensitive to a degree that would be almost impossible for a ground observer.

30. First Complete View of the World's Weather. This Global photomosaic was assembled from 450 individual pictures taken by Tirox IX during the 24 hours of February 13, 1965. The horizontal white line marks the equator. Special photographic processing was used to increase the contrast between major land areas, outlined in white, and the surrounding oceans. The brightest features on the photographs are clouds; ice in the antarctic and snow in the north are also very bright. The clouds are associated with many different types of weather patterns. The scalloping at the bottom shows how the earth's horizon appears in individual pictures.
ESSA.

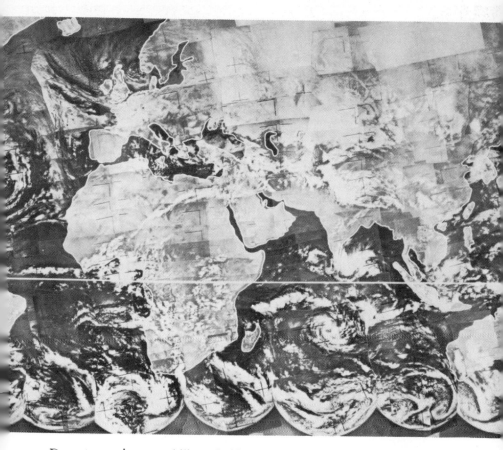

Remote-sensing capability of this type can already distinguish between various types of crops such as wheat, oats, and corn, and can also provide an early warning system for the spread of insect infestation or crop disease, lack of adequate water, or almost any of the changes that take the skilled farmer a great deal of time and energy to monitor and control.

Livestock movements, changes in grazing patterns, in forests, and in water tables, and even wild animal and bird migrations may be continuously surveyed in this fashion.

By measuring light and heat emanations, the flows of traffic in and out of cities can be computed; the patterns of human occupancy of buildings can be deduced from temperature changes. These kinds of data can be compiled to give direct viewing access to human ecological flows, data that were not possible to obtain before.

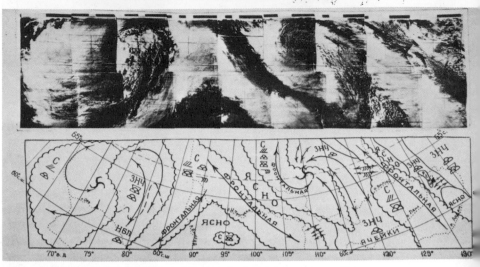

31. Analysis and television picture of cloud formation. Cosmos-122, July 25, 1966, 0708 Moscow time.

The Role of Meteorological Satellites in the World Weather Watch, Secretariat of the World Meteorological Organization, Geneva, Switzerland, Planning Report No. 18, 1967.

32. Cloud Cover Weather Satellite picture Northern Hemisphere. ESSA.

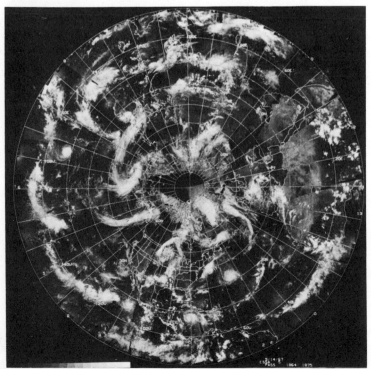

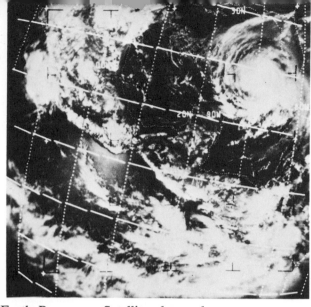

3. Photograph of Hurricane Inez west of Florida on October 5, 1966. The Gulf of Mexico, the western Caribbean, Mexico, and Central America are visible. SSA.

4. Sketch of the planned Earth Resources Satellite shows the multi-paddled vehicle flying over the Atlantic Ocean performing one of the scientifically-feasible feats of the ultra practical satellite, the outlining of the flow of the Gulf Stream. It contains a series of sensors and cameras that will be able to probe the earth below for economic gain—whether the discovery of oil, the prediction of rough sea conditions for ships, or the choosing of the best route for a new highway. High resolution color TV cameras will make it possible to pick out objects smaller than a city block. General Electric.

The track of a specially equipped automobile has been located repeatedly within 100 feet of its actual route on the Baltimore-Washington parkway by a satellite stationed 22,300 miles above the earth . . . the auto was moving 60 miles an hour and the satellite was in stationary orbit over Brazil.[7]

Apart from such discrete surveying, other advantages of resource satellite sensing are the huge areas that can be mapped simultaneously. With satellites that circle the globe in 90 minutes, and others whose changing path views all parts of the earth surface every ten to fourteen days, almost the whole of a continent like Australia can be mapped in one pass or variably sensed for comparative multispectral analyses over a series of orbits. Other synchronous satellites, such as the U.S. Applied Technology Satellite (ATS.1) can photograph half the earth in one viewing and relay this to earth in various frequencies.

For cloud cover analysis and weather forecasting, the automatic picture transmission (APT) system relays such photographs currently to about thirty-five countries linked within the system, where such transmissions may be received on relatively inexpensive equipment.

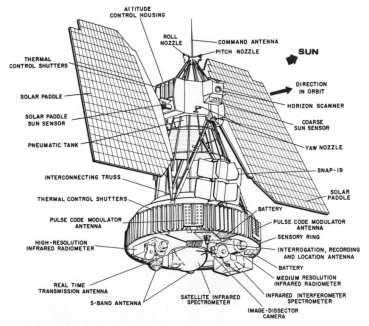

35. Nimbus "B" Satellite.
NASA.

The combination of this resource mapping, crop and livestock pattern changes, and weather-monitoring information can be of inestimable value to the developing countries; significantly, it overcomes previous obstacles to development that were due to lack of adequate specialists and technical personnel to carry out such work at ground level. In many cases, then, resource inventory, which would otherwise have taken decades of large-scale human and equipment energies, can be accomplished in a few months.

In context with the urgent need of an ecological basis for resource management, it is suggested that remote sensors may gather information for (1) inventory and mapping of resources; (2) quantifying the environment; (3) describing the flow of matter and energy; and (4) evaluating changes in the ecosystem.[8]

The management of resources generally has been potentially augmented to an incredible degree by these new tools.

In the control of water resources, hydrologists may check the seasonal buildup of mountain snows and the impounding of water in complex watershed relations to anticipate the forward regulation of rivers and dams for water uses. The regulation of crop irrigation relative to such changes is also an important factor in

Sensor	Sample Applications
	AGRICULTURE AND FORESTRY PRODUCTION
Metric camera..................... Panoramic camera................... Multispectral tracking telescope....... Multiband synoptic camera..........	Gather data on plant vigor and disease in order to aid in the increase of agriculture and forest production.
Radar imager..................... Radar altimeter/scatterometer....... Wide range spectral scanner.......... IR radiometer/spectrometer..........	GEOGRAPHY, CARTOGRAPHY, CULTURAL RESOURCE Gather data to permit better use of rural and metropolitan land areas and to update topographic base maps and census inventories.
Microwave imager.................. Microwave radiometer.............. Laser altimeter/scatterometer........	GEOLOGY AND MINERAL RESOURCES Gather data to aid in (1) the discovery and exploitation of mineral and petroleum resources; (2) the prediction of natural disasters.
Ultraviolet spectrometer imager.......	HYDROLOGY AND WATER RESOURCES
Radio frequency reflectivity.......... Absorption spectroscopy............ Magnetometer.................... Gravity gradiometer................ Viewfinder[1]....................... Earth-based sensors[2]............... Advanced TV system...............	Gather data to aid in the location and better usage of water resources. OCEANOGRAPHY Gather data to aid in ocean transportation and to aid in more efficient utilization of fisheries.

36. Instrumentation Potentially Required of Earth Resources Surveys.
Aerospace Technology November 20, 1967.

37. Potential Applications of Earth Resources Data Gathering Systems. NASA.

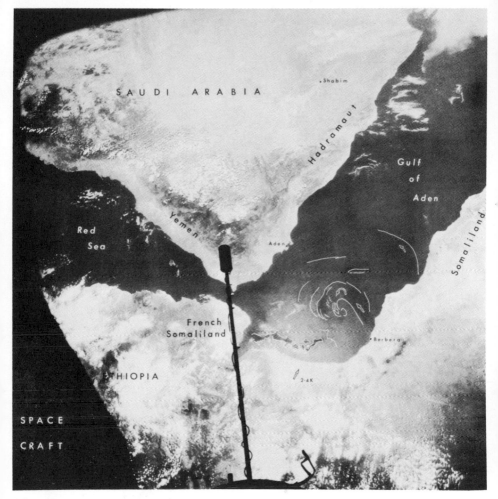

38. Photo from Gemini XI, September 14, 1966, with analysis
overlay.
NASA.

forecasting, and in forestalling droughts (or floods) by giving longer lead time for preventive measures.

The use of the oceans for both scientific study and increased food supply may be similarly advantaged. The flow of currents, the courses of great tidal movements such as the tsunami, and the concentrations and migrations of marine animals and their feeding beds of plankton and other organisms may be charted and analyzed on a scale never possible before.

Ocean and aerial navigation already derive assistance from satellites, and the former may particularly benefit from the tracking of icebergs and floating ice packs, as well as from more accurate navigational fixes and weather forecasting.

Besides these positive advantages, the monitoring of air, water, and soil pollution, whose scale in recent years seemed to be slipping

39. Photo taken from Gemini XI at an altitude of about 200 miles shows all of Israel and Jordan and portions of Turkey, Lebanon, Syria, Iraq, Saudi Arabia, and the United Arab Republic. Scientific and Information Division, Office of Technology Utilization, NASA.

beyond human grasp, is now subjected to more direct human viewing, assessment, and new possibilities of *anticipatory control*.

At present the range of predictive control in the use of much satellite information, and also its more immediate uses, is retarded by the slower development of facilities and equipment to process the volume of incoming data. But in the step function relation of such technologies this phase will pass quickly. The automatic analysis of weather and other information by means of on-line scanning and coded computer map printouts is becoming more routine. As more periodicities and regularities in such patterns become discernible, greater accuracy and reliability is fed back into the automated aspect of the process, freeing human analysts for further development of the process itself.

(One) can foresee the possibility that the techniques for remote sensing will evolve into a highly automatic operation, in which an unmanned satellite orbiting the earth will carry multiband sensing equip-

40.   The Augmented Target Docking Adapter during one of three rendezvous accomplished by the Gemini IX-A crew.
Scientific and Information Division, Office of Technology Utilization, NASA.

ment together with a computer. Thus equipped the satellite could, for any particular area, take inventory of the resources and produce a printout that would amount to a resource map of the area. The computer could then use the inventory data in conjunction with preprogrammed (i.e., human regds.) factors and could reach a decision for the optimum management of the area.[9]

The type of decision and management envisaged here, for example, is the sensing of drought in fields and remotely controlling the irrigation valving until further sensing shows that the condition has been dealt with; or in sensing a forest fire, storm, or tidal wave, and computing the various optimum measures to be taken to control or avert damage.

The concomitant growth of transnational world organizations is a not inconsiderable factor with this increasing use of global satellites. The World Weather Watch, Automatic Picture Transmission service, already mentioned, are only examples of a great host of interlocking stations, institutions, and scientific services that have become involved. This global network, if assessed numerically and in terms of its regulatory potential in relation to the planetary ecology, would probably be much greater than the defense network that we described earlier.

An equally important factor is the increasing dependence of the various world regions and national blocs on such global service networks for the communications, weather, and other information that they now provide. When we refer to an invisible metabolic system, we necessarily infer that once we have become dependent on such globally shared networks and capabilities, it becomes progressively unlikely, and even more unreal, that nations may be able to go it alone in making the kinds of unilateral decisions that affect the rest of the human community. Given our present rate of increased interdependence on local services such as telephones, airlines, weather forecasting, and the range of environmental monitoring, and the vital linkage of these systems to the global system, the threatened withdrawal of any or all such linkages would be a more extreme deterrent than any bomb. To "unplug" any of the advanced nations from the world telephone network could alone be a more drastic sanction than any yet devised. This was indicated in recent years by the withdrawal of only local telephone, airline, and power services through breakdown or labor disputes.

The possibility of such coordinated action by the emerging world of service organizations may seem remote. But the fact remains that many of the world key metabolic decisions, such as the allocation of broadcast frequencies, the regulation of air traffic, and the control of communicable pests and diseases are already being made by way of the concerted agreement and action of many such bodies.

When we turn to the use of satellite systems for more directly human communications, this situation emerges with more clarity. Again the development has been swift, and its broader and more long-range implications are not yet generally recognized.

The first recorded voice was heard from a satellite only eight years ago; four years later the first live telephone, television, data, and facsimile transmissions were made between Europe and the United States via Telstar I and II. Since then, Syncom, Echo, and the Early Bird satellite relays have transmitted between Russia, Japan, the United States, and Europe.

Such communication has become a fundamental part of our society; three operational systems have come into being: the Intelsat, the Department of Defense series and the Soviet Molniyas. At the end of the decade the possibilities for direct relay from satellite to home or individual have become the next useful and logical step.[10]

Worldwide television coverage, which is now partially in operation through satellite relay transmission, has already brought an immediacy and personal quality to global events that man has never before known. When a public figure is assassinated or another human immolates himself in protest against war, the world literally watches and is emotionally involved. The movements for change around the world participate visually in communications, which again chain-react swiftly around the world. The so-called mass medium of television is shown to be a highly selective and personalized communication in terms of its audience response, remaining mass only in the quantitative number and global distribution of individual viewers.

The real TV dramas are not the soap operas and late movie spectaculars, but the newly dimensioned acts in which protagonists

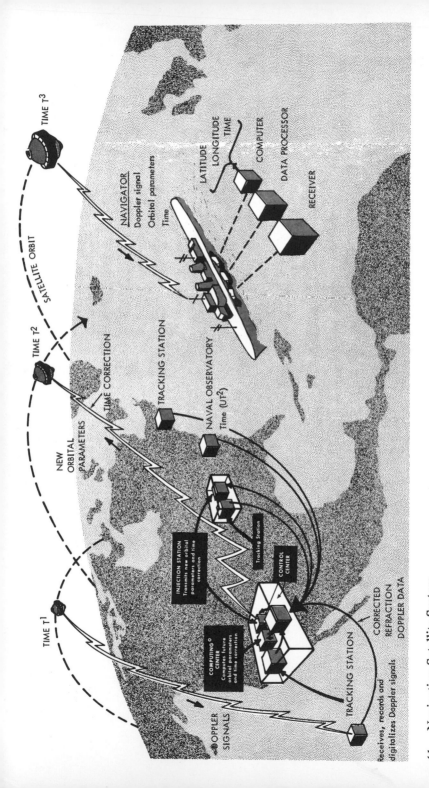

41. Navigation Satellite System.
U.S. National Council on Marine Resources and Engineering Development.

may be face to face though physically at great distance, or temporally displaced as in the rerun and further interaction sequences. The dramatic act of a space walk or an Agena docking maneuver is conducted on a planetary stage upon which performers, their actions, and dialogue are separated from one another by thousands of miles, yet conveyed in compact simultaneity to an audience as widely separated.

The potential and impact of such satellite-relayed communication is still relatively untouched in terms of its capability of breaching old barriers of time and distance, which restrained greater participation in the world's affairs by the larger community. The world's town meeting is now a conceptual, and may soon be a physical, global reality.

More routine communications, such as satellite-relayed telephone with facsimile or photographic printout are now possible on the same globe-circling scale.

We may note also that the introduction of satellite telephony—already functioning with a number of 900 two-way voice-circuit units and anticipated new ranges with 5,000 circuits per unit—is not assumed to increase the cost of such service. The reverse has

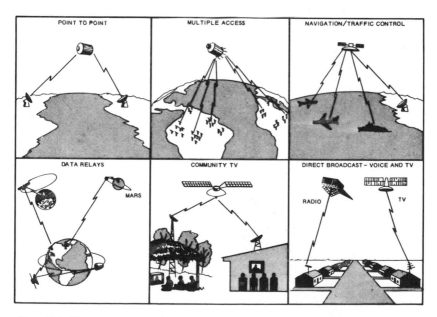

42.   Satellite Communications Capabilities.
NASA.

occurred. In computing the economy of administering differential costs per call distance, it was found that it may be best to cut the billing cost and use a flat rate to anywhere. The technological jump wiped out the traditional economic concept of more-distance-more-cost when it was determined that it could be far cheaper to call halfway round the world than to use a local system to call a nearby town.

As David Sarnoff, of RCA, stated some time ago:

The way is open technically for the establishment over the next few decades of a communications system by which governments, business organizations, or individuals may establish contact with anyone, anywhere, at any time, by voice, sight, or document, separately, or in combination. . . . A person sitting in his home or office, or in movement will be able to [communicate] with any other person anywhere in the world. Written information, computer data and facsimile will be capable of instant transmission from point to point over any distance.

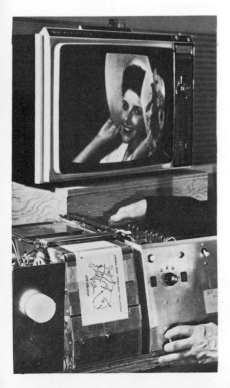

43. RCA Experimental Home Facsimile System. RCA has developed an experimental television system which makes it possible to broadcast printed copy and standard programs to the home simultaneously and over the same channels. In the illustration the image of a pretty girl is sent to the TV screen at the same time a weather map and prediction are sent to the print-out unit. Radio Corporation of America.

We are presently only in the first stage of this revolution, wherein point-to-point messages are relayed from ground transmitters via satellite to relatively high-power ground receivers for further broadcast. The second stage will involve the use of distribution satellites capable of service to less powerful receivers; the third stage of direct satellite-relayed broadcasting to quite small portable receiving units opens up the possibilities that Sarnoff forecasts. In mid-1968, NASA announced a unit of cigar-box size which would enable lunar astronauts to keep contact with each other and with earth stations, and which would itself transmit biomedical data on the condition of the lunar explorer.

Apart from ordinary communications these possibilities will also revolutionize the development pattern of many vital services, particularly for the poor nations. Like resource survey satellites, they tend to cut across the traditional infrastructure of highly trained and scarce personnel. For example, the expert medical diagnostic advice of any specialist anywhere in the world could be available in the remotest hamlet; complex physiological analysis requiring the most advanced equipment could similarly be on hand by way of telemetering devices. The highest application of human knowledge, through libraries, computer banks, human specialists, and technical personnel, could be within the reach of any local community.

We have all these developments presently working in prototype form in the United Nations, the World Health Organization, the International Labor Office, and other organizations, but they have been enormously hampered by the different modes of communication and implementation in use. Implicit within the new wave of communications technology is the reduction, where required, of the many different modes of voice, print, picture, telegraph, etc., to one possible channel through which they may be transmitted simultaneously as identical electronic pulses for reception in any preferred form.

The same may be said for satellite-relayed education, which can bring all or any of these communicative modes to bear on the deployment of educational services anywhere in the world. But here one must say that so far the results in the advanced countries of airborne TV broadcasts and the interlinkage of television, computers, and other systems connecting educational institutions have not been spectacular. As in other areas of the application of advanced technological means to traditional social processes, the tendency is to try to convey the old content in the new channels.

Each technical advance poses a new challenge toward reconceptualizing and transforming the process in which it is used. If this challenge is not recognized, the added technique may even be a retrograde step. At present, much of our educational technology is being used in wholly negative fashion. Rather than enhancing and expanding education—by refashioning its content, decentralizing its means, and allowing for more personalized instruction and more time for human interaction—new techniques are merely superimposed upon a largely obsolete system in a manner that perpetuates its malpractice in more repetitive and more bureaucratic forms.

It is worth restating at every opportunity that the negatives of our present situation are not inherent in the technological revolutions as such, but in the conceptual approaches and social attitudes that determine how new technical means will be employed. *We* are the active instruments that create a technological passivity.

Notwithstanding, therefore, the optimism with which one may review the positive employment of advanced technologies, there is the requirement for increased vigilance over their negative uses. Our present discussion has reiterated the possibilities of newly found sensing, control, and communications techniques with which we may extend our control over our environment. Of course the same possibilities exist for providing new forms of surveillance and control over human actions. Yet was not this also implied in the use of the stone club? The answer is the same. *We* decide. The hope within our evolutionary situation is that the "we" becomes more informed, more cooperatively organized and interrelated, and directly and more individually critical of, and resistant to, the perversion of technical means to inhuman ends.

6
Problems and Prospects

As industrial civilization has expanded in a few generations to encompass the entire globe, it has been paced by the expansion of all the problems that threaten human existence. The problems themselves are not new. All human history is a long record of man's struggle against hunger, disease, war, and ignorance. What is new, and menacingly urgent, are today's expanded dimensions and accelerating frequencies. Their scale and magnitude have been compounded, paradoxically, by the measures that man has developed to combat them. By shrinking the physical distance between his fellows, he has increased the critical interdependence of all; by alleviating hunger and disease, he has added astronomically to his numbers; and by displaying the material results of his increased knowledge and capabilities, he has created a tremendous demand by all people to share in the accumulated industrial wealth and knowledge.

As populations grow, people pack ever more densely into the cities in search of better living. As the general expectation of life rises, so does the drive for higher standards for: more food, houses, clothes, autos; lighting, heating, and cooling; more roads, airplanes, telephones, television, and radio; more packages, bottles, newspapers, toothpaste tubes, and beer cans. More people now not only require more in quantity, but in far greater diversity and materials quality than ever dreamt of in any other period. To keep pace with these growing demands, man has measurably extracted more materials, metals, minerals, and fuels from the earth and atmosphere in the past century alone than in all previous history.

But the concentrations of population, the increase in extraction and production and use of huge amounts of material and energy are also accompanied by the massively accumulating by-products of such human actions: the sewage, garbage, scrap and junk, the effluents and fumes, and all other discards and excess wastes that poison the air, overburden the lakes and rivers, and pollute the offshore waters and beaches. Where more power also means more destructive power, we have the added menace of radioactive fallout from the testing of "overkill" weapons, now sufficient in quantity to destroy each living being many times over.

The growing crisis in human development begins to affect the whole balance of the global ecology. What is the point at which the explosive growth of the human species, and its enormously increased scale of activities, will overwhelm the natural checks and balances? How long can the earth sustain such growth, absorb its by-products, and still remain a viable habitat for human life?

Our present levels of development already interfere substantially with the natural cycles of energy and materials in the biosphere, and we now probe beyond these toward outer space. A recent U.S. congressional report asks:

Is it too soon to inquire if these factors, plus others, may be contributing to an upset of nature's delicate balance? Are we slowly overturning the oxygen-carbon dioxide system upon which all life is dependent? Is that cycle being disturbed by high oxygen consumption and low oxygen yield? Are we thus shifting basic weather patterns upon which our various civilizations have come to depend?

It is no longer adequate to consider any such problems in isolation or with sole regard to their unilateral solution at local, regional, or national levels, whether they be pollution, hunger, or population pressures.

A cosmic numbers game is being played out; one whose patterns are hidden, like picture puzzles, in series of intricately related curves of birth, growth, and decay. According to many authorities, the rules of the game may be discerned in a few mathematical laws of simple addition and multiplication, which seem to govern all the players, their business, and exits and entrances—whether they be fruit flies in a jar, bacteria on a culture plate, or human populations on the planetary scale. The stakes in our phase of the game may be survival or oblivion.

The laws governing growth are rigorously simple and have a

close similarity to the rates of growth governing all types of energy, mass, and unit increase. Stated succinctly by Derek de Solla Price:

Mathematically, the law of exponential growth follows from the simple condition that at any time the rate of growth is proportional to the size of the population or to the total magnitude already achieved— the bigger a thing is, the faster it grows. In this respect it agrees with the common natural law of growth governing the number of human beings in the population of the world or of a particular country, the number of fruit flies growing in a colony in a bottle, or the number of miles of railroad built in the early industrial revolution.[1]

The growth law can be separated into two phases: the *exponential* curve of growth, and the S-curve phase, beyond the exponential. For example, in the first phase, colonies of insects or microbes in a closed laboratory system may be observed to multiply swiftly to the limits of the environ, until a specific point is reached when they stabilize, decline, or decay. Initially growth proceeds slowly until a critical population mass is reached; then the numbers curve begins to climb explosively at an exponential rate of increase, measurably doubling within each given time period. The saturation point is reached as population growth begins to outrun food supply and as the environ system becomes clogged with its own wastes, which have also been accumulating exponentially.

The trend of the curve, from this point on, depends on specific situational and species conditions. It may oscillate out of control, gradually decline, or transform into the second phase.

Where growth continues beyond the crisis point of exponential increase and enters the second phase, it typically conforms to an S-curve, rounding off to a steady-state plateau line of relative equilibrium. In the early 1920s, Raymond Pearl reported this curve as governing the rate of increase of flies in a bottle, of yeast cells in a given environ, of cell increases in white rats, etc. In the natural environment, such growth patterns may be more complexly structured. To the nutrient supply as a controlling factor may be added the role of predators and parasites; for example, the balance cycles of rabbits and foxes or deer and wolves in an area, the density stress syndrome leading to self-destructive drives, and other growth-inhibiting factors.

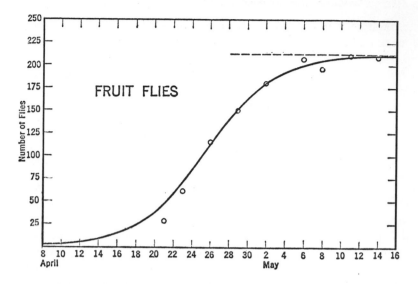

44. Patterns in Growth of Organisms.
Biology of Population Growth, G. Pearl, 1925.

45. General Form of the Logistic Curve.
Science Since Babylon, D. J. de Solla Price, Yale University Press, 1961.

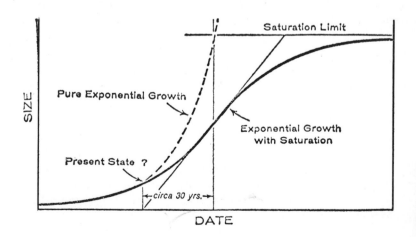

For present relevance, we can consider the planet earth as a closed laboratory system with man as the dominant species.

In 1967 a United States environmental task force unequivocally reported that, "There is no sign of any stability or plateauing in man's collision with his environment." John Wilkinson strongly underlines the same negative finding:

Every area of the world, even the "underdeveloped," is participating in a "technological-information-explosion." Substance can be given to this cliche: Many of the most important cultural indices are following an exponential curve, that is, a law of growth representing an "explosion" in a system that was hitherto more or less stable but either is already out of control or very soon will be. We are accustomed *ad nauseam* to hear of the so-called population explosion and the dangers it represents to the future well-being of mankind. But, lung cancer, coronary infarctions, bankruptcies, the Gross National Product, the destructive capacity of weapons of war (and the velocity of the vehicles which are designed to deliver them), the number of book titles and scientific papers, the pollution of air and streams—in fact, an indefinite variety of things—are participating in that same exponential curve which is formally identical with the law regulating the growth of money at compound interest.[2]

If we examine similar illustrations we can find many to support these viewpoints. The so-called population explosion may still be the most dramatic.

From 6000 B.C. to the beginning of the Christian era, world population grew relatively slowly, from 10 million to about 250 million. In the next fifteen centuries (A.D. 1500) it doubled to around 500 million. Within four centuries (A.D. 1850) it doubled again to 1 billion. In less than one century (A.D. 1925) it jumped to 2 billion. In the 1960s it passed the 3 billion mark; and by the year A. D. 2000 it will be over 6 billion. At the present world rate of increase it is doubling about every 80 years.

Focusing down to regional examples makes this rapid increase even more dramatically apparent! India's population has increased:

12 million between 1891 and 1921,
27 million between 1921 and 1931,
37 million between 1941 and 1951,
78 million between 1951 and 1961.

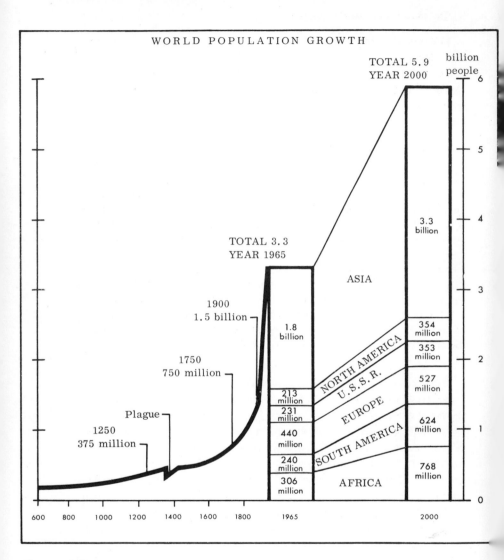

Figure 46.

In referring to the explosive power of such unchecked exponential growth, Isaac Asimov has calculated that, ". . . by A. D. 3500 (world population) would reach 630,000 billion! Our planet would have standing room only." An even less sanguine estimate was made by three scientists, Von Foerster, Mora, and Aimot, in 1960. In a sardonic plea for more urgent population control, the crisis point was stated precisely in the title of their paper, *"Doomsday: Friday, 13 November A.D. 2026."* On the basis of the trend curves, they suggested that, "at this date, human population will approach infinity if it grows as it has grown in the last two millenia . . . our great-great-grandchildren will not starve to death. They will be squeezed to death."

What about other exponentials? Almost all show their most abrupt upswing in the past hundred years and are those most closely associated with scientific and technological growth, with population density, and the increased magnitude of human operations.

Of wild life species rendered extinct (107 kinds of mammals and 100 species of birds), 70 percent have occurred in the past century and have been mainly due to human agency, less through hunting than destruction of habitat.

Other uses of the earth have also increased enormously. As against approximately 50 tons of raw materials per person consumed in 1880, we now use over 300 tons per person annually. When this is translated into amounts of iron, coal, oil, wood, and other extractions, it is an operation of considerable ecological magnitude. For example, of all the coal mined by 1960, only 20 percent was mined before 1900, and the remaining 80 percent since then.

The enormous energies used in our industrial processes are mostly obtained from burning the fossil fuels (oil and coal), each ton of which releases large amounts of carbon and dioxide and other gases into the atmosphere. From 1860 to 1960, this has been calculated to have increased atmospheric carbon dioxide by 14 percent. In the past ten years the average role of such increase has been 5 percent, which in the coming years may give an overall concentration capable of grossly distorting the earth's atmosphere.

Such pollution curves begin to read as if man were engaged in chemical and biological warfare against himself. Four thousand Londoners died in one week in 1952 from causes variously attributed to air pollution; one thousand, in 1956. The World Health Organization reports that Europe pours millions of tons of sulfur dioxide into the atmosphere every year, Britain alone accounting for five million tons.

Air pollution affects almost everything in our environment, from clothes, skin, and lungs to buildings, metals, and paints. Material damage costs caused by it in the United States already run more than $9 billion annually. Out of the exhaust system of each of our 90 million United States motor vehicles this year will come 1,600 pounds of carbon monoxide, 230 pounds of hydrocarbons, and 77 pounds of nitrogen oxides.

A further ironical twist is that in making our land more productive through the use of chemical fertilizers and other nutrients, we indirectly destroy the crops in the process. Each calorie of food produced in highly mechanized agriculture requires another calorie of fuel to power the tractors. This fuel burning adds agricultural smoke to industrial smoke; hence, in at least half the states in the United States, vegetation damage is reported from smog, sulfur fumes, fluorides, and ethylenes. Livestock damage is more indirect and chronic.

The pesticides we use to combat crop pests also increasingly contaminate the soil, lakes and rivers. Massive fish kills of around 10 million in the Mississippi basin and Gulf of Mexico during 1960–1964 were traced to pesticide runoff and other toxic effluents flushed into streams and rivers thousands of miles away. Added to these poisons from agricultural practice are the city sewage, the detergents, the leftovers from steel, chemical, pulp paper, cement, and glass plants, such as acids, oils, cyanides and other lethal agencies. Into Lake Erie alone goes 18,000 tons of such wastes every day, turning a sparkling lake into a fetid cesspool. By 1980 it is calculated that the continued dumping of such effluents will be sufficient to consume all the oxygen of all the dry weather flow of twenty-two river basins in the United States. Yet our need for fresh water has so increased that in 20 years it will go from 370 billion gallons to 600 billion gallons.

Concern with this poisoning of the land, air, and water, with the coming of "the silent spring," is not confined to the United States. Pollution is apolitical. Thus, a Soviet report in Pravda states:

Over the years of rapid industrialization and urban development, we have polluted hundreds of small and large rivers. The Volga has been very badly contaminated. The factories and rivers along its banks dump 280 million cubic feet of raw sewage into the river every 24 hours. . . . Before a cellulose mill was built in Northern Dvina delta fishermen caught 130 tons of salmon a year, now they barely catch a sixth of that.

With no monopoly on water pollution and fish kills, America may still take wry consolation in being the world's leading trash maker—by more than half. One official figure sets the possible amount for 1967 as able to "fill 36 lines of box cars from coast to coast." Total refuse production is already on the doubling curve, but recent estimates suggest that less than half of our cities have satisfactory refuse disposal systems.

The rising curve of garbage is underlined by the official figure of roughly 1,600 pounds now produced by each person per year— 125 million tons in total—48 billion metal cans, 25 billion bottles and jars, 65 billion metal and plastic caps and crowns, plus almost 20 million tons of paper packaging. As one newspaper reported, "Americans last year bought and presumably squeezed 1,244,126,428 metal squeeze tubes, half of which contained toothpaste."

To an extent, however, these are all visible—mounting garbage and junk piles, smog, scummy rivers, and dead lakes—and their public presence provokes action and corrective measures. What about the invisible killers, the thousands of new chemical compounds introduced into industrial and private use, the by-products of new and exotic technologies?

As the 1967 Environmental Health Task Force states:

Modern technology brings man into contact with a vast array of substances new to the human race which have the potential of causing new health problems . . . the American people are being exposed to some 500,000 different substances many of them over very long periods of time. Yet fewer than ten per cent of these have been cata-

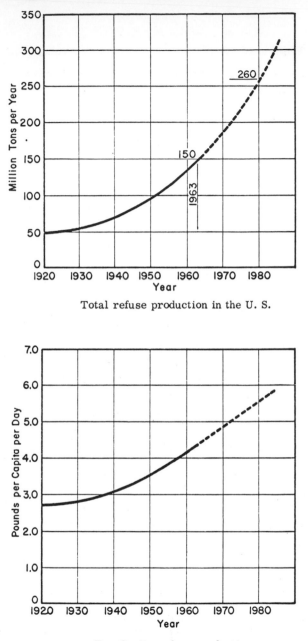

Total refuse production in the U. S.

Per Capita refuse production.

Figure 47.
Public Health Service, U.S. Department of Health, Education and Welfare, February 1964.

logued in a manner that might provide the basis for determining their effects on man and his environment . . . our ignorance of potential hazards is perilously great.

The thalidomide scandal awakened the legislative conscience toward the need for better medical drug controls. More recently, concern with the side effects of even seemingly innocuous food additives, such as artificial sweeteners, has brought to light the lurking dangers from the excessive use of all such materials without careful long-range monitoring. Even the increased use of electromagnetic waves in radio, television, radar, and microwave has recently come under scrutiny, since growing evidence suggests that such radiation may have definite effects on human functioning.

Many commentators suggest that the social pathology of uncontrolled growth in urban density and in technological complexity is now shown in the mounting curves of mental illness, divorce, and family breakup. The rise in the numbers of murders, robberies, rape, juvenile delinquency, and general crime is matched with the decline in public morality, with violence, and with the pornography purveyed in the mass media. The most materially prosperous nation on earth is preoccupied with the successive assassination of key public figures and reels from waves of arson, looting, and rioting in its major cities; at the same time it spends billions of dollars to destroy its enemies, halfway round the world, with the most sophisticated instruments of human destruction ever devised by man. Violence, corruption, and social deterioration in the adult world are mirrored in the increasing withdrawal and isolation of the young from the basic norms and avowed goals of the society. The "stress syndrome" point seems to have been reached in such a situation of mass and individual breakdown.

Yet we may pause here to question both the curves and the rhetoric. Is the prospect so bleak? Have we reached the point of no return in a society now irrevocably doomed to succumb to its own self-generated destructive drives?

There is no simple answer. Rather we must accept a certain amount of the evidence as strongly indicative that we are indeed approaching the most critical juncture in human affairs in all history.

But we must discount much of the more simplistic extrapolation of exponentials that has been adduced so far. Exponential curves do not grow in isolation; they are related to other growths and values, in simplest relation: as one value goes up, its opposite declines. As Price says:

In the real world things do not grow and grow until they reach infinity. Rather, exponential growth eventually reaches some limit, at which the process must slacken and stop before reaching absurdity. This more realistic function is also well known as the logistic (or S) curve, and it exists in several slightly different mathematical forms.

Growth, size, and change itself are all relative measures. What looks like separate rates of increase of abnormally explosive growth in one narrow frame of reference, such as a span of time, may be a slowly changing distribution relative to a wider context or longer time span.

Human beings are not fruit flies, and while their aggregate activities may conform to the natural growth patterns, the point of plateauing in human trends is not necessarily saturation before

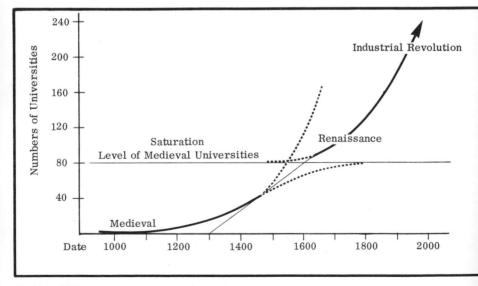

PLATEAU CURVE WITH NEW TAKE-OFF POINT

Figure 48.
Science Since Babylon, D. J. de Solla Price, Yale University Press, 1961.

the onset of decay, but may be a more or less consciously exercised control function.

The numbers game itself is not infallible—even though its more skilled and scientific operators bid fair to become our new theocracy! Adequate statistical compilations are of quite recent origin, and in many areas are still crudely approximate. Their enthusiastic and overcredulous use in recent years is often more reflective of the human need for some stable authority image ("figures can't lie") than it is for the reliability and predictive accuracy that statistics claims.

Many recent and alarming curves, as in the case of certain physical and mental disorders, are evidence only of better bookkeeping; we could maintain no earlier growth records until the illnesses were precisely identified and duly documented. Other statistical increases share the same defect: crime, deviance, and the social pathologies are as you label and count them. The divorce rate rise may not be indicative of social deterioration but rather of greater ability to afford the court fees or of wider flexibility and choice in human relations. The rising toll of deaths on the road (or in the air) rarely includes the enormous increase in the number of safe miles that are traveled in proportion to the number of fatalities and the increased numbers of vehicles operating on them. And so one might go on to reappraise each specific trend and curve within its specific context and in relation to all pertinent contributing factors.

The content and type of exponential growth is also important. The rising curves of knowledge, of international cooperation, higher education, health, material living standards, and similar societal derivatives may more than offset the curves of alarm.

Concealed within the enormous growth in the use of metals and other materials is the fact that the bulk of these resources are not simply used up but go through various scrapping and reuse cycles that render them virtually inexhaustible in the long run. We constantly use less material and less energy input per function in advanced technologies, and therefore the gain in performance for each material used is in many cases a reverse curve.

The materialism exponential that associates the growth of products and systems with a decline in spiritual values is possibly one of the most questionable.

The trend toward microminiaturization, invisible electronic linkages, and self-adjusting and self-serving machine equipment means that as technologies gain in reliability and efficient performance, they tend to require less human attention, are more unobtrusive in their function, and are less materially constraining upon our human activities. The more advanced the technology, the more it tends toward such dematerialization.

Then, too, the more material goods, services, and systems become available, more freely available, the less they rank in importance. The younger generation is now being reproached for its *lack of interest* in the material values and goals of the respective societies. The youth of the world demonstrate for the renewal of more spiritual values. In the advanced economies, the trend away from material ownership in favor of use/rental is such that people have to be persuaded to *own* goods in order to avoid changing some of the basic economic premises of the society.

Many of the other exponentials mentioned are only phases of larger patterns and cycles whose overall rhythms are not perceptible in the shorter range. Of course this in no way absolves us from more vigilance; it suggests rather that we apply our vigilance to the larger possible consequences of exponential growth.

The Malthusian theory of overpopulation and famine is now second only to the H-bomb in its capacity to induce despair, with figures and trend charts that have become unassailable dogma. A reappraisal of fertility programs and food production by Donald Bogue suggests:

For more than a century, demographers have terrorized themselves, each other, and the public at large with the essential hopelessness and inevitability of the "population explosion." Their prophecies have all been dependent on one premise. "If recent trends continue. . . ." It is an ancient statistical fallacy to perform extrapolations upon this premise when in fact the premise is invalid. It is my major point that *recent trends have not continued, nor will they be likely to do so.* Instead, there have been some new and recent developments that make it plausible to expect a much more rapid pace in fertility control. These developments are so new and novel that *population trends be-*

fore 1960 are largely irrelevant in predicting what will happen in the future.[3]

Bogue's point is particularly borne out in the differential fertility rates between the underdeveloped, agriculturally based countries and the industrialized and highly urbanized regions of the world. High birth rates are associated with low industrial energies and poor living standards. While the situation cannot be viewed with complacency, the most dramatic gains in population control seem to flow from rapid industrialization in conjunction with other programs, as evident in Japan. The associated food problem is no longer traditionally tied to the soil; more people may be fed off the land than on it. Archaic equipment, maldistribution, and ancient prejudice are still prime factors in the hungriest regions; 20 percent of India's grain crop is eaten by rats and 200 million cattle still forage without restraint in a country where food output could be quadrupled by modern methods.

The growth of population *may* have been retarded for centuries, and may now be climbing swiftly toward a new optimal size required by the next phase of human development. Decreasing amounts of land per capita, though often cited as an obvious limiting factor of human expansion, is a relative measure and is crucial only during a critical transition period. The amount of land surface available and still unused may be gauged from the fact, for example, that the entire population of the United States occupies less than 10 percent of its land area. And we have noted, man has now expanded his ecological niche to include the whole planet. His activities are no longer constrained to horizontal deployments around its surface, but go increasingly into and beyond the atmosphere, beneath the earth, and deep into the oceans.

The exponentials of such ecological expansion are not unidimensional, but include many interrelated and complex variables. The plateaus of one curve in such an overall context may be the take-off point for another. This is formally shown in the increase in vehicular speeds and in the successive curves of accelerator energies.

We may also redress our semantic bias on pollutants, garbage, and poisons. Pollutants are as we perceive and designate them; poisons are natural substances out of place or in excess of tolerable levels. The gases and dust of forest fires, volcanic ashes, pollens, marsh effluents, and other natural airborne particles are all pollutants of the environment. The problem aspect of man-made pollutants has been an outgrowth of lack of foresight and inadequate planning. We can refashion our major undertakings toward more efficient ecological function so that the wastes of one part of the process cycle become the raw material of another in "closed loop" systems. Natural forces can be more selectively used to absorb sewage and reprocess discards and residues on a much vaster scale than at present.

Apart from the tendency to enjoy the thrill of impending doom, of being on "a collison course with destiny," our major problem is lack of perspective. We think of the immediate past—in terms of one of a few generations—and try to constrain the technological present within the traditions, conventions, and seasonal rituals of an agriculturally based society. But many of the trends now disturbingly apparent have been under way from a few decades to a thousand years.

We mythologize the more distant past as a golden age when man and earth were young and vigorous, issues and problems were clear-cut, and life was infinitely free and less complicated. This could hardly be farther from the truth! There is considerable archaelogical evidence to identify the organic diseases and the physically stressful and debilitating conditions with which primitive men were plagued within their brief lives. The so-called golden ages of civilized periods were often anything but that for the ordinary person. In Europe during the sixteenth centry, half of the children never reached the age of five. Violence, sudden death, pestilence, and local warfare were everyday hazards; unremitting toil, monotonous diet, and low life expectancy were the standard lot of most people.

In terms of life expectancy, man in the materially advanced countries has gained approximately twenty years of extra life since 1900; his gain in personally disposable time, alone, is almost equal to the total life expectation of many primitive peoples. The conquest of many traditionally killing diseases and other ailments has greatly reduced the incidence of unnecessary physical pain and suffering. In terms of personal freedom, most men are less bound and socially limited than in most previous societies. Where free-

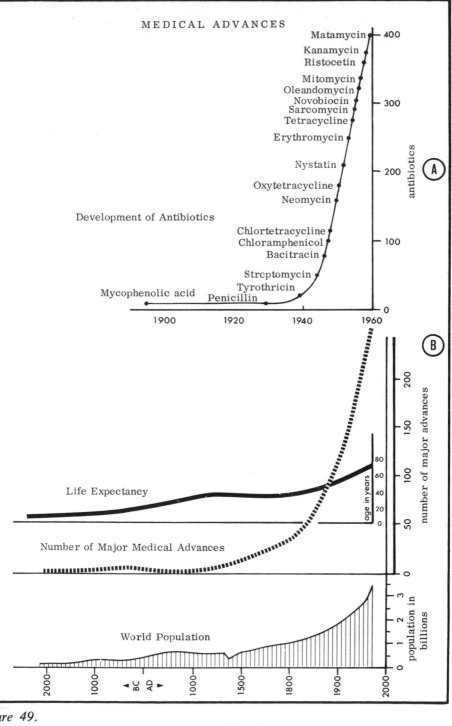

MEDICAL ADVANCES

Development of Antibiotics

- Matamycin — 400
- Kanamycin
- Ristocetin
- Mitomycin
- Oleandomycin
- Novobiocin — 300
- Sarcomycin
- Tetracycline
- Erythromycin
- Nystatin — 200
- Oxytetracycline
- Neomycin
- Chlortetracycline
- Chloramphenicol — 100
- Bacitracin
- Streptomycin
- Tyrothricin
- Mycophenolic acid
- Penicillin

antibiotics Ⓐ

Ⓑ

Life Expectancy

Number of Major Medical Advances

World Population

number of major advances

age in years

population in billions

ure 49.

elopment of Antibiotics, Dr. H. Striner, Upjohn Institute, 1963; *Man Study*, J. McHale, Southern Illinois University, 1964.

doms are reduced and constraints imposed, these are, more often than not, due to attempts to maintain old orders and securities rather than to accommodate changes. Besides the enlargement of the physical world available to his direct experience, new extensions and communications media make the whole earth into man's psychic environ. Access to these means becomes less rather than more complex and *less conditional* upon his conformity with some locally prevailing ideology, societal rule, or mandate.

Many of these gains have come about only through planning, organization, and control. Though applied to physical means more frequently than to persons, the idea of such planned change is still negatively tied to loss of individual participation and choice within the process. This remains one of our more crucial questions. Its redefinition may lie in examining the ways in which we have exercised some conscious, or unconscious, control over our past historical development.

Our access to, and comprehensive viewing of, long historical trend patterns is presently fragmentary. Theories of history have concentrated on impersonal forces, laws, environmental determinants, and the singular effects of local religious, political, and other leaders. Other variables, such as series of individually identifiable decisions leading to changes minor in themselves, but cumulatively effective over long time spans, have been too numerous and complex to account for within the record.

What has defeated us has been sheer quantity. The forces whose resolution is represented by the words, "so-and-so's victory" are so overwhelmingly numerous that it has been impossible for human minds, unaided by technology, to identify each of these multitudinous human beings, to trace their myriads of relations with each other, and to follow out each separate strand in this network of relations until, having started with individuals we arrive at the end product of their interaction in the shape of a "victory" or one of those other "historical" or "social" events for which we have invented mythical labels. . . . The problem of linking up Everyman's individual acts with the historical end product is a problem with which historians have wrestled so far, without success. Here the computer may come to the historian's rescue.[4]

It is significant that cybernetics, noted earlier as the science of control systems, or steersmanship, for the future, should be cited as an aid toward clearer understanding of the manner in which we have controlled or steered our way in the past.

Toynbee's suggestion, in the preceding quotation, is viable, and has the important quality of reducing teleological theories of historical explanation to the dimension of individual intervention. Evolutionary teleology, in terms of the preset goal orientation that explained the adaptive behaviors of organisms, has lacked this dimension, from the simple adaptation of species to environments to the Bergsonian "vital force" idea to the present DNA/RNA "life code" hypotheses.

Lester Ward, a nineteenth-century American sociologist, proposed the interesting idea of "social telesis" in explaining man's adaptive behaviors as governed end-purposes progressively controlled by his intelligence, replacing instincts and drives as prime behavioral determinants. Individual actions are defined as teleological or ends-oriented in a conscious sense. We may extend this idea further to consider society as an aggregate of such individual behaviors.

Society is thus conceived as partially (consciously and unconsciously) self-directing in its development through the reactive interrelationship of individual decisions.* In order to determine the difference in behavior of the complex form (society) from the sum of individual behaviors, Ward introduced the concept of synergy,† which suggested that the behavior of the whole cannot be predicted in terms of the isolated behaviors of its parts.

*This idea has been revived in recent years; for example, the "society as a learning system" concept. The function of Teilhard de Chardin's "noosphere" (or confluence of organized human knowledge around the earth) comes close to Ward's (and earlier, Bacon's) exposition of cumulative knowledge as the developing conscious governor of overall societal directions. Basically, the notion of social telesis is related to the idea of feedback, the adjustment of goal direction by the corrective relation of output to input signals.

†This concept is an old one, but seems to have been first used with clarity in eighteenth century chemistry to explain the behavior of inert compounds resulting from the combination of reactive elements; thus common salt is not predicted from the isolated behavior of sodium and chlorine. Auguste Comte used the term in the social sense, and it also appears in contemporary anthropological explanations. R. B. Fuller has used it most incisively in his structural exploration; and lately it has reappeared in systems and cybernetic theory.

Our hindsight evaluation of macrohistorical patterns in terms of such conceptual approaches has, so far, lacked the practical means of correlating the huge numbers of variables, which the computer now affords.

It is interesting to speculate on the extent to which we may find that much of our past development has been avoided, not by the operation of deterministic laws, but by the interrelation of individually conscious responses.

Particularly evident in the recent past is that the *need* for carrying out some extremely complex operation became apparent at almost the same time as the *means* were developed to enable man to deal with the emerging level of complexity.

The size of cities was controlled by the etiology of infectious disease, adequacy of food supply, and other natural regulators until man developed the necessary preventive procedures and the necessary accounting/logistical procedures to organize himself effectively in numbers above one million. The sixfold to eightfold growth of city size in Europe in the nineteenth century is usually imputed to the migration of labor to the factories, but it was part of a much larger pattern, which included the chemicalization and mechanization of agriculture as no longer binding men to the land yet ensuring adequate food supply for new macrocenters, improvements in transportation, in organization, and in public health necessary to maintain large numbers of people in one place. We have also noted the acceleration of education, professionalism, and other developments. All these "phased-in" developments were part of a larger mosaic of communication and response, operating so as to change the human ecological pattern at a specific time.

The early empires were particularly restricted in their size by their modes of communication. The Roman empire, as a positive ecological advance development, reached an optimum growth through its command and control technologies—such as close-order drill, rational chains of command, and the use of the wax tablet and stylus to transmit orders and return accurate information on the state of the empire's frontiers. These, and the aqueduct, the thermae, and other measures of environ control served to sustain a larger and more consciously organized ecological pattern than was possible before. When this particular form of large-scale organization reached its point of maximum value for development and when its continuance might have adversely affected man's continued growth, the empire outran its capabilities and declined.

One does not attribute here some "collectively conscious" decision that led to the breakup of the empire; rather it was the result of individual and group decisions in terms of a vast array of reasons, of self-interest. Historical forces suggest barbarian pressures due to the overcrowding of pastures, failure of crop lands, or internal decadence. Whatever the contributing factors ultimately, there was also, and importantly, a human decision to pursue this or that course of action.

We customarily refer to the Renaissance as the dawn of a new human consciousness, but this was preceded by the Middle Ages, during which there occurred the myriad linked discoveries and developments that were integrated at a specifically swifter rate than previously, possibly because of the increased number of literate individuals. The use of the breast harness and stirrup, the introduction of the spoked wheel, the shift to Arabic numeration with its gains in computational accuracy and reliability, new timekeeping and work regulation procedures, the use of windpower, increased food yields through crop rotation, the invention of printing, paper, canvas, and oil paint—all these and many other elements necessarily had to be matured to the state of critical renaissance mass. When this state of information level, social organization, and learning was reached, another surge forward took place.

Whether the forward surge connoted progress need not immediately concern us. There was a further elaboration of cultural development, which was also pertinently available to more people.

Gradually, as we approach our own period, much of the process of the relationship and cross-fertilization of individually creative innovation and discovery becomes more conscious of itself in the overall pattern of increasing human relatedness.

The point about this excursion is simply that which relates to human control. The resolving focus of many of our present dialogues about man and his world is that, having voluntarily ejected one or another quasi-divine external agency from the driving seat of our development, we cannot quite accept that we may be in self-drive after all!

In our most recent development we have begun to learn how to learn, how to invent and even to institutionalize, or create, favorable climates for the encouragement of creativity and innovation. Clearly our way forward lies with the more conscious and reflective control of much that has been unconsciously carried forward.

A U.S. National Academy of Science report takes the view that in the long range, future progress depends

. . . in large measure on whether the cultural lag can be sufficiently reduced between the inhibitory sacred-cow behaviors which we have inherited from our recent past and the action requirements which are now necessitated by the socio-industrial complex with which we have to deal. If such impediments can be overcome, it is entirely possible that with only minor extensions of our present knowledge . . . we shall be able to make the transition to a stabilized industrial civilization with a decent standard of living and a high standard of health for all the world's human inhabitants.[5]

The way beyond the exponentials lies between evasive optimism and an equally dangerous, but more inhibiting, despair. It requires, rather, a cool pragmatism that affirms a strong belief in man's innate capacity to solve his problems, but covers its bets by more consciously devising and applying the ways and means to avoid catastrophe.

Our chances of survival are clearly based on our capacity to meet the largest challenge ever offered to man. Technologies and "know-how" are more than adequate to solve many of our largest problems. What we lack is that combination of vision, understanding, and innovative action that will enable us to use our knowledge more immediately and more effectively.

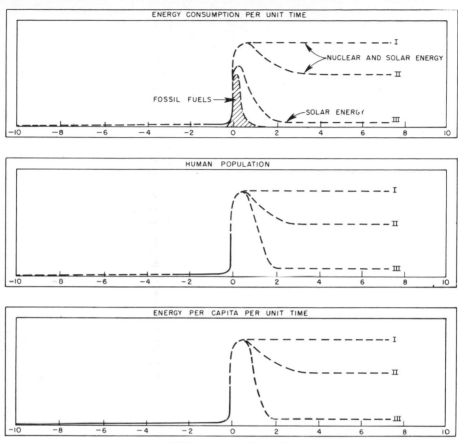

50.   Human Affairs in Time Perspective.

"The present state of human affairs can perhaps more clearly be seen in terms of a time perspective, minus and plus, of some thousands of years with respect to the present, as depicted . . . On such a scale the phenomena of present interest—the growth in the rate of consumption of energy, the growth of the human population, and the rise in the standard of living as indicated by the increase in the per capita rate in energy consumption—are all seen to be represented by curves which are near zero and rising almost imperceptibly until the last few centuries. Then after an initial gradual increase, each curve, as the present is approached, rises almost vertically to magnitudes many times greater than ever before.

On this time scale the consumption of fossil fuels is seen to rise sharply from zero and almost as sharply to descend, with the total duration of the period of consumption representing but a brief interval of the total period of human history."

Energy Resources, M. King Hubbert, Chairman of the Energy Resources Study, U.S. National Academy of Science, 1962.

IV

The Future of
the Future

1
Outer Space

Despite the emphasis on change, much of our discussion so far has ranged through ideas, institutions, and processes that are related by continuities of human experience. Everyday life in the past "century of revolutions" still had a sufficient number of familiar characteristics resembling those of previous periods to allow changes to be assimilated almost unnoticed. The impact of change was felt only when there were breaks in the continuity that were less recognizable and explicable in terms of previous experience.

Our conceptualization of the present is focused on the stability and continuity of ecological processes as a necessarily continuous and relatively permanent matrix of life itself. Any suggested re-orientation is toward an understanding of the larger patterns of change within which we may accommodate our current transitions with comparative ease.

In engaging with the future of the future, however, we confront those trends in human development that are more *discontinuous* with the past, in which man encounters situations and new environmental relationships more or less alien to any previous human experience. Thus, "walking in space" beyond the earth's gravitational clasp is roughly comparable to sojourning at the bottom of the ocean, and both are voyages into the extremes of environmental experience for which we have no acceptable terms of reference. That we are able to integrate them into our everyday events says much for our increased tolerance of the widening options and possibilities of human experience. But their full import still needs to be understool and emotionally grasped.

The exploration of outer space and of the inner space of the oceans has often been likened to the discovery of the New World during the Renaissance. The implications and reverberations of ocean exploration have not yet been fully worked out, but those pertaining to outer space are already radicalizing many areas of present society.

The visible technology of space research and its accomplishments has provided an arresting image of scientific and technological progress for some years. Its detractors have made great play with its enormous cost in human and material energies and the obviously indirect and apparent tenuous relation to the many grievous terrestrial problems that those energies could be used to alleviate. Its apologists have been hard put to find the directly promised "spinoffs," which they asserted would swiftly accrue from this massive effort.

In a sense, both simplistic detraction and apologetic defense in terms of the immediacy of practical application may miss the point in assessing the overall phenomenon. The relationship of theoretical, or intangible, science to usable technology is difficult to gauge in that technologies emerge from a very great number of both discrete scientific discoveries and technical advances. Discovery in pure science is often spurred, for example, by an advance in technical instrumentation, which may in turn represent many developmental movements from other scientific and technical fields.

The discrete discoveries and applications of space research are also difficult to elicit; its larger import and implications may be, paradoxically, much simpler to understand.

The central point would be that of *convergence*. We have noted, a possibly negative trend in scientific and technological development, the increasingly piecemeal and specialized nature of an enterprise whose basic nature is the integration of individual discovery or invention through the collective validation of its results.

In a period, therefore, of increased divergence of human inquiry, space research is particularly characterized by the way in which all its effort and directions converge upon a unitary undertaking: the exploration of space, of conditions beyond the earth's atmospheric shields and electrogravitational forces, an area that man may yet physically explore and possibly inhabit. Almost every brand of science—from physics and chemistry through biology and medicine to psychology and parapsychology, and every field of engineering—has been pressed into this development, so that seemingly space research seeks to sum up and draw upon the whole of accumulated scientific knowledge discovered in the past few hundred years.

The reasons for the convergence of these sciences are to be found within the central purpose of space research. To transport and maintain the human organism *off* the earth and outside its sustaining envelopes requires a duplication of the earth itself—a protective enclosure and complex life support system that is, in effect, a rudimentary earth in miniature.

The developed space vehicle—with its protective shields and energy collectors and converters; with its internal closed ecology for the cycling of air, water, and wastes; with its sensors and communicating devices—is a microminiaturized version of the earth itself a simulated planetary vehicle for the larger human community.

What we refer to as the "space effort" is one of the latest stages in man's extension of his ecological niche beyond the limits of his home planet. Notwithstanding, therefore, that the manifest impetus to the various space programs may be a combination of chauvinism and weaponry, their most tangible by-product is an entirely new way of regarding the earth, man himself, and the full range of his relationships to it.

In these senses, both the drive toward space and the ultimate "spinoffs" are biologically and psychosocially oriented, rather than technologically centered. This may seem to be a curious assertion, in view of the central role of the physical technologies in the space effort. But these technologies are directed wholly toward the single purpose of maintaining the human organism off the surface of the earth or, at the next level, toward extending human sensing and communications even beyond this limit. The central problems of research, application, and operational reliability of the technological components are phrased in terms of the parameters of extreme environments.

In sum, the most massively organized deployment of human knowledge and expertise is now concentrated on how man, through his technical capabilities, may maintain himself optimally in a "shirtsleeve" environment under conditions more stringently hostile than any he is likely to encounter on earth. In terms of our terrestrial problems and prospects, this direction is not without significance.

At the point where man's relationship to his planetary environment has become extremely critical, he launches with seeming spontaneity the largest controlled experiment ever carried out. He devises the model and defines the mission to determine how man may best use his most advanced scientific and technological capabilities to sustain the human organism in the most advantageous physical conditions, assisted by the most refined environmental control and communications facilities. Rather than being peripheral to the more urgent problems of human society on earth, this represents a major direction of human intelligence toward their solution.

The "closed ecology" of life support systems for sustained flights, even where no prolonged residence in space is projected, is a systems model for the redesign of many of our large-scale industrial undertakings whose ecological malfunction degrades the quality of our environment. The problems of waste management, materials reuse, and recycling of clean air and water are stated precisely in these terms. A similar model may also be applied to the refashioning of the metabolic support systems of many of our other human conveniences in the city, the private dwelling, transportation, communications, and similar services.

Overall biomedical research focused on the internal environ of the space capsule has already augmented the operational specification for physical living standards, for remote health monitoring and service, and other benefits that might have been achieved by a more directly ameliorative concern for everyday human welfare. In addition, the microearth capsule is not merely planned for survival, but for *optimal* human integration in observation, communications, decision-making, and control.

Although any brief references to the present state-of-the-art of such life-support systems emphasizes the wholly physical aspects, the larger psychosocial requirements for multiple crew missions of longer duration are also a major focus of such work.

The basic human functions are the baselines for such closed

CLOSED ECOLOGICAL SYSTEM

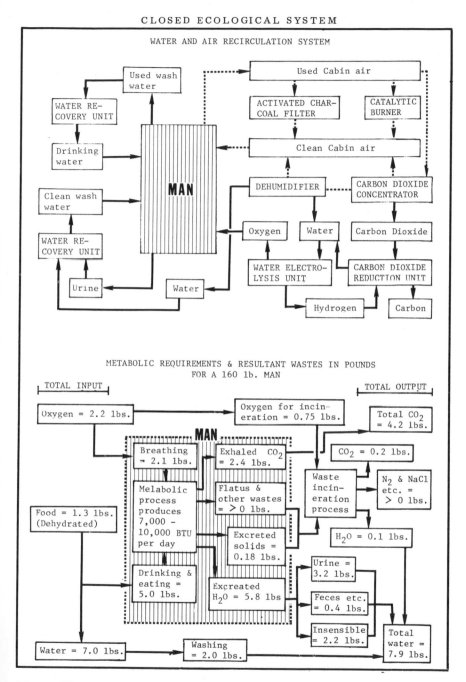

Figure 51.
E. S. Mills, R. L. Butterton, Douglas Missile & Space Systems Development,
Interplanetary Mission Life Support System 1965; NASA: ASD Report TR
61–363.

ecologies. Man's required physiological intakes are food, water, and air. His output materials are solids, including undigested materials: metabolic wastes (shed skin, hair, fingernail clippings, etc.) and salts; expired gases, including carbon dioxide and water vapor; liquids, respiration, and perspiration moisture, urine, and fecal matter. His daily metabolic turnover is in balance so that the main considerations in the physical aspect of the ecology design are the "looping back" of various exchanges to form a closed system. For example, in breathing, we exhale about 2.2 pounds of CO_2 per day; on earth this is largely taken up by growing plants, which convert it to oxygen and cycle. In a closed spacecraft, the CO_2 can be funneled outside, absorbed through chemical combination, fed to an oxygen recovery unit, or used in a "food cycle" resembling the terrestrial man/plant exchange.

The ideal system would be a completely regenerative, self-sustaining one in which water and oxygen would be recovered from metabolic wastes. Air conditioning, temperature regulation, food synthesis, preparation and disposal, sanitation and hygiene requirements, and other functions would be linked in one integral system: "In a truly closed cyclic system . . . all molecules entering the body are eventually excreted, purified physiochemically, and then reused by the spacemen."[1]

The present state-of-the-art is exemplified in an interplanetary mission scheme for the launch period between the 1970s and mid-1980s. Emphasis is placed on the air and water recirculation systems, which are integrated in certain aspects with temperature conditioning, waste management, and atmospheric conditioning. The food cycle remains open as an area of critical forward development.

The full system projected is for a regenerative "closed loop" microecology capable of maintaining a nine-man crew on a 500-day planetary mission without resupply.[2] This covers the entire range of physical life maintenance, including waste management, personal hygiene, nutrition, and clothing. Waste control will be nonmanual, both disposable and reusable clothing will be used with cleaning and storage provisions, a full bath/shower unit will be included, and other personal services will be provided. Each man will have approximately 1,000 cubic feet of space in the module.

The design of power supply and heat sources for such a large

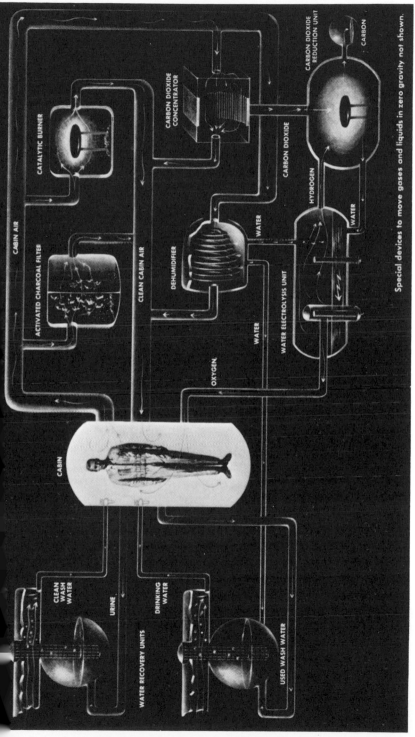

Special devices to move gases and liquids in zero gravity not shown.

52. Life Support System.
General Dynamics, Inc.

system are interesting, in view of our earlier discussion of terrestrial systems. Three possible alternative, or combined, designs are described: (1) solar cells in conjunction with batteries to provide heat and power; (2) solar cells used for power but heat obtained from a radioisotopic source; (3) isotope source for both heat and power.

What is actually being studied here is the prototype for an autonomous, self-servicing house that could function anywhere on earth, without sewer lines or power utilities, and with minimal maintenance and real estate linkage.

Omission of the food cycle from the project described above reflects the comparative developmental lag in this area. The earth, its regenerative cycle, and its food chains through plant, animal, man, microbe, and so on, is a closed-cycle feeding arrangement of relatively envious size whose miniaturization is a greater problem than that of the individual air-water-waste cycle that it subsumes. Biological food systems under review have almost all dropped the earlier "algae" based models or other photosynthetic units because of their light-energy requirements. The more recent approach is the chemosynthetic, using microbial populations that assimilate carbon dioxide and urea, obtaining their energy from hydrogen rather than from light conversion, and hence able to work in the dark. As (theoretically) edible products, these organisms are composed of proteins, fats, carbohydrates, and water.

Various other biosynthetic processes include combinations of bacteria, algae, turnips, sweet potatoes, and reportedly a small colony of duckweed, which is at present in orbit. The Russians have broached the idea of a carefully programed chicken battery, reusing processed wastes and algae to achieve an endless chicken supply. Serious studies have also been put forward for using edible materials for all internal partitions, control knobs, furnishings, the functions of which would be programed so that they would be expendable at various mission stages.

Forward work on this part of the cycle involving eventual duplication and miniaturization of natural food synthesis will eventually result in applications of direct value to terrestrial food problems.

A further aspect of space travel is the possible effects on men living away from earth periodicities for long periods. Many of man's internal rhythms are based on twenty-four-hour cycles.

You can take man away from the earth . . . but you can't take earth away from man, for he is an earth animal and his entire biological system and biochemical process is a function of the environment of the diurnal cycle. He takes with him his own rhythm . . . what happens [then] if men are desynchronized over long periods . . . with abnormal physiological cycles? It may well be that an understanding of this problem will help develop a revolution in medical diagnostics and chemical research in the use of drugs and the predictive health assay of the individual.[3]

Apart from the increased understanding and acquisition of knowledge about the internal metabolic requirements of the human organism, there is also within the space-satellite sensing program the extraordinary development of new and more comprehensive knowledge about the external metabolic processes of the global ecology: the composition and cycles of the atmosphere, mapping and monitoring of vegetation changes on the earth's surface, sensing of electrophysical changes in the earth structure and its radiation shields, and many more. These, by their relation to other developments, may be treated best separately.

Rather than seeking for the direct technological transfer of space research applications to traditional artifacts, we may stress again that it is the conceptual approach and the coordination of efforts toward its unitary purpose that may be of greater value.

In practice, the spinoff is characterized by applications in both the hard and soft technologies: in the hardware of new materials, instrumentation communication devices, and instruments; and in the software of new organizational and logistical capability, in scientific concepts, and in the range of new systems approaches to the solution of various problems.

Telemetry, for example, the sensing and transmitting of information on the state of a man or an object at great distances, owes its recent rapid development to space activity. Obviously, this can be used in any situation where monitoring at a distance is required, but at present its most positive developments are in medicine. In ways that are now beginning to revolutionize hospital design and various chemical procedures, this family of devices includes microminiature individual patient sensors that feed data to centralized computer or human/machine diagnostic and treatment centers. These telemetric instruments thus provide new and more efficient forms of medical care.

A six patient physiological monitoring system, which evolved from Mercury and Gemini technology, has been installed in a St. Louis hospital and is being marketed commercially. The system includes bedside consoles, oscilloscopes, multiple recording apparatus for monitoring various ongoing physiological conditions, and an audio alarm to alert staff to radical changes in various critical rates.[4]

Compact power sources for heart pacemakers, inert materials for surgical replacement, and a range of new instrumentation for diagnosis and treatment owe much to space-medicine research. With the emphasis, however, on the anticipatory optimal care of healthy spacemen, the greatest gains may be in the area of preventive medicine, in the maintenance of health rather than the curing of disease.

The development of automated medical component systems, such as those for routine microbial, blood, urine, and other biochemical analysis, and of other diagnostic instrumentation could point the way toward the provision of high-standard medical services for the lesser developed countries. Such services are presently hampered by the shortage of medical personnel and the lengthy training period necessary for their provision. This shortage could be compensated by the use of advanced systems capable of remote deployment, which could greatly increase the range and accessibility of expert medical skills far beyond those normally encountered in everyday social relations.

As plans develop for larger crew missions, moon colonies, and other space enclaves, we shall need to structure new patterns of social interaction. Perhaps we can adapt older models, such as those of the Eskimo and other groups who have intricate systems for closely contiguous enclave living in protracted isolation. Our current social models, emphasizing stability and equilibrium, will be of little value in the design of such microsocieties, for essential to their survival will be their swift adaptation to change and their alertness to cope with the ever-present threat of dire physical emergencies.

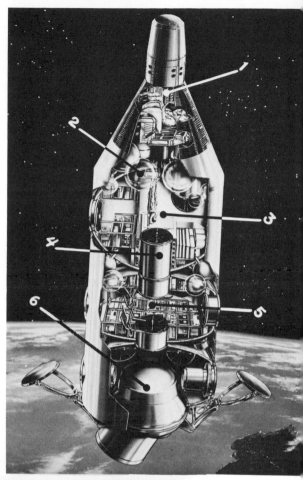

3. Manned Orbiting Labora-
ory.
1. Gemini capsule
2. Sphere for cryogenic fuels
3. Living compartment
4. Airlock
5. Laboratory
6. Camera

ockheed Missiles and Space Co.

4. Drawing of the United
ates' most advanced unmanned
acecraft, the Orbiting Astro-
mical Observatory (OAO).
is 3,900-pound observatory
ll give astronomers their first
stained look into the universe
m above the obscuring and
torting effects of the Earth's
nosphere, at about 500 statute
les.
SA.

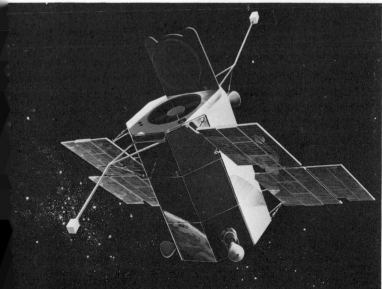

The structural aspects of spacecraft systems have as wide a spectrum as that displayed in life-support systems. These structures —which will perform under the most rigorous conditions, sustain loads, insulate, and protect against radiation and meteoroids— are strictly computed on a more precise performance-per-pound basis than any type of environment-control structure employed on earth.

Again it is the changed conceptual level of approach that is important. Our private dwellings and city structures are still put together in relatively medieval craft fashion (with attendant demerits and human energy costs) using components that have changed little in materials use and design since the nineteenth century. The space structure designer, on the other hand, must work on the more radical and fundamental level of functional molecular concepts. He selects from the microlevel those materials that are integrated into the macrosystem. For instance "whisker" fibers of 0.2-mu diameter are spun into composite lightweight matrixes of flexible metallic and nonmetallic materials of a durability and strength far in excess of our present steel, concrete and brick buildings.

In terms of external configuration, form is determined by functional criteria, but in ways that bear little relation to such determination by other designers. Apart from the projectile type of launch vehicle and present cone-shaped, manned capsules, space structures now in orbit or under development present an extraordinary range of design strategies. These range from rigid structures of various types, exhibiting greater variety in the unmanned "Surveyor" and "Nimbus" types, to developments in the variable-geometry folding, self-expandable structures that have been pioneered by R. Buckminster Fuller. The latter are particularly under investigation for manned lunar-base needs, for which large-span enclosures will be required to fit into a nose-cone volume for automatic opening and erection.

Similar close-packing studies for the first space station include a full-scale, three-story prototype of an inflatable doughnut-shaped structure of neoprene-coated Dacron and foam rubber. Like a giant innertube, the station connects to a central hub through a tunnel spoke. The prototype has a 30-ft diameter, and production-model calculations allow for a 150-ft diameter station within which the crew would work in a shirtsleeve environment equipped, of course, with inflatable furnishings.

Nuclear structuring of the materials and miniaturization of the electromechanical components of our present home environment controls is a by-product of space research that will go far beyond the Teflon-coated saucepan. The direct influence on the external forms and interior is, for the moment, confined to the symbolic: transparent and inflatable furniture, exotic metallic finishes, and spacecraft-type kitchen control consoles. But this symbolic use is a normal mode in the communication of innovation, marking the necessary psychosocial adjustment that accompanies more fundamental changes in a reconceptualized environment.

The development of microminiaturization, which in large part derived from space needs, is one of the most dramatic technical gains of the past two decades. Though presently more visible in the progressively smaller and again symbolic gadgetry of the transistor radio and portable TV, it represents another aspect of the dematerialization of the physical presence of technology.

About fifteen years ago, packing densities of microelectronic units were around 10^6 parts per cubic foot; present "off-shelf" components now run to 10^8 and 10^9 parts per cubic foot. At this scale, for example, more than 100 circuits comprising around 150 parts are packed in a silicon wafer an inch wide and less than 1/100 inch thick. If trends hold, this capacity could reach 10^{15} per cubic foot within the next thirty years. The resulting electronic "grown" components would begin to approach biological units with equivalent long-life spans.

Apart from weight and volume savings, the development of microminiaturization was spurred by *reliability* requirements, an equally important conceptual parameter of space technology. In terrestrial environment control, reliability, like most other factors, is of an extremely low order. In the hostile environ of space, crucial part failure can be literally the end of the mission.

Apart from exhaustive testing and extremely high reliability standards, another operational aspect is the software design of anticipatory schedules for emergency procedures and the integration in elaborate "backup" and self-repairing subunits. Typically,

TREND TOWARDS MINIATURISATION
(MAXIMUM PERFORMANCE PER POUND OF UNIT RESOURCE)

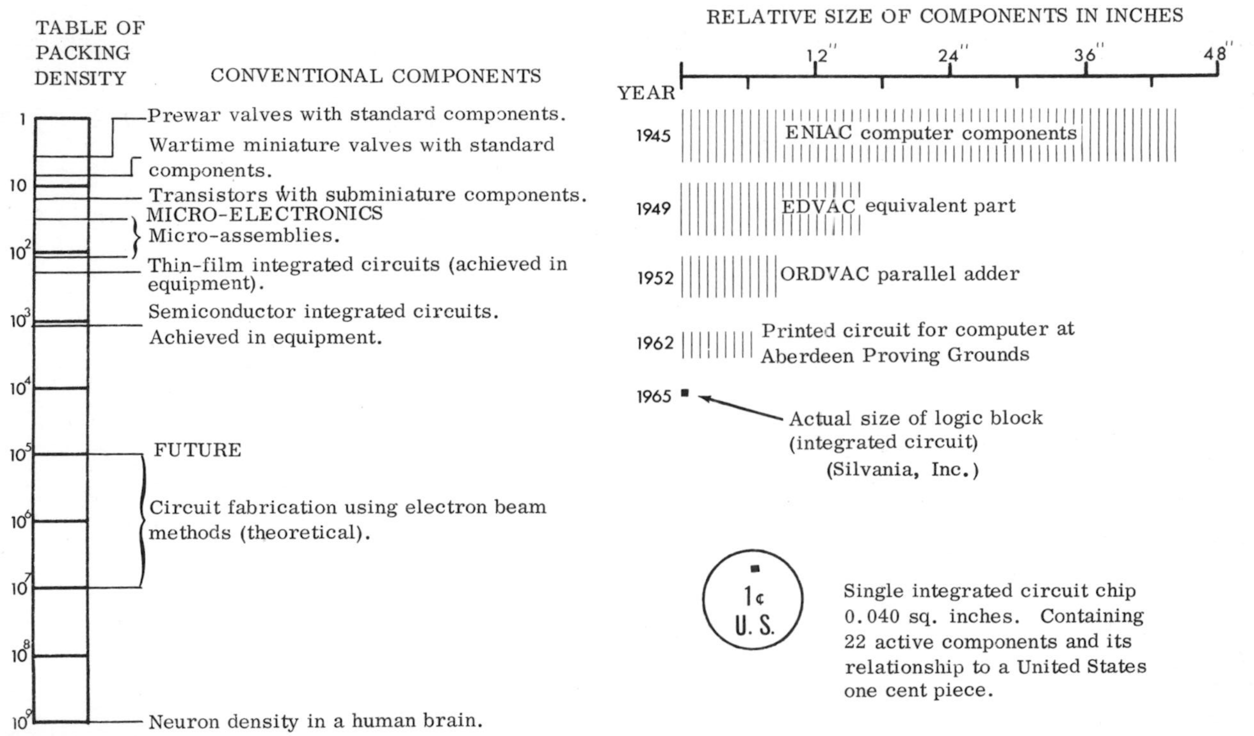

RELATIVE SIZE OF COMPONENTS IN INCHES

12" 24" 36" 48"

YEAR

1945 ENIAC computer components

1949 EDVAC equivalent part

1952 ORDVAC parallel adder

1962 Printed circuit for computer at Aberdeen Proving Grounds

1965 Actual size of logic block (integrated circuit) (Silvania, Inc.)

Single integrated circuit chip 0.040 sq. inches. Containing 22 active components and its relationship to a United States one cent piece.

1¢ U.S.

TABLE OF PACKING DENSITY

CONVENTIONAL COMPONENTS

Prewar valves with standard components.

Wartime miniature valves with standard components.

Transistors with subminiature components.

MICRO-ELECTRONICS Micro-assemblies.

Thin-film integrated circuits (achieved in equipment).

Semiconductor integrated circuits. Achieved in equipment.

FUTURE

Circuit fabrication using electron beam methods (theoretical).

Neuron density in a human brain.

1 10 10^2 10^3 10^4 10^5 10^6 10^7 10^8 10^9

Figure 55

in life-support areas, units may be split in parallel half-loads for normal conditions and assume full load in the event of either failing. Electromechanical modules are interchangeable, allowing emergency repair "piracy" from one area to another. As far as possible, control and maintenance functions may be degraded successively on malfunction, from automatic to semiautomatic, to eventual manual operation of all vital units. The contrast with the design of terrestrial operations is acute, say, in relation to the recent United States power-grid failures and the general lack of anticipatory design in our local environ control.

The next stage in space will be the lunar base and manned orbital space stations. Current thinking on lunar base design goes in many directions. Ancillary transport equipment designs vary from Buck Rogers jet suits (already operational for the recent Gemini/Agena docking program), to balloon-wheeled mobile laboratories, moon trains of various types, transport modules as mobile bases, flying platforms, and the like.*

The moon race aspect brings in the Soviet work in space. So far, due to local accessibility of materials, our emphasis has been on United States equipment and thinking. Though roughly parallel in technical development, there are certain interesting cultural differences in approach. The first obvious one would be that the Russians already have a woman cosmonaut.

The female organism is more stable, compared to that of a man, to the influence of a number of unfavourable conditions. This is the result of physiological traits of woman connected with her intended by nature functions of motherhood. Thus the female organism more easily endures deficiency of oxygen and unfavourable conditions of environment. But, at the same time, the nervous system of the female organisms is more excitable, more strongly reacts to an unusual situation.[5]

The Americans have been rather silent on this aspect. A second difference may be the view of man and his role in the space-man/machine relationship. The Soviet effort has concentrated on

---

*Similar to the Wanigan mobile bases in use in the Arctic. These are long trains of snow wagons, in some cases two stories high, accommodating a small village of technicians who travel from fixed base to base.

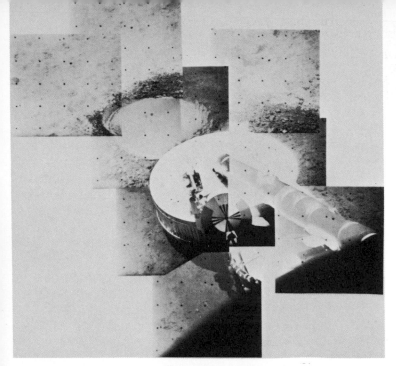

56. Mosaic of narrow-angle pictures taken by Surveyor III on April 26, 1967 moonlanding.
Jet Propulsion Laboratory, California Institute of Technology, NASA.

57. Surveyor VII's surface sampler furrowed a 12-inch-long trench in the moon's surface at midnight Friday, January 12, 1968.
Jet Propulsion Laboratory, California Institute of Technology, NASA.

58. Bendix Corp.'s version of the Lunar Scientific Survey module. A similar vehicle will be used to extend lunar surface mission stay-times.
Aerospace Technology, November 20, 1967.

59. A simulation technique (Reduced Gravity Simulator) developed by NASA's Langley Research Center, Hampton, Virginia, is used to simulate the low lunar gravity under conditions suitable for a man to perform self-locomotive tasks on earth.
NASA.

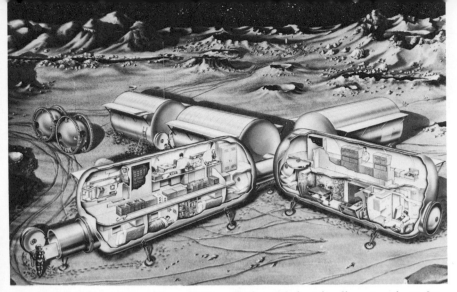

60. Design for a lunar base. Each cylinder, 20 feet in diameter, is to be delivered to the moon as a completely assembled, pressurized unit with all equipment, provisions, stores, and supplies installed and ready for operation. Each six-man shelter is self-sufficient except for power supply, to be obtained from a central nuclear power plant.
Lockheed Missiles and Space Co., Inc.

massive boosters and the lifting of relatively large capsule units into orbit, with earlier emphasis on more directly controlled maneuverability from the spacecraft rather than ground control. For example, referring to the "Polet-1" of 1963:

Now man in outer space no longer is a prisoner of his own ship. He controls it, he directs its flight. The spaceship becomes all the more obedient to the will of man.[6]

The Russians tend to emphasize more rigorous training of human functions with less reliance on a tailored environment for the astronaut. This is a more rough-and-ready approach than the American emphasis on a shirtsleeve cabin environment with greater dependence on machine augmentation of human function.

Other interesting divergences may be found in the available translated material. Russian extrapolation of present technological development seems more literary and poetic in imagery. This may be a characteristic of translation. One paper[7] describes a rocket-rail system of interplanetary travel, using an "ion drive" engine, which runs between solar electrical station guidelines that furnish additional drive energy and guidance. Others often refer to Yefrenov's novel *Andromeda Nebula*, and various science fiction works when discussing travel to other galaxies, which is not quite so characteristic of American reports in this area.

An exception would be the work of D. M. Cole, a senior space scientist at U.S. General Electric's Space Technology Center. His various papers, and a book, *Beyond Tomorrow*, published just before his recent death, explore far beyond the development of hardware to that of artificial intelligence, modes of immortality, and extraterrestrial styles of life. He gives a detailed exposition of the evolution of man based on the terraforming of meteoroids and other planetary bodies, and of developing new forms of macroecological relationships that enable large, 10,000-people colonies to cruise space in their own self-powered, closed-cycle worlds.

Among the larger-range implications of space exploration are those questions of a social and cultural nature that relate to:

1. The presence of intelligent life elsewhere in our solar system.

2. The modification of man or of other planetary environs to permit humans to colonize other "earths" on a more permanent basis.

3. The contamination of earth by organisms brought back by interplanetary probes, and conversely, the introduction of terrestrial life forms to alien environs.

It is generally thought that life as we know it may not exist in the other bodies circulating our local sun, and is more likely to be encountered through long-range communications from sources outside the local system. The possibility remains, however, that evidence of extinct life forms or of past civilization artifacts might be found on the lunar or Martian surface. The sociocultural response to the latter would, of course, be quite different from the former. Where the discovery of an alien life form might trigger a feral hostility in a human society that felt threatened by such a presence, the discovery of traces of long-dead civilized forms on the moon might be equally traumatic in its pessimistic overtones. Of course, both reactions are already being modified by increased human understanding brought about by psychological experiments with dolphins and other creatures with acute perception. Continued archaeological exploration of the earth places man's own civilized origins so far back in the past that this knowledge may afford him sufficient antiquity to assuage the feeling of having been preceded in time by other forms. There is, of course, the no less possible and intriguing theory that man himself may have originated on other worlds, or at least that his original life forms may have so developed.

The modification of man to live in extreme environments has also proceeded naturally on earth, and current biomedically engineered prosthetics may be the forerunners of further designed alterations. The re-forming of extraterrestrial bodies to maintain human life is obviously a task requiring vast amounts of energy and considerably more knowledge than we presently possess. However, as we may note, this would be:

. . . analogous to an earth bound modification project that has been underway with increasing success for almost 2,000 years, the reclamation of the North Sea lowlands. Although only the last century or so of this effort has utilized modern technology it has always required the combination of physical and biological operations—and, of course, social cooperation—which will also be requisite for the expansion of extraterrestrial colonies.[8]

61. Commercial space station concept envisioned by Douglas engineers would accommodate privately owned laboratory modules docked at sides of the 130-foot core vehicle. A nuclear power plant trails on a 100 foot boom. The core vehicle would be 33 feet in diameter and house up to 32 men. *Aviation Week & Space Technology*, May 15, 1967.

Contamination of other planetary surfaces by *earth* organisms seems more likely in view of our projected manned lunar landings within the decade. Past instrument landings have already been carried out under relatively stringent precautions to avoid any such events. Though the reverse effect of earth entry by alien forms seems more directly harmful, the overall emphasis derived from both possibilities has been the emphasis on anticipatory microbiological procedures. These include the design of automated remote and local sensors and recorders capable of refined microbiological analysis. Again, we may conclude with the observation that even the negative threat within such a far-reaching program of organized human enterprise may be converted, through anticipatory procedures, into positive gains.

.   Anticipated Pattern of Spacecraft Development.
acecraft Development in the Next Decade, by A. K. Theil; American Astronautical
:iety Meeting, Hindsville, Alabama, June 1967.

COMMUNICATIONS	NAVIGATION	EARTH RESOURCES	METEOROLOGY	GEOSCIENCES	LUNAR	PLANETARY
1500 CHANNELS	FEASIBILITY	RESEARCH AND FEASIBILITY	LIMITED OPERATION IN PHOTOGRAPHY, RESEARCH IN INDIRECT SENSORS	SMALL OBSERVATORIES	APOLLO	MARINERS, PIONEERS
		LIMITED OPERATIONAL				
20,000 CHANNELS, 5000 LB, 3 KW	GLOBAL OPERATION		LIMITED OPERATION IN PHOTOGRAPHY AND INDIRECT SENSORS	EXPLORATORY MANNED REASEARCH IN ORBIT	PERMANENT STATIONS AND MOBILE SURFACE PROBES	VOYAGER
						OUTER PLANETS PROBES
DIRECT BROADCAST, 10,000 LB, 50 KW						
20-TON MANNED PLATFORM SYNCHRONOUS ORBIT ●VOICE, DATA, TV ●TRAFFIC CONTROL ●SYNOPTIC EARTH RESOURCES ●SYNOPTIC METEOROLOGY			2-5 TON LOW ORBIT AUTOMATED PLATFORMS	60-100 TON LOW ORBIT MANNED RESEARCH STATION		

2
Inner Space

The oceans cover approximately two-thirds of our planetary surface, yet our knowledge of this vast area is rudimentary. In the sense that we are able to look directly into the sky and scan the stars, we already know more about the reaches of outer space than we do about the oceans on our doorstep.

As man's most hostile environ for centuries, only the surface of the oceans was traveled upon and its depths were virtually unknown until the present. Barely 1 percent of all sea organisms have been studied, and the cyclic migrations of its larger creatures are comparatively uncharted. Our mapping of the ocean floor is at about the same stage as that of our earth-land mapping in the mid-eighteenth century.

In terms of space, resources, and the challenge of exploration, it is rather like having two other worlds at our disposal: the shallow and accessible edges of the land continents and the great deeps beyond, which are calculable not only by their floor area, but also as a three-dimensional volume of space inhabited by a vast number of life forms.

The continental shelves alone afford a possible work, research, and recreation area approximately three times the land surface size of the United States, or about half the area of the world's lowlands where most of humanity lives. These shelves slope gradually about 10 feet for each mile out to the deeps; their extension beyond the shorelines of the continents varies in width from about 700 miles off northern Europe and Siberia to less than a mile off parts of the western coasts of the Americas. They comprise about 7 percent of the lands under the oceans.

While neither so heavily funded nor so dramatically in evidence

196

as outer-space developments, underwater research may have a more immediate impact on our way of life in the next few decades.

The material resources of the oceans are relatively enormous, and though the difficulty of access to them is in proportion to their richness, human ingenuity in exploring them has already afforded a considerable extension of man's environ control possibilities.

The ocean is the ultimate repository of everything eroded from the continents. Over 40,000 million tons of materials are washed into the oceans every year by rivers. The winds also transport many millions of tons of materials per year.[1]

But the material exploitation of the ocean's mineral resources is only one area of its potential overall value. Like the exploration of outer space it provides a focus of convergence for almost all facets of human enquiry, ranging from the earth sciences to historical and archaeological studies and to the psychosocial aspects of undersea living, work, and play.

The floor of the ocean contains a wealth of history of the past life on our planet . . . core-sampling the sediment of the ocean bed . . . in some areas one inch reveals 1,000 years of history. In other areas it has been determined that a thirty foot length of core reveals history as far back as nine million years.[2]

Our pressing requirement for more intelligent use and reuse of land resources is not so stringent in relation to oceans, in which there is much more frequent ecological recycling than in land areas. Fish and other organic populations have higher growth rates, and the harvest of undersea vegetation is less subject to capricious weather problems.

In the past two decades alone, the yield of the world's fisheries has increased at a rate considerably greater than that of other food producers, and at a rate greater than that of the human population. Yet this yield, immensely valuable when translated into animal protein (the major shortage in the world's diet), is still much less than could be gained by a more organized and systematic cropping of the ocean's food resources.

The amount of fish and invertebrates taken from the ocean in 1964

(45 million tons) represented about 2% of the approximately 2 billion tons of such animals actually produced by the ocean per year in size large enough to be caught and used by man. The other 98% died, decayed, and returned to the web of ocean life . . . the ocean is capable of producing for man's use about 400 million tons of animal protein per year . . . if distribution were timely and equable to all people in the world 24 million tons per year of animal protein would keep 3 billion people in good health from the protein need standpoint.[3]

Of course, as this writer states, the protein presently gained from the sea is used more in processed feed for land animals than directly for human consumption. But given an increase in the use of sea protein in human diet, the oceans could provide still more (by a factor of 10)—up to 240 million tons per year of additional animal protein.

In addition to the food harvest, as mentioned before, the oceans are a great potential source of metals and other materials. The concentration of elements in certain bodies of ocean water—the Red Sea, for instance—is virtually fluid sea mines. The extraction of metals and minerals is a complementary process in the large-scale operation of desalination plants for fresh water supplies.

The more immediate source of ocean ores may be the nodule deposits recently discovered on the ocean floor. In many areas, thick concentrations of high-grade manganese ore nodules have been located which assayed up to 50 percent; other ores included cobalt, nickel, and copper to 3 percent respectively, and other metals in varying amounts. One specifically interesting quality of these nodules is their continuing growth formation. Referring to the speed with which such nodule deposits grow, one authority has suggested that, ". . . as these nodules are being mined, the minerals industry would be faced with the interesting situation of working a deposit that grows faster than it could be mined or consumed."[4] In terms of ecological design, that is, using the naturally occurring growth cycles, this phenomenon of nodule growth has interesting connotations.

Other characteristics of water mineralization are relevant to ocean mining. A number of marine plants and animals can concentrate elements found in sea water, much as land plants and animals selectively accumulate soil elements. Seaweed concentrates iodine from its normal dispersion of 0.001 percent in sea water to up to 0.5 percent; absorption rates of certain coral species reach to 8 percent levels. Oysters concentrate copper from sea water, and a certain sea slug has the capacity to concentrate vanadium in its body even though the quantity in its environ is quite minute.

Apart from the minerals already present in the ocean waters and floor, it has been estimated that in the United States some 200 tons of copper, in various forms, are lost to the oceans in sewage per year for each million people, together with 50 tons each of such metals as manganese, lead, aluminum, and titanium. Such naturally occurring agents could possibly be designed into processing systems for mineral concentration and recovery. Our use of domesticated land food, plants, and animals is precisely such an ongoing system for intermediate processing of food energies and materials.

Apart from bulk supplies of materials, the medical aspects of drugs extractable from sea organisms and plants is only now opening up into a new area of research into marine pharmacology.

We already know that chemicals isolated from certain toxic marine fishes are 200,000 times more powerful in blocking nervous activity than drugs currently used in laboratory research on nerve and brain activity . . . Toxicity is a useful indicator of biological activity and, therefore, provides important leads to other valuable pharmacological properties.[5]

Offshore drilling for oil and natural gas has been an ongoing aspect of ocean work for many years. Recent dislocations and shortages of the strategically located land fields have shifted attention increasingly to the exploitation of oil and natural gas deposits under the bed of the continental shelves. Particular areas of increasing commercial activity are the continental shelves of southeast Asia and the Pacific islands. Apart from the value of exploitation, the impact of such undertakings has already had considerable effect on the political and economic situations in these areas.

As with outer space, much of the present impetus and funding to explore the oceans is largely of tactical military/commercial origin. The nuclear-powered submarine and its missile-launch pattern is one instance. The vast economic potential and obvious scientific interest have encouraged ocean research and development and have served to reorient man in his overall relationship to the ocean. Official interests in the direction of conservation have been aroused just in time to prevent further indiscriminate spoilage, particularly of the coastal shelves. Old minefields of past wars still make many parts of the shelves unsafe and will do so for some time to come; sewage and industrial waste pollution have already ruined other large areas of the coastal waters, in particular where these are critical for recreational and other living purposes. Over-fishing has led not only to greatly reduced catches, but to the near extinction of certain unique marine species such as the great sperm whale. Other species are threatened by continued encroachment upon spawning and breeding areas. As man fills and builds on these marine lands, the species decrease and in time will disappear. Dispersal of nuclear power-plant wastes into estuaries increase water temperatures in these spawning grounds so that a thermal pollution of as little as a 5 percent increase in temperature can kill fish.

Ocean Technology

The design criteria of undersea vehicles and environ control structures are, in some respects, the reverse of those for outer-space exploration. In building to withstand very great outside pressures, there is less configurational freedom in external hull design; also, hull weight varies sharply according to operating depth. Propulsion speeds need to be increased, drag and resistance must be overcome, and special problems of surface coating to resist chemical erosion, microbial growths, and other salt-water effects must be solved.

At greater depths, no external work can be carried out by human operators and remotely controlled manipulators are required. Vehicle speed, relative to energy source, imposes certain limits. For example, to double the speed of submerged vehicles requires roughly eight times more propulsion power than is now available. Communications problems are, again, different from those in space flight.

The most singular differences in the two areas of sea and space penetration are in travel speeds and range. However, maximum ocean depth penetration was established relatively early in underwater exploration. The bottom of the deepest ocean trench known, the Challenger Deep at 35,000 feet, was reached by the bathyscaphe Trieste in 1960.

Apart from scuba equipment used in shallow waters, or heavy diving-suit gear limited to about 200 feet, present commercial undersea vehicles are two- to five-man units having a top speed of about 4 knots with working depths up to a few thousand feet. Some of these are equipped with external remote manipulators for specimen collection. In development are larger, more maneuverable, longer-range vehicles.

Separation of the manipulatory system from the manned vehicle is also being pursued. The latter, called "telechiric" systems, are essentially a family of general purpose work robots. Equipped with arms, sonar, and television, these machines are an extension of their human operator, who may be in, under, or on the sea.

These telechiric, or robotic, systems may be the developmental direction for both shallow and deep ocean mining where human

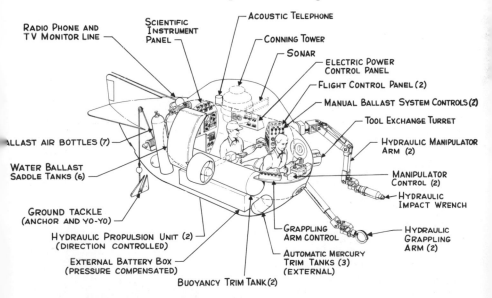

63. Deep Submergence Vehicle.
North American Aviation, Inc.

work capacity is greatly reduced by pressure and other atmospheric characteristics. They can already be linked remotely by television and other electronic instruments that give the land or sea-based operator a control position as sensitive as his own physical senses. The further refinement of such robotic systems could have implications for many land tasks under hostile conditions; their initial remote-handling capacities were partially developed for the movement of "hot" radioactive materials.

Though many of the undersea craft in use and under development are for variable depth use, the most immediately significant area for the establishment of work environment controls are the continental shelves, averaging between 600- and 800-foot depths. These comprise about 10 percent of the total sea floor area only, but are estimated to contain half of the ocean's important biological population and many of its mineral deposits. It is logical, therefore that these will be the first areas to be fully exploited.

These coastal borders still require deep-submergence work craft, and a great many of these vehicles have already been built and used with increasing success.

64.   One of two research submarines, Autec I and Autec II, being built for U.S. Navy, at Electric Boat division (1968). They will carry three-man crews. In emergency, crew can separate front section of craft and float to surface. General Dynamics.

During a dive on the Blake plateau off Florida, the *Aluminaut* (craft) brought up a single manganese nodule weighing 200 lbs. Subsequently, on a deeper dive, the submersible recovered a 2,100 lb. current meter array, thereby establishing the deepest known heavy load recovery to date.[6]

The location and recovery of the lost H-bomb off the Spanish coast in 1967 publicized this aspect of weight recovery from depth by manned and unmanned submersibles.

Though our illustrated examples of such submersibles are mainly of U.S. origin, European and Soviet work in this area has been comparably developed. Recently reported Soviet work includes many types similar to those in use here and also smaller craft that are more specifically designed for shallow depth work and which are made of fiberglas and incorporate external manipulators. The latter type of small lightweight submersible is also under commercial development in the United States for recreational uses.

One of the key features of the recent U.S. Occan Systems, Inc., *Deep Diver*, is that it is the first to permit a diver's entrance to or exit from the craft at great depths. This facility is an important one, obviously, relative to extended undersea exploration work.

Undersea Living

The pioneer in undersea living and working is, of course, Jacques-Yves Cousteau, who set up the first manned undersea work station in 1962 off Marseilles. In Conshelf One, as it was called, two men remained submerged for a week at 33-foot depth and worked outside daily for 5 hours at depths up to 85 feet. Conshelf Two, "the first human colony on the sea floor," as Cousteau has called it, was 36 feet down in the Red Sea and housed five men for a month, including a two-man work camp at greater depth.

Both Conshelf One and Two were cylindrical-domed structures tethered by umbilical communication cables, supply pipes, and other connections to surface and shore stations. Conshelf Three, a spherical structure weighing 140 tons, was established at 328 feet off Cape Ferrat, housing six men for thirty days. During this time, the oceanauts breathed a helium and oxygen mixture inside the base, and conducted heavy duty work for up to 7 hours per day outside. An unusual first time communication link was made when Conshelf Three's crew spoke by telephone from under the Mediterranean to the crew of the U.S. Navy's similar experimental station, Sealab II, located 205 feet down off the coast of La Jolla, California.

The problems of life-support systems for extended underocean residence are somewhat similar to outer-space requirements. One particular difference is in the breathing atmosphere where, due to pressures and the problems of nitrogen narcosis and oxygen toxicity, helium-oxygen mixtures are used. This type of atmosphere transmits sound at a different frequency than does air, and by alteration of the speech resonance the human voice takes on a peculiarly high Donald Duck quality.

Another problem is encountered in the variable compression and decompression effects at different depths and their incapacitating effect on sustained undersea work. To combat this, Edwin

65.   Artist's concept of TEKTITE I habitat (1968), being constructed by General Electric's Missile and Space Division, shows the four compartment home-laboratory. Cupola on top of right chamber permits additional observation capability for the crew.

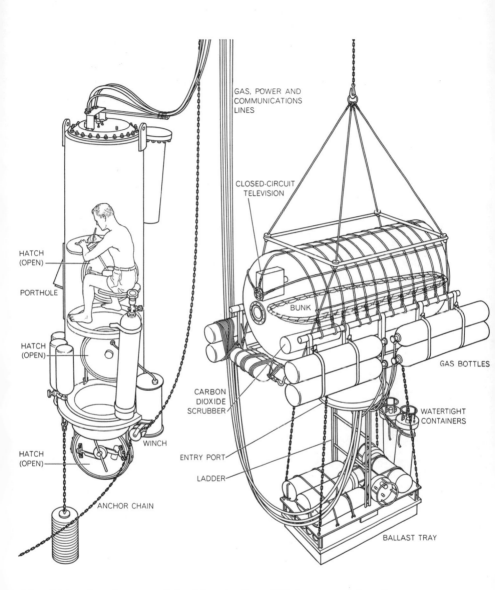

GAS, POWER AND
COMMUNICATIONS
LINES

CLOSED-CIRCUIT
TELEVISION

HATCH
(OPEN)

PORTHOLE

BUNK

HATCH
(OPEN)

GAS BOTTLES

HATCH
(OPEN)

CARBON
DIOXIDE
SCRUBBER

WATERTIGHT
CONTAINERS

WINCH

HATCH
(OPEN)

ENTRY PORT

LADDER

ANCHOR CHAIN

BALLAST TRAY

66.   Two chambers used in *Man in Sea* 432-foot, two-day dive
are diagrammed.
"Living Under the Sea," by Joseph B. MacInnis, *Scientific American*, March
1966, Vol. 214, No. 3.

A. Link, inventor of the Link trainer, has developed the "Man in Sea" system of three related chambers, one of which serves as an elevator to the upper decompression chamber. Using this system, oceanauts have been able to sustain work for longer spaced periods of great depth, than previously—over 400 feet.

In late 1968, the *Sealab III* system of a fixed undersea habitat, with parent ship overhead and semiscuba vehicles for sea-bottom work and excursions, will be anchored for three months at over 400-foot depth off the coast of California. Five eight-man teams will take turns for twelve-day periods of living in the habitat and working on the ocean floor.

There is the more radical possibility of men living under the ocean without elaborate breathing apparatus. Jacques Cousteau has speculated on artificial gill prosthesis, providing direct transfer of oxygen from water to a main blood artery, to adapt man temporarily (or permanently) to undersea living. Some years ago, the Dutch scientist Johannes Kylstra discovered that mammalian lungs can actually extract oxygen directly from water as well as from air. In animal experiments, various subjects have survived long periods of fishlike underwater breathing. The ocean diver using such a system would breathe in water adjusted to the same chemical concentration salts as the bloodstream and charged with dissolved oxygen under pressure. The gain here seems mainly to be in circumventing the need for decompression after diving, and possibly the use of an apparatus that could adjust sea water directly as the breathing liquid. A more promising technique may be the development of artificial gills made of ultra-membranes of silicone rubber. These allow the absorption of air from water and permit escape of carbon dioxide from breathing.

Several patents on this type of underwater breathing apparatus are now being processed.

The sea as a recreation and adventure area is being pioneered by a generation of scuba divers, snorkel swimmers, and surfers. As previously noted, various types of light submersibles are already being marketed. One recent report describes a portable, underwater, inflatable shelter designed by three Russian skin divers, so compact that its main fabric can be stowed in a rucksack. We may be certain that Cousteau's pioneer directions have already gathered a great and enthusiastic following, which will result in many such experiments.

The planned recreational use of the sea and shore "interface" area has, on the other hand, been rather unimaginative. A few beach resort hotels with undersea lounges and living areas, connected by tunnel to the main shore building, are in somewhat basic development. Landscaping the ocean floor, designing undersea gardens, and entertainment grottoes (and comfort stations) will probably require the imaginative combination of a Capability Brown and a Walt Disney.

Schemes for extended large-scale dwelling under the sea range from the General Electric Corporation's "Bottom Fix" project of chains of huge glass spheres for the occupation of the mid-ocean ridge by the late 1970s, to the "Rock Site" of a U.S. Navy engineer, who envisages large caverns carved out of the ocean bottom to house surveying, mining, and other sea working teams.

Whatever the feasibility of such ideas, they presage an era in which man's activities will open up the ocean depths more and more.

The danger, as with outer space, is that part of the manifest drive toward these activities will be in terms of military and commercial strategies. Technology has swiftly outstripped the terms of the 1958 Geneva Convention that deal with the continental shelves. These are involved mostly with national ownership and exploitation rights to depths of about 600 feet off the coasts and are not applicable to the deeper sea bottoms that are available for exploitation. Much lip service has been given to suggestions that the trusteeship of the larger deeps be administered by, and assist the funding of, the United Nations. But most governments and their associated commercial interests are already in overt and open competition for exclusive rights to greater areas of the ocean deeps.

The oceans, patently, do not and should not belong to any specific national group, any more than the earth's atmosphere or the Van Allen radiation belts. This question is only another aspect of the basic problem of the various obsolete local and short-term interests that press closely on the larger survival interests of the global community.

3

Resources of the Planet

ENERGY

The maintenance of man on earth is accomplished through the use of the energies incoming from the sun and from the stored energies of past evolutionary transformation of the planetary surface.

Our concern here is with those resources that are more specifically industrial in character, rather than with agricultural and animal food resources, which are now in more dependent relation to such technological development. We may divide resources, for convenience, into energy and materials, but the prime resource is man himself, since it is through his knowledge and inventive capacities that resources are identified, and then only in terms of human purpose.

Solar Energy

Solar energies have been received on the earth for millions of years and much of present-energy advantage is derived from the stored layers of past animal- and plant-energy converters in the earth surface. These are our fossil fuels: oil, coal, and the gases associated with such deposits. The biomass—that is, the entire complex of all life forms on earth—also represents a long and continuous impounding of solar energies.

We have, then, the division of *stored* energies—the fossil fuels and fissionable elements in the earth crust—which comprise a finite, nonrenewable source, and the division of *income* energies from the sun and other sources, which are constantly renewed.

The material course of human society may be related to various stages of energy exploitation:

1. The use of collective human energies to perform tasks beyond individual capacity.

208

2. Draught animal energies; wood burning; wind and water sources.

3. Inanimate machine energies, dependent largely on the fossil fuels, but related to more direct use of the energy of chemical and biochemical processes.

4. Post-mechanical energy phases, in which atomic energies derived initially from the limits of fissionable fuels go toward fusion processes and relatively inexhaustible sources.

5. With, and beyond, the atomic phase, the more directly efficient use of solar energies of ongoing biological, biochemical and bioelectronic energy conversion.

For the greater part of human history, until a few hundred years ago, most civilizations were based on the first two stages, with men and animals as the main muscle energies. The emergence and diffusion of cultures is related to the gain in free energies as surplus to basic survival. Our own period is uniquely the first in which man has had technical access to abundant energy supplies from inanimate sources.

Though many in the lesser developed regions of the world are still dependent for their survival on their own function as muscle-energy converters, man's role is increasingly that of a designer of high-energy gain systems, which are now passing the routine control of such systems to other electromechanical devices.

The gain from low- to high-energy converters is not only in quantity but also in quality and flexibility. Electric energy is most efficient because it is more adaptable and can increase the speed with which energy is made available for a given task. Moreover, it makes possible the conditions under which inanimate energy converters can work round the clock with no organic rest periods.

Zimmerman gives an interesting comparative example of the speed and energy cost differentials between man-labor and machine production:

If we assume that the building of an Egyptian pyramid required the work of 50,000 slaves for twenty years, while a skyscraper of comparable size can be built by 5,000 laborers in six months, the number of workers at a given moment is as 10 to 1; but if the time element is taken into account, the ratio is 400 to 1. This means that it took approximately 400 times as much food to generate the manpower that built the pyramid as it took to feed workers who built the skyscraper.[1]

This comparison between total human slave-labor energy and man-labor plus machine energy was early elicited, for example, in Sir William Ramsay's "Presidential Address to the British Association" (1911). In his estimation, "each British family then had an average of twenty energy 'helots' in its service. This concept of the electromechanical "energy slave" measure has been further developed by R. Buckminster Fuller.*

The significance of this energy measure in terms of living standards may be noted in comparing European with African and Asian figures for recent years[2]:

Map Area	Population 1960	Percent World Population	Energy Slaves per Capita
Asia	1,679,000,000	56	3
Europe	641,000,000	24.1	81
Africa	254,000,000	8.5	10

We may note that since Ramsay's calculation of 20 such energy units per 5-person family in 1911, the European measure is now 81 per person, or over 400 energy slaves per family.

Though reduced here to the amount of energy directly or indirectly available to each person, the increase in the vast amounts of inanimate energies now required to sustain our evolved societies is evident. A further contrast may demonstrate this more vividly:

The power produced by the Bratsk Hydroelectric Power Station alone is greater than the amount of energy that would be obtained by using the muscular efforts of the entire able-bodied population of the U.S.S.R.[3]

*Fuller's energy-slave unit is computed by taking the world's energy consumption in a year and dividing this by 25 to give a 4 percent figure of energy gainfully employed at present rates of overall efficiency. This (4 percent) net energy used, as expressed in kilowatts per year, is divided by one manpower year; that is, the amount of energy that could be provided by the world population of the year, working 8 hours per day per year. This gives the number of electromechanical energy-slave units available in terms of industrial products, household appliances, autos, telephones, heating, lighting, and other productions.

Our past and present uses of industrial energies and the projection from such continued full uses are a critical factor for both the developed and less developed regions of the world.

The production of world energy, which is also roughly comparable with consumption, increased about 3 percent annually from 1860 to 1960. In the past decade this percentage has almost tripled as a result of population rise and the increased rate of industrialization of previous agrarian regions.

Much of the rise in energy consumption is still within the high-energy economies. In 1964, the industrial regions, with one-quarter of the world's population, consumed 75 percent of the world's coal, 80 percent of its oil and electric power consumption, and 95 percent of the natural gas produced. In the nonindustrial regions, with three-fourths of the world's people, energy still came mostly from human and animal sources plus wood fuels and wastes.

In round terms, during 1964 the most fortunate individual in the developed world regions consumed more than fifty times the industrial energy of his counterpart in the poorer regions of the

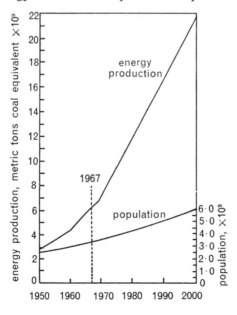

67.   World Population and Energy Production.

world. The paradox in the use of the word "poorer" is, of course, the fact that many of the industrial raw materials and energy fuels used in the high-standard regions came from the so-called poorer regions.

In other comparative measures we may note, for example, that the United States, with only 6 percent of the world population, accounts for one-third of the world's total industrial production, using 32 percent of all minerals and 39 percent of all oil produced. Given our present global trend toward increased interdependence of one region upon another, such countries, in the even short run, "cannot hope to survive as an island of plenty in a sea of international poverty."[4]

When such disparities between the two worlds are compounded by expected population increases in the next few decades and by the increase in industrial energy uses, there is a twofold dilemma. First, the present rates of increase in use of the fossil fuels raises serious doubts not only about their reserve capacities and deleterious effects on the environment, but also about the wisdom of using up such an accessible, but swiftly exhaustible, store. In a world increasingly dependent on inanimate energies, it seems foolish to clean out the cupboard without checking on present and future income energies or unforeseen emergency needs.

Secondly, with present population increases and rates of industrialization, by the year 2000 we may require not double but up to five times more world energy. In terms of fuel-energy usages in current industrial practices, this means an approximate 60 percent rise per year in the overall use of fossil fuels.

Assuming that the nonindustrial regions would be industrialized to the present levels of the advanced countries with the continued rise in use of such energy fuels, this would allow about one century until present accessible reserves were exhausted. In this relatively short term, therefore, to expect to bring the poor nations up to industrial parity with the rich by means of current technological practices is rather unrealistic. We need several, relatively massive, developmental approaches in order to do this effectively.

The first approach is the already ongoing phase of increased resource exploitation, although under present auspices this can hardly be regarded as being conducted for the benefit of the lesser developed regions. Coal may not supply the world energy needs at the year 2000 level for more than 150 to 200 years. Proven oil and natural gas reserves are much greater than the extent of our present knowledge; oil reserve estimates are roughly forty times the world total consumption figures for 1960. Oil, shale, and other sources increase estimates further. The extent of our knowledge is the critical factor in projecting such reserves and their utilization. We not only discover more deposits, but also increase our knowledge of how to extract more energy from them. The existence of very large untapped oil fields on the continental shelves and delta lands of southeast Asia, rivaling those in the Persian Gulf and Caribbean, has been noted in a recent paper:

Actually it has, by now, become obvious (1) that the world's effective reserves of oil will run into trillions of barrels; (2) that a large part of these reserves exist in the shallow water and delta coastal-plain areas of the Western Pacific and of the Southeastern Asian nations; and that the development of these resources can be of immense benefit to hundreds of millions of people, pending the further "breakthrough" in connection with the harnessing and use of atomic and thermonuclear energies.[5]

One may also speculate as to the relevance of such large-scale oil sources, extending as they do through southeast Asia, to the present power struggle being waged in this area. Unfortunately, there is as yet no world resource authority to decide such conflicting interests in terms of the real needs of the human community. The point may still be stressed, however, that even with other reserves, both in resources and knowledge, we patently cannot continue our present political attitudes at the expense of human requirements for these energy sources.

Apart from by-product effects and extravagant valuable deposits in storage, the petrochemicals and those derived from natural gas are now the bases for innumerable different products, including the swiftly developing range of plastics. Recent advances in microbial research also suggest the biosynthesis of food materials from such fossil fuel bases.

It is indeed prodigal to waste our reserves of oils and gases, even when considering them solely as industrial fuel, but when we realize their additional uses in the categories of valuable construction materials and enormous food and medical supply reserves, such waste is catastrophic abandon.

Overshadowing all other considerations in this regard, then, is that of diversifying our overall world energy economy—of more swiftly developing our income energy sources on a massive scale, and of investigating new sources, means of storage, transmission, and more efficient process use.

Water Power

Hydroelectric power represents less than 10 percent of the world's energy consumption. Its potential is considerable, particularly as those regions that are poor in fossil fuels are often rich in untapped water power. For such regions its demerits remain in the developmental costs of manpower, transportation equipment, and other resources that are in equally short supply.

Only about 13 percent of the estimated potential hydropower is presently being used. If all were developed, it would still provide only a fraction of world power needs.

Tidal Power. The tidal surges of the occans into and out of the large river deltas and coastal bays are largely unharnessed. Neither have the general massive movements of ocean water had sufficient investigation. Much work needs to be done to exploit this energy source.

Geothermal Sources. Hot springs and other outlets from the interior heat layers of the earth have not been widely considered. Their additional value as an energy source lies in their more accessible availability, in areas of recent volcanic activity, which are also rich in minerals such as potash for fertilizer.

Solar Energy. Methods for utilizing solar energy have received much attention. As the annual solar radiation received by the earth is about 35,000 times our present yearly energy consumption, the sun is comparable to a huge atomic reactor safely located millions of miles from earth.

Although solar heaters, cookers, and coolers have been developed for various areas of the world, they are still in a relatively unsophisticated state of development. The most promising overall area of development, and use, is in aerospace work. The solar cell, converting sunlight directly into electric energy, has made possible much of the space exploratory data collected so far. One system, of almost 30,000 cells covering 70 square feet, powered all instruments (including cameras and other recorders) in a satellite track lasting seven months and covering 325 million miles. Such units in the near future may therefore be powering the entire satellite-routed global telecommunications system already partially in operation.

Nuclear Power. Much is said about nuclear power as the fuel source for the future. Since 1 pound of fissionable uranium is equivalent in energy to about 650 tons of coal, its energy production is much greater than that from any of the fossil fuels. Part of its present limitation lies in manner of use—to produce steam, for instance, and thence to electric-energy generation, rather than producing electricity directly. Despite these developmental limitations, nuclear reactor installation and successful economic operation has increased considerably.

Its advantages for the underdeveloped regions of the world have been noted:

It can function anywhere. It is independent of geography, climate, and the general cultural level of the inhabitants. Upkeep is minimal. . . . Needed amounts of nuclear fuel are easily transported, and the consumed weight is negligible. Operation is automatic and can be managed by a limited personnel. And because initial costs are high (and nuclear fuels are and will remain government property), installations will continue to be planned and financed by national or multinational agencies. They can, therefore, be placed where they are needed.[6]

The author of this statement also draws attention to the fact that the nuclear revolution (of dispersed autonomous power centers as well as those providing large concentrations of power) would be less difficult transition than the introduction of traditional fossil fuel based industries for developing peoples.

. . . where the airplane is supplanting the bullock cart or dogsled, where radio (and television) directly superseded the village drum for communications, and where manufacturing goes from handicrafts all

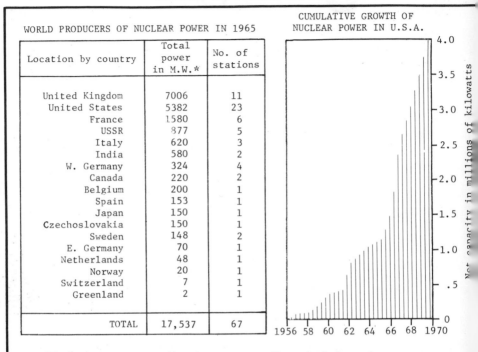

WORLD PRODUCERS OF NUCLEAR POWER IN 1965

CUMULATIVE GROWTH OF
NUCLEAR POWER IN U.S.A.

Location by country	Total power in M.W.*	No. of stations
United Kingdom	7006	11
United States	5382	23
France	1580	6
USSR	877	5
Italy	620	3
India	580	2
W. Germany	324	4
Canada	220	2
Belgium	200	1
Spain	153	1
Japan	150	1
Czechoslovakia	150	1
Sweden	148	2
E. Germany	70	1
Netherlands	48	1
Norway	20	1
Switzerland	7	1
Greenland	2	1
TOTAL	17,537	67

*Estimates vary according to sources. These include nuclear power plants operating or under construction. One megawatt (M.W.) = 1 million watts = 1,000 kilo watts (K.W.).

"There are only 3 commercial nuclear power stations in the whole of Asia, 2 in India and 1 in Japan. A site for a third Indian station has just been chosen, near Madras.

The U.S.A. and U.K. are the main suppliers of commercial reactor units to other countries. So far U.S. manufacturers have obtained 8 contracts and U.K. 3." - Dr. Peter R. Mounfield

Figure 68.
"Nuclear Power in the World Today," Peter R. Mounfield (notes from lecture given at S.I.U. May 9, 1967); "Environment Contamination from Nuclear Reactors," Malcolm L. Peterson, *Science and Citizen*, November 1965.

the way to automation without having to pass through the states symbolized by the steam railway and the assembly line.[7]

Though, as compared to present fossil use, nuclear power is a clean source, the disposal of radioactive wastes has been and remains a problem; however, its emergence as a competitive source in the advanced regions will probably accelerate solutions to this. Recovered wastes from uranium fission have also been used in other types of power plants specifically designed for use in remote areas—in space or unattended Arctic weather stations.

Our energy prospects are predicated not only on available sources, but also on our conversion and transmission efficiencies. Energy conversion, in overall world totals, based on production and consumption in various types of engines attains only about 6 to 8 percent—at best, up to 20 percent. This runs roughly from automobiles at approximately 10 percent efficiency in terms of energy produced for full input to steam turbines at 40 percent to the potential 80 percent of various fuel-cell developments.

When we speak of improving material standards of living, of bringing lesser developed regions up to parity, high-energy yields per fuel unit is an obvious requirement. Our current uses of fossil energy fuels in the advanced countries is prodigally wasteful, a criterion that might not be so critical in using income energy sources where use taps in to a short-term renewable cycle.

Single-engine efficiencies are only part of a larger system function; present emphasis of the malfunction of the automobile in cities could be fruitfully extended to heating, lighting, household and public energy uses, including sewage- and waste-disposal systems. Much of the hidden costs of human energy wastage in such urban aggregate ecologies may be traceable to the piecemeal uncoordinated uses of energy in their physical systems. Though there has been much discussion of the ecology of cities recently, little attention has been given to this aspect.

When we refer to efficiencies in this context, the criterion is not economic, but one of a more overall concern with a more facilitated *human use* of the environment.

Electric power use has been one of the signal advances in this direction, in efficiency, ease of use, and, depending upon its generating fuel, least damaging to the environ; the introduction of nuclear power generation has further enhanced these qualities.

Recent developments in the miniaturization of generator substations give similar capacities for a tenth of the size of plant. This is also accompanied by the additional possibility of extending power transmission through ultrahigh-voltage lines, carrying power over much greater distances with less transmission loss.

Many European countries are already running such lines up to 600 miles; the U.S.S.R. is developing capacities to transmit power from Siberia to the industrial areas of western Russia, and if this can be done, then it is feasible to extend them from Europe to India or to Africa. Efficiency in power networks is through the largest network interconnection for load sharing at varying peak uses.

For overall developmental planning, of course, the large centralized power grid is only usable if the system is there to use it; many world regions would have no way of using such large amounts of available power. The requirement goes, rather, through linkage to the relatively massive amounts of industrial power, down through local generating plants to small autonomous power sources such as battery sources capable of running radio, TV, and small transmitters to provide news, education, entertainment, and other communications uses. There are various stages of development, obviously, without necessarily retracing the earlier stage developments of the advanced regions.

Reference is usually made here to cultural barriers, but electric light, movies, telephone, transistor, and television could not have been more eagerly adopted wherever they have been made available, even in the most tradition-oriented societies. There appear to be no social and cultural barriers in the swift transfer of advanced military technologies!

The presently advanced countries are characterized by the plurality and variable scale of their energy production and consumption systems. The process of development should also share this plural approach. There are no fixed rules to be followed other than those of speed and urgency, and it is mandatory that the most immediate advantage be gauged within a framework of future consequences and contingencies.

ENERGY CONVERSION EFFICIENCIES

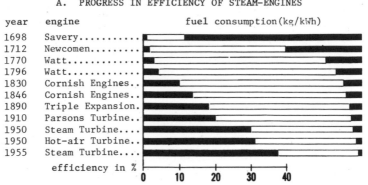

A. PROGRESS IN EFFICIENCY OF STEAM-ENGINES

year	engine	fuel consumption(kg/kWh)
1698	Savery..........	
1712	Newcomen........	
1770	Watt............	
1796	Watt............	
1830	Cornish Engines..	
1846	Cornish Engines..	
1890	Triple Expansion.	
1910	Parsons Turbine..	
1950	Steam Turbine....	
1950	Hot-air Turbine..	
1955	Steam Turbine....	

efficiency in %   0   10   20   30   40

A. "The left-hand side of the diagram gives the efficiencies, the right-hand side the fuel consumption, which is inversely proportional to the efficiency."-- H. Thirring

B. OTHER ENGINE EFFICIENCIES

engine type	efficiency in %
Steam Locomotive.............................	7
Automobile Engine............................	12
Ram Jet (at 1,300 m.p.h.).....................	21
Reciprocating Aero Engine....................	23
Turbo Jet (at 40,000 ft.)....................	24
Gas (general)................................	30
Diesel Locomotive............................	35
Steam Turbines...............................	40
Fuel Cells (potential).......................	80
Hydro-elective Turbine.......................	90

Figure 69.
Energy and Man, Hans Thirring, New York, Harper & Row, 1962; *The Ten Year Program*, John McHale, Doc. 4. World Resources Inventory, Southern Illinois University, 1965.

There is, for example, the growing trend toward a shared pool of the large-scale world technological instruments, even where this is masked by local "brain drain" and the balance of competitive markets. Advanced global services such as telecommunications, world airlines, large-scale energy generation, and distribution systems, go increasingly beyond the capacity of any one national group to create and maintain them. No country has all the necessary resources to develop these entirely alone; few manufacture all the items necessary for their maintenance. They are, by their nature, systems that operate most efficiently in the service of the largest possible numbers of people.

We may question, therefore, the often assumed need in the developing process for the prior buildup and duplication of heavy industry in national units. In some, by reason of size, it is obviously impractical; in others, it may be due to prestige need rather than actual operative value. This may also apply to large-scale energy production. Rather than wait for the buildup of specifically national industrial bases, we may need to go further ahead with both variable scale and locally autonomous energy generation and large-scale regional generation and distribution.

Generally, we need to assume that no matter what the artificial constraints may be—those that are customarily put forward, such as exchange economics and balance of payments—we can no longer afford the disparity between the energy-rich and the energy-poor regions of the world. The present costs in global tensions are already great; the future costs are likely to be ecologically enormous.

MATERIALS

The flow of industrial materials and technologies is now as essential to the ecological maintenance of the whole human community as the natural flows and cycles of air, water, and light energies. Our present modes of conceptualizing the operation of the industrial econetworks relates more to the preindustrial past than to the present reality. We still operate in terms of the restrictive barter practices of local agrarian societies in survival competition with each other and with the environment. Such obsolete modes of accounting and control now clog the operation of the global industrial ecology. They may be as dangerous to its forward and healthful maintenance as glandular malfunction in the internal human body or large-scale pollution in the overall ecology. No local society can now go it alone; all are in critically dependent relations.

When we focus on the historical development of materials, the importance of reorientation becomes clearer. Most of the industrial resources presently in use were not even *conceptually* recognized as such a hundred years ago. Aluminum was a scarce metallic curiosity, radioactivity was a laboratory phenomenon, and many of our present essential metals were regarded as waste impurities in other ores. Our material resources and capacities are dependent on the way we view our environment; they are ultimately as we conceive them to be.

Industrial raw materials are generally found in the earth's crust, the 10 mile thick shell of geologically formed deposits of metallic ores and nonmetallic minerals that can be extracted and processed within our present technological capabilities. Additional to these crust materials are the elements of the atmosphere and ocean, also used in the industrial process. Eight elements make up 98.6 percent of the earth crust. These are:

Oxygen	46.6%	Calcium	3.7%
Silicon	27.7%	Sodium	2.75%
Aluminum	8.1%	Potassium	2.6%
Iron	5.1%	Magnesium	2.1%

Other materials of present importance occur in lesser percentages:

Nickel	0.019%
Tungsten	0.005%
Tin	0.0004%

The major concentrated deposits of these resources are inequably distributed around the earth with little relevance to national boundaries and "natural" ownership. This has been an important factor in the location of industries, the growth of the advanced nations, and the present disparities in living standards.

Until about two hundred years ago, the numbers of known metals were quite small, and the scale of their use comparatively insignificant in our present terms. There were the noble metals of gold, silver, and platinum and the base working metals such as iron, copper, lead, and tin; mercury was known but little used. The main alloys were brass and bronze, but their precise combinations of copper, tin, zinc, and antimony were not clearly understood until the eighteenth and nineteenth centuries.

The Industrial Revolution of the nineteenth century started the production of metals on larger scale than at any previous period. In the first quarter of the twentieth century more metal of every type was extracted and processed than in the whole of all recorded history; this output was doubled in the second quarter of the century. Ninety percent of this production was iron alloyed with a smaller proportion of other metals to form the range of steels which, until now, have been the fundamental material basis for our industrial civilization.

From this point on, there are three distinct and characteristic phases of industrial growth and materials use:

The *first phase* is marked by the localized growth of iron and steel production, when large-scale mechanical industry developed in those countries where supplies of iron ore, coal, and limestone were available in close association with developing power and transportation facilities. The swift take-off of the industrially advanced nations owes much to these locally coincident factors of relative self-sufficiency in this first brief phase. Even where their own iron ore supplies had to be augmented as production increased, industrialized nations had the transport facilities and political and trade power to obtain ores from nearby countries. The increased demands for such materials led to a polarity of trade exchange, characterized by the flow of manufactured goods from the industrial countries in return for raw materials from the industrially underdeveloped areas. This pattern, with its latent restrictive functions, persists up to our own period.

The *second phase* occurred in the late nineteenth and early twentieth centuries when new ferrous and nonferrous alloy production required access to constituents that were relatively scarce in many of the industrialized countries. Such materials as manganese, tungsten, nickel, and cobalt were widely distributed and unevenly deposited around the globe, with little relation to previously conceptualized territorial and power balances. Within a few decades, the separate national systems of industrialization found themselves acutely dependent for vital alloying and other materials on distant, and often competitively controlled, sources of supply. The whole industrial network, both of manufacturing centers and raw materials areas, became locked in a critically interdependent global relationship, since no one nation could be self-sufficient in the vast array of materials now essential to the maintenance of its industrial system.

The *third phase*, into which we are just entering, is characterized by the possible displacement of steel, as the prime industrial material (for structural, machine, transport, and other major use), by other metals, composite materials, and plastics. The forward pattern of development may lie in:

1. The pairing of aluminum/magnesium/titanium as prime metals with electric power from hydro or nuclear sources.

2. The increased use of metallic and nonmetallic composites and plastics in conjunction with similar power sources.

3. The introduction of automation into industrial processes.

STEEL CONSUMPTION/PRODUCTION TRENDS

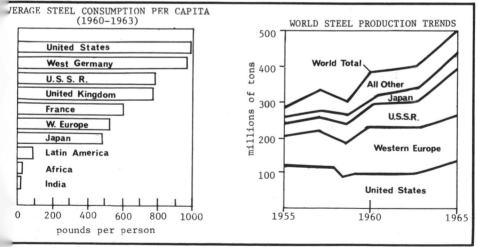

This moves the core orientation in society from mass quantitative production and development towards a qualitative concern with consumption, that is, with the service of individualized requirements beyond wholly material needs.

Automation could alter the present industrial power balance and turn the present advantage of the older established industrial regions into a restrictive disability. The speed of technological change no longer favors long-term stable amortization in heavy plant facilities. The rapid recovery of those industrial countries (Germany and Japan) whose capital plant equipment had been largely destroyed in World War Two and their subsequent rise to industrial parity and a competitiveness with the other advanced industrial nations, within two decades, is striking evidence of this trend.

The Future Phase

As we advance in materials research and energy production, the only unique resource is the organized human knowledge that converts one resource into another and finds new ways of tapping the larger and renewable energy patterns of the ecological systems.

The capacity to restructure material resources to almost any desired range of physical properties, and to produce energies in quantity from any locally preferred source, would be so close to nature's organic capabilities as to constitute a nontechnology.

With the decline in importance of heavy industry, the invisible ubiquity of miniaturized technologies and the increasing detachment of human energies from direct industrially productive work, we come toward a post-technological society, just as we are now in a post-agricultural phase.

In the past, agriculture was the survival machinery that dominated the landscape and influenced the institutions and life styles of most peoples. In the more developed regions, it has receded from such dominant visibility as a human malformation of the environ and has indeed reverted to "nature." So we may expect our presently dominant technological landscape to phase into relative obscurity and, where remaining, to become "natural." The windmill and the waterwheel (and the railroad almost) have undergone this metamorphosis and are now picturesque reminders of the time when man was more in harmony with his environment.

In the preceding synoptic review, we have devoted most attention to metals and metalworking. Many other materials and technologies played major roles in this development, but were closely interwoven with, and dependent upon, metallurgical processes. These, in turn, depended upon the general growth of industrial chemistry, which changed manufacture from being predominantly mechanical in nature into processes of diverse modes relying on chemical, electrochemical, and electromechanical industrial transformations.

Metals have a continuing centrality within the industrial ecology. Until other materials are more fully developed and available in the same abundance and with the same necessary ranges of fusibility, hardness, durability, conductivity, density, and malleability, we are dependent upon the primary metals.

The high living standards afforded by advanced technological facilities are predicated largely on the amounts of metals and inanimate energies available. As the amount of metal used in maintaining such living standards increases in overall consumption in proportion to the numbers of persons served by an increasing range of industrial facilities, the amount of metals actually available per person decreases; we use less materials per function.

Within the immediate range of our present technologies we are dealing with a relatively limited amount of metal resources. Alloying chemistry extends the number of their combinations and provides an increasing range of qualities; the reuse of the metals and their alloys through progressive cycles of scrapping and refabrication in different products means that they are not lost or used up. In the long run, when we consider such factors, the supplies of metals are relatively inexhaustible.

This relative inexhaustibility is, however, predicated on a developing technology, not in quantity or development but quality. Successive technical improvements use less materials and less energy per function. The "doing more with less"* is masked by the emphasis on gross quantitative increase in materials and energy use and by traditional economic (that is, fiscal) criteria.

More fundamental indicators of technological directions measure growth in terms of end-point human service gained with the least human constraint or loss of freedom in using technology. Though little academic attention has been given to the development of such indicators, they may be noted in, for example, the minimal human energies required in mechanized agriculture and in the increase in computer performance with declining weight, energies, and space required. In more mundane human needs like illumination and heating, which previously required much human labor, this human energy expenditure has been reduced to the mere flicking of a switch or adjusting a thermostat. The electric light bulb is an interesting example of such intangible performance gain; tungsten filaments are four and one-half times more efficient than the earlier carbon filaments, and since less than 2 tons of tungsten are required to make 100 million electric bulbs, the annual world use of tungsten for such purposes does not exceed approximately 200 tons.

Reserves and Future Uses

Most analyses of resources deal in "years of supply in exploitable reserves." For example, expressed in years,

Aluminum	570	Copper	29
Iron	250	Lead	19
Zinc	23	Tin	35

The use of such estimates, while useful for general economic criteria, is limited by lack of appreciation of the degree to which such metals are actually used up. Most are highly recoverable

---

*A phrase coined by R. B. Fuller who has pioneered the study of industrialization in terms of "Dymaxion" principles, that is, the gain of maximum physical advantage through minimal energy investment through constantly increasing "performance per pound."

through their scrapping cycles and are therefore used over and over again.

Our reserves, therefore, include all metals in present use and those recoverable from the lowest-grade ore deposits in the earth's crust, which are not usually accounted for in terms of exploitability because they are not economically exploitable in present terms. Of course present availability is important in the next critical transition to full industrial parity for all.

In dealing with resource reserves, the key question is how we may bring the underdeveloped nations up to higher standards of living, as measured by present materially advanced regions. As we have noted, the United States, with only 6 percent of the world's population, consumes approximately 30 percent of the world's total current production of minerals. How much more would be required to bring the total world population up to the same level of material consumption? A conservative estimate would be about five times the present world production of minerals, far more than we can attain with present levels of materials and energy performance efficiencies.

Using an ordinary example, suppose we tried to extend the 1960 level of United States automobile use (at roughly one auto per three persons) to the entire world population? This would require approximately 2,300 millions tons of steel, as compared with total world steel production (1963) of 425 million tons only. We have a long way to go.

In the same way, when we consider extending full-scale electrification to the underdeveloped nations, the average use of copper per capita in fully industrialized nations is approximately 120 pounds. The increase of even 1 pound per capita consumption in present world population terms would require about 36 percent increase in world copper production. Even the slightest rise in living standards can require vastly increased amounts of metals use in our present terms. Again this emphasizes the fact that the only way to advance the living standards of the under-advantaged countries is through overall increase in the performance per pound of all invested resources. This is, as we have noted, inherent in the advanced technological development processes. It requires, however, to be more immediately realized and used as an overall planning principle.*

Given abundant supplies of energy (for example, nuclear), we may secure almost inexhaustible supplies of minerals from the earth's crust and oceans, plus the developing capacity to increasingly construct or synthesize materials from many different element sources. The critical period lies in our present transition from one kind of world to another, of more equable distribution of life advantages.

Synthesis of Materials

The term "synthetics" is somewhat misleading. We do not create new materials but rearrange the basic chemical elements in different configurations to provide some desired material properties. Strictly speaking, man has always been synthesizing his environ by restructuring it to his needs, from the earliest use of fire, foods, fibers, and ceramics up to the latest alloys and plastics.

There is therefore no *intrinsic* difference between natural and synthetic materials; the one is not truer to nature than the other.

Materials synthesis now runs through many fields, from molecular and chemical transformations to the use of biochemical systems. A few of these are:

Plastics. Though first used commercially in the late 1860s, these did not reach their present widespread use until around 1927. Since 1942, a major new group of plastics with relatively unique properties has been introduced almost every year. The world's total volume consumption of such materials is now about one-third that of metals. By 1980 it is estimated that their overall use will surpass that of iron products.

Composites—nonmetal substitutes for metals. They combine the properties of metals with those of ceramics and fibers in their forming and stress properties. In general, such composites give new and extremely favorable ratios of strength to weight and can withstand higher temperatures. They have the promise of unpreced-

*This planned increase in more efficient use of material resources is the central premise of the "World Design Science Decade" program initiated by R. B. Fuller in 1961.

ented strengths, even surpassing the theoretical limits of their separate constituents.

Structural plastics of the fiber-reinforced, epoxy-resin types have become one of the most important ranges of structural materials for general purpose, and have already made considerable inroads on conventional metal usage. The rate of invasion of traditional-use areas is, of course, impeded by prior investment in plant production facilities adapted to older materials.

As synthetics are generally of less bulk weight and provide higher use performance per unit of energy and materials investment, their increased usage tends to be underestimated in classical economic and industrial analysis. One weight unit of plastic may replace the same weight unit of metal, but the volume use displacement may be much greater because of their difference in density. Many synthetics are already cheaper than steel and other metals on a cost-per-cubic-inch basis.

Structural polymers are a good example of this trend:

They are already replacing many metals in consumer products to such a degree that in United States industry as a whole the volume of polymers used already exceeds the volume of steel . . . [due to] the density difference averaging about seven times in favor of polymers. But relative growth rate of usage is such that polymers will soon overtake steel, even on a weight basis, and they may have already done so . . . polymers will indeed become the basic materials of the future. We will be manufacturing the bulk of our products, and even the machines that make them from new, man-made, synthetic polymers. And, inevitably, the elements from which we will fashion these new polymers are common inexpensive ones.[8]

The full range of synthetic materials engages us with new electrochemical industries, now extending into bioelectrochemical technologies. This, as we have noted, is the leading edge of a form of industrialization whose development and implications will be quite different from the older steel-based complex.

Many other issues necessitate a fresh perspective, particularly in the use of fossil fuels. The chemicals derived from these fuels are the basic materials for most of the synthetic resins and elastomer plastics, and importantly for the synthetic rubbers—sufficient reason to reconsider our presently prodigal use of these fuel deposits.

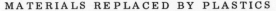

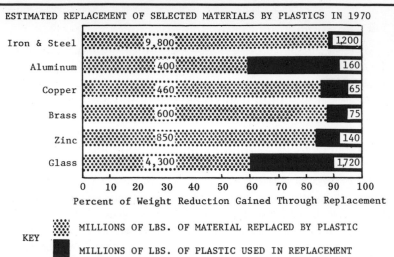

ESTIMATED REPLACEMENT OF SELECTED MATERIALS BY PLASTICS IN 1970

Iron & Steel 9,800 1,200
Aluminum 400 160
Copper 460 65
Brass 600 75
Zinc 850 140
Glass 4,300 1,720

0 10 20 30 40 50 60 70 80 90 100
Percent of Weight Reduction Gained Through Replacement

KEY
MILLIONS OF LBS. OF MATERIAL REPLACED BY PLASTIC
MILLIONS OF LBS. OF PLASTIC USED IN REPLACEMENT

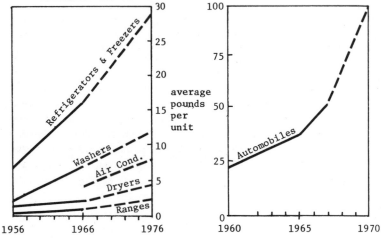

ESTIMATED USE OF PLASTICS IN APPLIANCES & AUTOMOBILES

Refrigerators & Freezers
Washers
Air Cond.
Dryers
Ranges

average pounds per unit

Automobiles

1956 1966 1976
1960 1965 1970

"Since 1955 the average plastic has dropped in price by about 35%, whereas steel has increased in price by more than 20%....On a weight basis, plastics probably never will be as cheap as steel; but on a volume basis the price difference could all but disappear.

"....Tooling costs are lower for plastics than for metals. Also, complex shapes can be molded in a single operation, and finishing of parts is virtually eliminated. A metal part often involves the assembly of several components -- this means additional labor cost and a higher price for the finished part." --"Chemicals and the Auto Industry," Special Report, Chemical and Engineering News, October 22, 1962, p. 117.

Figure 71.
Technology Behind Investment, New York: A. D. Little, Inc., 1965; "Cost-Price Sq Tightens Materials Battle in Major Appliances," *Steel,* July 1966.

When we begin to use the most commonly available and abundant elements in the earth's crust, atmosphere and oceans, within a pattern of recycling and reuse, we come to an almost entirely different picture of our material resources. Questions of resource balances, reserves, the dependence of industries and whole economies on access to this or that resource change radically.

We will be less dependent on the given configurations and properties of naturally occurring rare deposits, and on the ownership and control of strategic minerals. Our most important resource will be the possession of organized knowledge, that is, trained human beings, their requisite standards for full creature living, and the facilities for their continued pursuit of further knowledge. Many of our present natural resources will be supplanted by substitutes created in the laboratories. With these new discoveries we will be able to advance our less advantaged peoples more swiftly. As we survive this period of resource disparities, many of the older bases for conflict and competition will be reoriented toward other areas of human activity. Notions of territoriality, and strategic rights and control of material resource deposits, will shift to the "brain mines" of the world.

The older patterns of heavy industry and massive centralization of production facilities are no longer viable. The developing nations would be better encouraged by, and for, the world community, if they were to move directly into the new forms of industrial process—into the age of synthetics, light metals, nuclear power generation, and the full range of automated production, transportation, and communication facilities. Such questions as how, at what monetary cost, and by whom these will be supported may become increasingly irrelevant. We already spend more materials, energies, and human lives in our present global conflicts than such development would cost.

THE FUTURE ECOLOGY

Until recently our technological systems were hardly considered as an organic part of the ecology; hence little attention was given to this aspect of their function. Now, when they are polluting the air, earth, and waters with their discarded materials and by-products, we begin to examine their pathology without, in a sense, having engaged first in some overall assessment of their physiology.

Generally, when the problem is stated simply in terms of technological hazards, this tends to produce various piecemeal programs of filtering industrial smoke or car exhausts, or checking the level of effluents into rivers and streams, or legislating natural conservation and beautification projects. As laudable and as useful as these may be, they do not solve the problems precisely. Technology is an extension of the human metabolism—one which processes millions of tons of material each day—yet we have no very clear picture of its operation even to the extent that we have such knowledge of our own internal workings.

We need to reconceptualize our global, man-made environ facilities within more comprehensive and coherent schemes. For example, even where refined and advanced econometric models of whole regional and national economies are presently used, they concern themselves largely with the inputs and outputs of the industrial system almost solely from the viewpoint of its economic operation, in terms of fiscal and material balances. There is little sense of the complex ecological relationships that obtain even when we consider the industrial-economic system in isolation. We need to reappraise our industrial systems in terms of models that are not based on simplistic notions of production/consumption.

We do not produce things in the sense of manufacturing them out of new raw materials only, and then *consume* them so that their constituent materials no longer exist. They are used in a well-defined life cycle, then broken down in such use, and are repaired or discarded and replaced. Some of their material constituents are returned to the process and fabrication cycle (directly or indirectly in various time lags of secondary uses), others are further decomposed, returned in part to the earth or atmosphere, or flushed into the oceans.

Most of our currently prodigal modes of using the earth and biosphere systems are potentially dangerous. We dissipate vast quantities of capital energies that may be needed in future emergencies, and we disperse valuable concentrations of materials for which we have no present means of substituting, reconstituting, or replacing.

POPULATION/MATERIALS: Projected Consumption

YEAR	1966	1970	1980	1985	1990	2000
POPULATION (billions)	3.4	3.7	4.6	5.0	5.6	7.0
IRON						
Mil. tons	469.0	560.0	900.0	1130.0	1400.0	2250.0
Lbs./person	304.0	332.0	431.0	497.0	550.0	706.0
ALUMINUM						
Mil. tons	7.7	11.3	32.0	55.0	90.0	250.0
Lbs./person	5.0	7.0	15.0	24.0	35.0	79.0
COPPER						
Mil. tons	5.4	6.2	9.2	10.0	13.5	20.0
Lbs./person	4.0	4.0	4.0	4.0	5.0	6.0
ZINC						
Mil. tons	4.3	5.0	7.2	8.7	10.4	15.0
Lbs./person	3.0	3.0	4.0	4.0	4.0	4.0
TOTAL METALS						
Mil. tons	486.0	582.0	948.0	1204.0	1514.0	2535.0
Lbs./person	315.0	345.0	453.0	503.0	594.0	795.0
Mil. cu. m.	64.0	78.0	129.0	167.0	215.0	384.0
Liters/person	19.0	21.0	28.0	33.0	38.0	55.0
PLASTICS						
Mil. tons	16.0	27.0	105.0	240.0	420.0	1700.0
Lbs./person	10.0	16.0	50.0	116.0	165.0	535.0
SYNTHETIC RUBBERS						
Mil. tons	3.9	5.5	11.5	16.0	23.0	44.0
Lbs./person	2.0	3.0	6.0	7.0	9.0	14.0
MAN-MADE FIBERS						
Mil. tons	5.6	7.2	13.0	17.0	24.5	46.0
Lbs./person	4.0	4.0	6.0	7.0	10.0	15.0
TOTAL SYNTHETICS						
Mil. tons	25.5	40.0	130.0	273.0	467.0	1790.0
Lbs./person	17.0	24.0	62.0	121.0	183.0	563.0
Mil. cu. m.	23.0	35.0	114.0	236.0	409.0	1564.0
Liters/person	6.8	9.5	25.0	47.0	73.0	224.0
NATURAL RUBBER						
Mil. tons	2.2	2.5	2.6	2.7	2.8	3.0
Lbs./person	1.0	2.0	1.0	1.0	1.0	1.0
NATURAL FIBERS						
Mil. tons	19.0	21.5	30.2	35.0	41.5	60.0
Lbs./person	12.0	13.0	15.0	15.0	16.0	19.0
TOTAL NATURAL PROD.						
Mil. tons	21.2	24.0	32.8	37.7	44.3	63.0
Lbs./person	14.0	14.0	16.0	17.0	17.0	20.0
Mil. cu. m.	18.4	20.7	27.7	31.9	37.5	53.2
Liters/person	5.4	5.6	6.0	6.4	6.7	7.6
Million tons	533.0	646.0	1111.0	1515.0	2025.0	4388.0
Lbs./person	345.0	385.0	530.0	667.0	794.0	1379.0
Mil. cu. m.	105.0	134.0	271.0	435.0	662.0	2001.0
Liters/person	31.0	36.0	59.0	87.0	118.0	286.0

Metals (left margin)
Synthetics (left margin)
Natural Products (left margin)

re 72.
"Synthetics Age," R. Houwink, *Modern Plastics*, August 1966.

This extends to our use of income resources—soils, air, and water—and to our understanding of our complex interdependence on other organic life forms. We have already used up and destroyed a great many other living species with little inquiry as to their possible functional relation to our own survival.

In redesigning our industrial facilities as ecological subsystems, we need to determine the gainful and more efficient linkages that may be established between separately functioning processes. We may ask how the overall energy flows are disposed relative to each use and how more performance may be gained through different relations. We may redesign so that wastes and by-products of one sector of the network may become the raw materials (or energy source) of another.

One convenient focus of attention lies in the scrapping and reuse cycles of materials. We customarily design our structures and other facilities and artifacts only in terms of one-cycle use, with little attention to the eventual disassembly of components and their reentry into the processing cycle.

Very little has been known about the actual reuse and discard cycles in metals. For each billion tons of primary metal ores mined, about two-thirds is waste rock or mine tailings discarded at the mine site. From this point on through foundry processing and fabrication there is some control of process scrap, but as the finished products go into use, such control is lost and the scrap return cycle is left to the haphazard operations of the salvage market.

The obscurity of this pattern leads many authorities to talk about metals being used up through manufacture when, in effect, most metals are almost wholly recoverable, or could be with adequate cycling design. We may ask, then,

To what extent are they lost in use? To what extent do they follow man-made cycles like the well-known carbon cycle in nature, so that the world stock is not depleted?[9]

We can ascertain the cycle of a given material in its useful life in various products, but we have no clear picture, for example, of the changing pattern of reuse in specific industries, or of the various inputs of energy required at different parts of the scrap-reuse cycle, and how these relate to the overall energy costs.

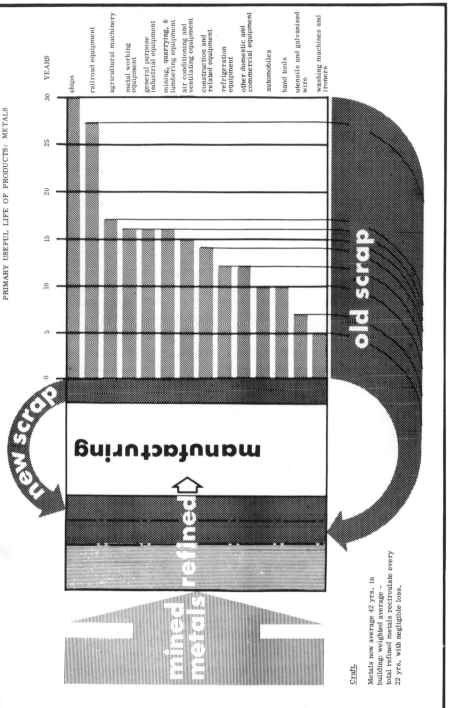

PRIMARY USEFUL LIFE OF PRODUCTS: METALS

YEARS

ships
railroad equipment
agricultural machinery
metal working equipment
general purpose industrial equipment
mining, quarrying, & lumbering equipment
air conditioning and ventilating equipment
construction and related equipment
refrigeration equipment
other domestic and commercial equipment
automobiles
hand tools
utensils and galvanized wire
washing machines and ironers

new scrap

old scrap

manufacturing

mined metals refined

Craft.

Metals now average 42 yrs. in building; weighted average - total refined metals recirculate every 22 yrs. with negligible loss.

73. Industrial Cycle.

Some indication of the importance of the scrap cycle may be gauged from the following figures:

About 957,000 tons of copper were recovered from scrap in 1963. This represented about 40 per cent of the total supply of copper in the U.S. for that year and 80 per cent of the total copper produced by domestic mines. The lead recovered from scrap amounted to about 494,000 tons—almost double the 253,000 tons of lead produced in the U.S. during 1963. The annual volume of aluminum scrap is about 25% of the total aluminum supply.[10]

Such examples of the recycling of metals may seem a narrow and specific one from the ecological viewpoint. In actuality, it is one of the key systems-model aspects of the entire industrial process.

In redesigning our ecological undertakings, we may sum up our more urgent objectives as follows:

1. *To recycle the metals and materials in the system*, so that there is a swifter turnover with the least lag in scrapping and processing cycles. In high-grade technological process, each use cycle tends, through overall development, to achieve more, not less, performance per invested unit of materials.

2. *To employ increasingly our income energies* of solar, water, wind, tidal, and nuclear power, rather than the hazardous and depletive fossil fuels. The latter represent major capital investments, which once used are not replaceable. They are too precious to burn up in our currently prodigal fashion, but they may be more efficiently—and more fractionally—employed in indirect conversion to plastics, foodstuffs, and other essentials.

3. *To refashion our food cycle* so that we may more swiftly augment the present starvation diets of more than half the developing world. We need, however, to go also beyond emergency satisfaction of immediate needs toward the more extensive ecological redesign of our whole agricoindustrial system; employing the most efficient natural means of food conversion through the plant animal chains and the possibilities inherent in microbiological, biosynthetic, and other processes.

4. *To set up ecomonitoring and control centers* that will act as early warning systems in relation to our large-scale scientific

and technological undertakings, analyzing and evaluating their immediate and largest range effects on the overall ecological matrix and their positive and negative implications for the quality of the human environ.

The future of our ecological maintenance depends on such re-design of our presently chaotic undertakings and on their coordination into more directly advantageous relationships within the larger planetary ecology.

V

Prophets of the Future

Any balanced account of past forecasting and current futures research would require many volumes. The range of predictions, and of prophets, is now relatively enormous. The brief comments made here are in no way intended to cover the field. Where individuals are mentioned, in addition to those quoted earlier, the purpose is to identify a directional development rather than to single out specific contributions.

We should also note that what is now called futures research, technological forecasting, or like terms, and conducted under various official auspices, has been brilliantly pioneered by utopian novelists and science fiction writers. This genre has been outside the province of our present text, but as a continuing tradition it still represents one of the valuable aspects of futures exploration. The literary utopia, the fictional extrapolation of trends in books and films, and even the transformative mythologies of science fantasy in "comics," all play an important role in forming our public and private images of the future.

We create our literary myths, legends, and epics of the future, not so that we will find our golden age, but because in the creation of utopian standards, we have created forms which make present action possible. . . . Every form of action makes use of ideals, as fictions in science, heavens in religion, utopias in politics or completely self-fulfilling acts in art . . . thus (creating) a means, model, a standard by which we determine the efficiency of present action.[1]

The visions of a Jules Verne and an H. G. Wells are supplemented by scientific and speculative works in our own period. Some, such as Velikowsky's *Worlds in Collision*, arouse considerable controversy in the area of science itself. Others, like *The Morning of the Magicians*,[2] extend speculation beyond customary scientific bounds. The protean work of Isaac Azimov ranges through the fictive invention of robot psychologies and scientific fantasies to encyclopedic ventures in the public communication of scientific discovery.

Within our narrower context of concern, the predictors of major changes are often their own self-fulfilling prophets, since they are also active in producing the conceptual and physical discoveries that bring about such changes. Of course science and technology have consistently surpassed many of even the most utopian projections. Vast social changes have proceeded in ways that were not predictable within our traditional social theories.

What prophets of utopias and anti-utopias have lacked has been partly a foreknowledge of inherently unpredictable inventions. Among these are the vacuum tube and the transistor, which have both had a profound effect on our civilisation . . . and a host of other discoveries and inventions. Any prophet, social or scientific, is bound to miss things of this sort and to the degree that the unpredictable and the unforeseeable strongly affect the future, a prophet is bound to miss . . . prophets of the past have underestimated both the adaptability of man and the phenomenally swift and strong impact of inventions and advances which, at their inception, seemed toys of civilisation . . . (showing) little promise of the revolutionary effects which they have had.[3]

As surprising, perhaps, is the degree to which men have been able to predict at all! The accuracy of prediction, on the other hand, often seems to be in direct ratio to its lack of contemporary acceptance. It is fitting, therefore, that our initial comments should be devoted to the *free-lance prophets*. Prophecy is a traditional function, both in the ecclesiastical and intellectual senses, but our concern here is to point up the more free-ranging predictive quality of individuals rather than to dwell on their institutional linkage.

Though the works of Wells and Bellamy are usually cited as key sources for much later prediction and achievement of various trends, the more recent work of C. C. Furnas has been somewhat neglected. In *The Next Hundred Years*,[4] published in 1936, Furnas sums up brilliantly what he termed "the unfinished business of science," and predicts with considerable accuracy many of the directions and accomplishments that have since ensued. Ranging broadly through all basic scientific disciplines, he elicits their forward linkages and possibilities in terms of large-scale engineering technologies, advances in communications, agriculture, air transportation, and many other fields.

Furnas is particularly perceptive of the social implications of these advances. Among the more gloomy prognosticators of a period emerging from the Great Depression of the 1930s, he emphasizes the importance of reconceptualizing education—less as training academic job skill than as

. . . an education for leisure. . . . Unless everything goes to ruin more leisure is coming. How better use it than for an extra year or so of education for every educable man or woman. Who will pay for the extra burden? . . . Who pays for the battleships, army, bridges, jails, highways and breadlines?

Though Furnas's work has been frequently neglected in citation, it has been a most valuable mine of scientific extrapolation, social insights, and resource analyses for a great many writers in successive next century forecasts.

On the other hand, he comments wryly in a recent address, that often his "1935 crystal ball was obviously operating under a cloud[5] —in missing the successive doubling and tripling of airplane speeds for example, and the possibility of manned orbital flight or lunar landing in his own lifetime. Furnas also points out his significant miss on the possibility of atomics: "The last word has not been said yet but do not buy any stock in an atomic energy development company. You will certainly lose!"

Actually, the formative work on such development was already under way. Though the realities of the atomic age were not apparent to most people until its negative effects shattered the world in World War Two, many key contributors to the uses of atomic energy had already predicted more positive directions.

In addition to those more strictly concerned with atomic research, one of the first physicist-engineers to project realistically the practical applications and wider potential of radioactive energies was Boris Pregel. In early 1941, before the inauguration of the Manhattan Project, he not only predicted that scientists would decide the war through the use of the atomic weapon, but also, and more importantly, that through the peaceful uses of this energy

We can look forward to unlimited cheap power and fuel, an indefinite supply of raw materials, comfort for all with the minimum of labor—those things that should remove the causes of poverty, envy and greed, make wars unthinkable and usher in a golden age for human beings.[6]

It was almost five years later, in New Mexico on July 16, 1945, that the first atomic explosion opened up this new era of reality!

Detailing the full social and economic aspects of the uses of atomic energy in terms of its rapidly lowering costs, Pregel emphasized the *dematerialization* that atomic power would bring about in the future world economy:

There will still be people who will find it impossible to believe that the possession of material things (beyond a few personal belongings of special sentimental value) is pointless, even in a society of unlimited physical power and unlimited (synthetic) raw materials. Our money economy is based on the notion of definite limited quantities of long lasting materials. . . . In the new generation, little will be permanent—except man himself and his ability, at last fully demonstrated, to control the world about him.[7]

In 1948, in projecting the wider social implications of such energies, he reiterated

. . . that these installations should be first started in the backward countries in order to bring the great masses of the population, as rapidly as possible to the level of abundance of the richer nations.[8]

In the same work he prophesied also that new multispectral analysis of resource-surveying of greater areas, through electromagnetic scanning of the earth, would bring to light the potential inexhaustibility of materials.

Another interesting exemplar of early accurate prediction is that of Arthur C. Clarke, the British scientist, writer, and founder member in 1936 of the British Interplanetary Society. At this early period, he was closely concerned with the theoretical problems of rocket flight, writing one of his first technical papers for the Society's journal on the mathematics of fuel-to-mass ratios relative to rocket escape velocities.[9]

Clarke has been consistently more accurate in his prophesies than many of his fellow scientists and science-fiction writers. In the mid-1940s, he described in operational detail the use of communication satellites for global television, and forecast 1959 as the probable date for the first moon rocket landing.

As a science-fiction writer, Clarke is in the tradition of H. G. Wells, with the same gift for technological extrapolation and insights into the manifold changes of the human condition which may occur in the distant future. His *Profiles of the Future* (1958) is still a remarkably prescient work, which sets future prediction within a credible framework of humanist concerns.

Much of the globally oriented work today is still done by physical scientists and technologists. A striking example, here, is Dennis Gabor, who furnishes one of the key concepts in the new "futurism."

The future cannot be predicted, but futures can be invented. It was man's ability to invent which has made human society what it is. The mental processes of invention are still mysterious. They are rational, but not logical, that is to say deductive. The first step of the technological or social inventor is to visualise by an act of imagination a thing or state of things which does not yet exist and which appears to him in some way desirable. He can then start rationally arguing backwards from the invention and forward from the means at his disposal, until a way is found from one to the other.[10]

Gabor is less concerned with ideal and utopian end states than with the more innovative ways in which we can consciously take each smaller step toward the future.

Whilst we cannot foresee the end, we can foresee the next steps. We can, following Karl Popper, adopt the principal of "piecemeal social engineering," fighting the greatest evils rather than fighting for the greatest ultimate good. The greatest evils and the most dangerous trends are not difficult to recognise.[11]

These latter comments raise an interesting question, which has been somewhat obscured in futures thinking: what is the extent to which social problems cannot be solved in the traditional way, but only in bypassing tradition through an appropriate technical advance or by circumventing the time required to solve the larger problems by applying technological measures that reduce their urgency? Alvin Weinberg states this explicitly:

Can we identify Quick Technological Fixes for profound and almost infinitely complicated social problems that are within the grasp of modern technology, and which would either eliminate the original social problem without requiring a change in the individual's social attitudes, or would so alter the problem as to make its resolution more feasible?[12]

A thorny question! To some degree, we already act on this premise. Its use as a change strategy belongs more within the realm of the social scientist. But as Winthrop notes in one of the most complete surveys of international futures research that has appeared to date:

The irony of current developments in studies of the future is that some of the natural scientists and engineers working in this new area are less modest and are assuming the role of social philosophers—a role which the more cautious sociologist has thus far been willing to abdicate.[13]

Sociology, which was founded in the nineteenth century as *the* previsionary social science, has been little interested in the study of the future. This may well be due to the manner in which it inherits Comtean prevision, as already emasculated by a pervasively conservative and past-oriented attitude.

Other areas of social science have been less lagging. The French political scientist Bertrand de Jouvenel has been one of the founders of the contemporary future research movement, with emphasis upon the social orientation. His work has ranged widely through rigorous studies of the forecasting process and theoretical exposition of its social methodologies, and has stressed the importance of wider public participation on studies of the future. In theory, and to a considerable extent in point of fact, de Jouvenel is rather like a latterday Saint Simon—of roughly similar background and outlook and in the general ambience of his work. A typical idea of his, which recalls Saint Simon's interest in parliamentary form is

... in other words a free market for surmises, allowing the thoughtful members of the public to derive their own views of what is most likely, to discern what should be done towards what seems to them most desirable among the possibles.[14]

But whatever the comparison, the contribution of de Jouvenel is particularly unique and outstanding.

His *Art of Conjecture* outlines a deeply humanist discipline, which utilizes the scientific tools of prediction and informs their rigor with a fundamental and central concern for those human qualities and needs that often elude logical schemes:

For man in his role as an active agent, the future is a field of liberty and power, but for man in his role as a cognizant being the future is a field of uncertainty. It is a field of liberty because I am free to conceive something which does not now exist will exist in the future . . . and indeed the future is our only field of power, for we can act only on the future . . . the only use of the known *facta* is as raw material of which the mind makes estimates of future. . . . The intellectual construction of a likely future is a work of art, in the full sense of the term and this is what "conjecture" means here.[15]

R. Buckminster Fuller represents a more thoroughly American type of free-lance prophet. He is a visionary of the American dream who combines the most utopian of ideas with pragmatic technological realism. In his first published work he writes:

Upon the premise that the sum total of human desire to survive is dominant over the sum total of the impulse to destroy, this book is designed. It does not seek a formula to attainment. To do so would develop dogma and nullify the process of individual rationalization that is essential to growth.[16]

Fuller's limits were metaphorically set by his first practical project of 1927, a series of drawings and plans for a "One-World-

Town Plan" in which each of the principal cities is the center of an air transportation network. This includes polar cities, set in the ice and fully environmentally engineered so as to provide as much comfort and liberty as those available in a more temperate zone. In the same year he proceeded to design the "Dymaxion House,"* which was to be demountable, transportable, with full air conditioning, automatic laundry, variable lighting, and many other inventions.

Almost a half century later, his "Expo '67" dome stood as the nth refined prototyping of this prevision, and one of almost 2,000 such structures used in various ways around the earth.

Fuller announced in 1965 his scheme for a great global indicators computerized "game"

. . . we are going to set up a great computer program. We are going to introduce the many variables now known to be operative in the world around industrial economics. We will store all the basic data in the machine's memory bank; where and how much of each class of the physical resources; where are the people, what are the trendings and important needs of world man?

Next, we are going to set up a computer feeding game, called "How to Make the World Work." We will start playing relatively soon. We will bring people from all over the world to play it. There will be competitive teams from all around Earth to test their theories on how to make the world work. If a team resorts to political pressures to accelerate their advantages and is not able to wait for the going gestation rates to validate their theory, they are apt to be in trouble. When you get into politics, you are very likely to get into war. War is the ultimate tool of politics. If war develops, the side inducing it loses the game.

Essence of "success in making the world work" will be to make every man able to become a world citizen and able to enjoy the whole Earth, going wherever he wants at any time, able to take care of all the needs of all his forward days without any interference with any other man and never at the cost of another man's equal freedom and advantage.[17]

*"Dymaxion" from the combination of dynamic with maximum, that is, the maximum environmental living advantage from the minimal investment of energy and materials.

This "Spaceship Earth Game" is now in considerable forward development, and its theme has become one of the key images of the period.

The Canadian futurist Marshall McLuhan remains a somewhat controversial figure. His work, and that of his associates at the Center for Technology and Culture, University of Toronto, contributes uniquely to our understanding of the sensory and symbolic transformations inherent in technological change. More space, however, has been given to misunderstanding McLuhan as charismatic medium than to comprehending his *Understanding Media*.

His basic tenet, stated in his book *The Mechanical Bride* (1951), is that the form of communication radically alters what is communicated, and conversely, that the receiving apparatus which screens such communication also alters what is perceived. This idea has been explored by many others since Berkeley and Hume, and in recent years by Whorf and Sapir, and particularly in the psychological optics of Adelbert Ames. McLuhan expands it to include all sensory modes involved in man's relation to his environ, the way in which they are affected by their extension technologies, and how the latter influence and condition what is experienced. This is of particular relevance to the study of change.

Electricity does not centralize but decentralizes, [is] equally available in the farmhouse or the executive suite. . . . The railways require a uniform political and economic space. On the other hand, airplane and radio permit utmost discontinuity and diversity in spatial organization.[18]

McLuhan presents a theory of social change that is strikingly apposite to our global requirements. Unfortunately his aphoristic and compressed communication of these theories has tended to emphasize the decline of linear, individualistic, print-oriented cultures and a return to the more inclusive sensory modes connoted as "tribal" in quality. Though perhaps not so intended, there is an *either/or* absolutism about the way in which this future is presented, and a latent assumption about primitive cohesion as against civilized fragmentation. Among all the electricity and cybernetic extension, we seem to come upon Rousseau, Fenimore

Cooper, and D. H. Lawrence in heated discussion about the "natural good." As McLuhan himself might say, "We are back in Bloomstown." But Joyce had the insight to call his hero Daedalus —no tribal lad but a hip artificer! In totality, however, McLuhan's work is about the extension of human consciousness and awareness in the present and future and how the understanding

(of) many media, the conflicts from which they spring, and the even greater conflicts to which they give rise, holds out the promise of reducing those conflicts by an increase in human autonomy.

Robert Jungk shares with de Jouvenel much of the credit for sensitizing Europe and the world to the need for systematic futures research. In 1958, his book, *Tomorrow Is Here Already*, particularly previsioned many of the growing dangers of overcontrol and exploration of the physical and social environs by technologies to whose long-range effects we had given little attention. Much of what he wrote is now reflected in the urgent legislating of early warning systems of technological hazards and the attempts to predict and forward-control the development of our large-scale technological systems.

Like de Jouvenel, Jungk has been particularly concerned with the communication of "the sense of the future," and the participative possibilities for the wider public, of forming and controlling the future. In 1964 he also initiated the "Mankind 2000" project. This is specifically concerned with communicating the wider implications of future changes to the widest public audience:

It is the purpose of those associated with the Mankind 2000 project to try and foresee what the basic alternatives requiring decision will be and to present these to people generally, through every effective means of communication, in the belief that by so doing a growing willingness on the part of the individual to bear the burden of involvement in the basic issues confronting mankind, now and in the years to come, will eventuate.[19]

Jungk's outline of a "European Lookout Institution" is devoted to the need for more official institutions—academic, governmental, and private—to study the future. It emphasizes

The need for such an institution, which might enlarge the horizon of executive, legislative, judicial, administrative and new functions of government, and thus help in their decisions . . . has been brought on by the unprecedented acceleration of change, which has become one of the main characteristics of our age, and even more by the sudden jump of incisive, even shattering power inherent in modern technology, making it imperative for human society to gauge and control the new forces.[20]

The idea of 'lookout institutions,' or social navigation centers, is drawn most recently from the work of de Jouvenel, as noted above. A key focus for the work of such centers would be to forecast the forward implications of technologies on society.

Erich Jantsch, Consultant to O.E.C.D. (Organisation for Economic Cooperation and Development, Europe), has been one of the major contributors to this latter area. We may note in the summary of Jantsch's description of the role of technological forecasting, that it goes beyond the wholly physical technologies to encompass their immediate and long range social implications:

We may note in the four-point summary of Jantsch's description of the role of technological forecasting that it also goes beyond the wholly physical technologies to encompass their immediate and long range social implications:

1. Technological forecasting is an integral part of the planning process unfolding between the levels of policy, strategic, and tactical planning. At policy-planning level, the scope of technological forecasting is the clarification of scientific-technological elements determining the future boundary conditions of the planning environment; at strategic planning level, its scope is the recognition and comparative evaluation of alternative technological options, in other words, the preparation of the technological decision-agenda; and at tactical planning level its scope is the probabilistic assessment of future technology transfer. Technological forecasting is never a straight prediction.

2. Consideration of the future potential technology transfer is set in a broad economic, political, social, and anthropological context—in other words, technological forecasting is integrative forecasting.*

3. Technological forecasting emphasizes the assessment of effects (for example, technological capabilities, such as speed, temperature resist-

---

*See also the chapter on integrative forecasts in: Frank P. Davidson, "Macro-Engineering: A Capability in Search of a Methodology," in *Futures*, Vol. 1, No. 2, Dec., 1968 (Iliffe, Guildford, Surrey).

ance, strength, etc.) and of impacts, not the actual description of a technical realization (a machine or apparatus, etc.). This implies that technological forecasting—in accordance with full-scale planning—is most useful in an outcome-oriented framework, not in an input-oriented one.

4. Technological forecasting takes an essentially nondeterministic view, combining exploratory (opportunity-oriented) and normative (mission-oriented) thinking. This implies, *inter alia*,:

The shift of emphasis from short- and medium-range tactical to long-range strategic and policy thinking; and

The trend toward large-systems thinking, going beyond the industrial and economic systems to include the joint systems of which society and technology are the constituents.†[21]

The rapprochement between the systems utopians and the more social previsionaries is more apparent in Europe than in the United States. This may be explicable in terms of the traditional continuity of figures such as de Jouvenel, Clarke, Jungk, and others. But in terms of the overall influence of futures research, we may expect considerable interconnectivity and a confluence of major ideas and methodological orientations in the next period. The first International Congress of Futures Research was held in Oslo in 1968 and included key participants from all the major countries, with the exception of China. From this and other meetings an International Secretariat was formed and since then more formal networks of communications and interchange have been set up.

Soviet and eastern European exploration into the future is characterized more by its direct linkage to the official establishment, a feature that is also shared by much American work.

As inaugurated by a series of five- and ten-year plans, forward extrapolation and futures planning has always been a central premise of the Soviet political and economic systems. In a recent survey of Soviet futures work, Arnold Buchholz sums up this close official relationship of ongoing everyday planning with longer range research.

Next to the Academies in the Soviet Union, the State Committees for Science and Technology were founded in order to coordinate scientific and technical research and, also, to relate their findings into better

†See also: Erich Jantsch, "Integrative Planning of Technology," in *Perspectives of Planning*, O.E.C.D., Paris (1969).

future forecasting. Working closely with these committees are also a series of "Problem Commissions" whose role is to apply concrete "interdisciplinary" solutions to specifically defined problems (e.g., the multidisciplinary focus on photo-synthesis processes in the study of air/water pollution).[22]

Buchholz notes also the widespread interest in the future in Soviet journals and popular magazines, which bring together futures thinking from many sources, particularly the work of Jungk, Arthur C. Clarke, and the German futurist Fritz Baade, author of *The Race to the Year 2000* (1962).

Bestuzshev-Lada, chairman of the Social Forecasting Research Institute of the Soviet Sociological Association, has recently published a new book entitled, *The Development of World Thinking on the Future of Man and His Earth.* His viewpoint on the focus of futures research was recently reported in a conference with Robert Jungk and Fritz Baade:

We must have a larger view. We need social forecasting in the broadest sense of the word—scientific, technological, economic, sociopolitical, geographic, demographic, ethnic, anthropological and moral-psychological forecasting. We must foresee the consequences of the scientific and technological revolution which is going on . . . we have reached the stage where we need a general theory that takes in all the methods we now use—modelling, polling, extrapolation. . . . Everything material in man's life—housing, food, clothes, constitutes only the conditions making socially creative work possible. The possibilities are boundless . . . the problem is to realise the possibilities we have.[23]

One of the most comprehensive futures studies in recent years was presented at the Prague 1968 conference, "Man and Society in the Scientific-Technological Revolution." The core of this meeting was a series of reports on a large cross-disciplinary project that had been under way for some time in the Philosophical Institute of the Czechoslovak Academy of Sciences. This project was first published in 1966 in three volumes entitled *Civilisation at the Crossroads.*

The main theme of this work deals with the ways in which the scientific and technical revolutions, now at world scale, are moving into a period of post-technological and, specifically, social concerns.

In contrast to many such official and academic futures reports published recently, this series of documents and its 1968 conference texts draw upon and discuss an extremely wide range of current futures papers, in every field and from almost every country.

This widening concern has also come to characterize those whom we might term the "establishment prophets" in the West. As their work often emerges from a preoccupation with systems engineering and control systems, sociologist Robert Boguslaw has dubbed them "The New Utopians."[24] The emphasis on predictive systems and cybernetics arises from the fact that these developments not only provided the tools, but also led to "the establishment"—large industrial-government research facilities whose central function has been futures prediction. The most obvious examples are the "think tanks" such as the Hudson Institute, RAND Corporation, Systems Development Corporation, and Institute of Defense Analysis. These were set up originally as weaponry analysis centers for maintaining scientific and technological parity in the cold-war phase. As captive institutions, their more directly prophetic work in the social sciences has been largely concerned with politico-military scenarios in which the various aspects of the compelling world-power systems are analyzed and projected so as to forecast necessary developments in weaponry, counterinsurgency and intelligence systems, and logistic and resource allocations.

The archetypal work of such institutions may be labeled "scenario," a term originated by Herman Kahn in his realistic discussion of sociopolitico-military projections. In his early work[25] on the analysis of nuclear attack capabilities, Kahn introduced the terms "overkill," "megadeaths," and other pleasantries related to predicting the choice between first- or second-strike possibilities. His most recent speculations[26] have been more optimistically inclined, and comprise a large-scale, multidimensional approach to the possible direction of various world conflicts and the solution to various socioeconomic and political problems, projected beyond the year 2000.

The general tone of this type of work is pragmatic in the traditional American sense of the term. There is a marked disavowal of idealism or commitment to any value stance other than that of objectivity, that is, Kahn adopts a realpolitik outlook on the present and the future. There is no *trahison des clerc* feeling admissible because the work was produced on contract for the government.

Assumed to be in the public interest, not treason but reason is its only governing principle. To act otherwise would be to admit of an ideological commitment, and an important assumption of the establishment prophecy that we have come to the end of ideology;

It is almost old fashioned today to admit an interest in ideas. The language of the social sciences is one of *hypothesis, parameters, variables* and *paradigms*. The procedures are multi-variate (i.e., the isolation of single factors or clusters, holding others constant, in order to measure the weight of a particular variable or the interaction of multiple variables), and quantified. Many social scientists, trained largely in technique, scorn ideas—and history—as vague and imprecise, while the humanist mocks the jargon and often minute conclusions of the social scientists. Both are talking past each other. No one can quarrel with language or procedures, however technical, that aim for precision rather than obfuscation. But even at best such procedures, by the modes of abstraction employed, narrow the range of one's vision.[27]

The author Daniel Bell, though identified with the "establishment," is pursued by what he calls the "restless vanity" of ideas and is therefore more alive to the perspectives of a sociology that, while avoiding ideology, may yet retain a more passionate commitment.

Bell is the chairman of "The Commission on the Year 2000," of which the title and participant composition would have delighted Saint Simon. The roster of the Commission is a pragmatic coalition of social and physical scientists, government administrators, corporate managers, and publicists.

Just as the gridiron pattern of city streets in the 19th century shaped the linear growth of cities in the 20th, so the new networks of radical highways, the location of new towns, the reordering of graduate school curricula, the decision to create or not to create a computer utility as a single system and the like will frame the tectonics of the 21st century. The future is not an overarching leap into the distance; it begins in the present.

This is the premise of the Commission on the Year 2000. It is an effort to indicate now the future consequences of present public policy decisions, to anticipate future problems, and to begin the design of alternative solutions so that our society has more options and can make a moral choice, rather than be constrained, as is so often the case when problems descend upon us unnoticed and demand an immediate response.

But what began a few years ago as a serious academic enterprise . . . has been seized, predictably, by the mass media and the popular imagination. The Columbia Broadcasting System has revamped its documentary program, "The Twentieth Century," into "The Twenty-First Century," to depict the marvels of the future. The *Wall Street Journal* has been running an intermittent series on expected social and technological changes. *Time* has published a compact essay on "The Futurists: Looking Toward A.D. 2000." The theme of the year 2000 now appears repeatedly on lecture circuits and newspapers. . . .[28]

The working papers of the Commission have the authentic flavor of the American commitment to committee, to consensus, and to return to,

. . . the realization of the promise of equality which underlies the founding of this country and the manifestation of Tocqueville's summation of American democracy: What the few have today, the many will demand tomorrow.[29]

Recently the question of "an end to ideology" has begun to affect the conservative idea of objectivity and the ideological commitment to the nonideology of a value-free science. Both the social scientists of the "think tank" and the physical scientist engaged in corporate research projection of ever-more sophisticated weaponry systems and delivery capabilities have become troubled by the burgeoning power of science itself and its increasing function as a quasi-sacred legitimizing agency for realpolitik expediency. The forbidding thought of Hiroshima and Nagasaki surfaces again in the Camelots, the Vietnams, and the defoliation and bacteriological warfare controversies, and is compounded within growing number of environmental changes and hazards—thalidomide, air and water pollution, increases in levels of radioactivity, and similar destructive possibilities.

As a result, even official oracular agencies have now turned toward the larger problems of the world society. The future of any locally sovereign enclave becomes severely limited within the longer-range context. Reflections from the future itself work change on the geopolitics of the present.

One important technique which marked the swing away from emphasis on political and military forecasting, was the "Delphi" method of Olaf Helmer and his associates at RAND Corporation. This is based on the polling of a series of expert panels, and collates the probabilistic weightings assigned to different future possibilities by the experts consulted. The range of possibilities and their cross-relationships are very great and do give a more informed way of forecasting, which takes into account individual opinions and field expertise. Helmer has been also closely concerned with the use of other simulation techniques using mathematical computerized approaches to extrapolate future possibilities.

Machine-derived forecasts have also been explored by Charles Osgood of the University of Illinois, who launched large-scale computerized investigation of various types of future contingency models. This avenue of research may be regarded as one of the most promising developments in the methodical approach to futures research.

One should enter a caveat here about the need to communicate with the larger audience, which is still neglected in futures work generally. We need to involve the public more dynamically and in a more directly participative manner. Important materials of the widest interest are still restricted to the more academic audience. As conditioned by this closed-circle concentration, modes of communication are also restricted and relatively incomprehensible to the larger audience.

Harold Lasswell has put this issue most succinctly:

. . . the methods by which the future is presented *do not foster vivid perceptions*. It is well known that a trained imagination is necessary before one can perceive a table of figures, a map, or a chart. Our perceptions of current and past events are facilitated by the context provided by the concreteness of news stories, anecdotes, and personal observations. By contrast, the charts, graphs and tables that refer to the future lack support. This is a problem especially for nonspecialists, since, if laymen are to grasp the meaning of a technical communication, they must rely upon equivalencies with common experience.

. . . presentations are often *lacking in transition*. Very often the potential future is described at a cross-section in time with no attempt to relate the cross-section to the state of affairs at present. This is especially common when rather "Utopian" proposals are put forward. Although the Utopian character of the recommended policy calls for particular attention to problems of strategy, problems of transition may be left out.

. . . I shall not carry the indictment further; the question is whether anything affirmative can be done about existing practice. What I propose can be quickly grasped by analogy to the planetarium, which was developed for the purpose of popularizing astronomical knowledge. I renew the suggestion of a social planetarium.[30]

The recent "social accounting" movement initiated by groups of establishment intellectuals, legislative spokesmen, and managerial analysts, is a step in this direction. In order to predict the future legislative course of government, this movement suggests and outlines a massive ongoing compilation of social indicators to augment the physical and economic indicators that have so far furnished only early warning and planning devices for societal navigation:

This paradox of a poverty of perspective in the midst of a growing abundance of data is a central problem for both the social scientist and those who attempt to guide our society toward a full realization of its potentials. To begin to cope with both the intellectual and the policy problems presented by this bewildering array of information, we must attempt to develop new overviews of society and social change. These must be of a different order than the *verstehen* theories bequeathed to us by such social philosophers as Spencer, Marx, and Weber. Our new overviews must confront the social problems of today, and not those of the turn of the past century. They must be open-ended rather than deterministic. They must be rich in concepts and at the same time deal directly with our growing array of empirical information.[31]

One could mention here a vast number of government, civic, and corporate institutions now at work on similar projects. Even the prestigious and hitherto conservative group known as "The American Institute of Planners," has had its second annual conference on "The Next Fifty Years 1967–2017. Almost every institution in American society now has its futures group* whose

---

*The World Futures Society was founded in 1965 in Washington, with an eminent academic board and its own journal, The Futurist.

concerns range from education for the future and museums of the future to plans for the construction of complete experimental cities.[32] The favorite benchmark is the year 2000, which now assumes the mythopoeic quality of Saint Simon's "Age of Gold." But a number of institutional groups are already engaged in predictions and forecasts that go beyond this date, well into the twenty-first century. These are more generally concerned with the extrapolation of physical resources and conversion technologies. The most typical representative of these forecasts is *Resources in America's Future*,[33] in which energy requirements, other physical and even human resources, and educational, recreational, and other needs are extrapolated forward for more than a century.

The Futures of Academe may be mentioned as fitting roughly within the establishment framework. There are, apart from the six major educational futures groups (now officially sponsored) a considerable number of futures-based curricular studies also progressing in many universities. A number of "institutes for the future" are planned and one is already in existence. The bibliographical listing and description of academic futures projects alone would require separate chapters and their more detailed consideration would comprise separate volumes.

One specifically interesting feature, which interpenetrates both the sponsorship of academic work and youth orientation toward the future, is the role of the church. Every major religious sect, from the Lutherans to the Baptists to the Methodists to Roman Catholics, now has its long-range task force or its study group on the future of society. Often, where local academic administrations are still somewhat hesitant to jump into the twenty-first century (having sufficient problems in the twentieth), many courses, visiting lectures, and seminars on the future are pursued by the university religious foundations.*

We have already mentioned the future orientation of corporate

---

*In part, this is intellectually traceable to influential works such as that of Teilhard de Chardin, *The Future of Man* (New York: Harper & Row, Inc., 1963). In part, it is due to the new ecumenical movement and also draws support from the newly militant engagement of organized religion with social problems and the attempt to regain and retain moral leadership of the youth.

industry. This is expressed partially in a concern with the markets of the 1970s and 1980s, and even later, and is somewhat conventional in these terms. However, there is a very real and financially demonstrable interest in the wider implications of the future, as already evidenced by internal support of long-range planning groups and the external support of individual futures consultants and quasi-academic seminars on the future of this or that area of society of importance to the industry in question.

Corporate futures work at one end of its spectrum tends particularly to shade off into utopian systems. Belief in the business ethic has been transferred to an equally pervasive belief and deep trust in the systems mystique. There also is an interesting and direct linkage between the systems thinking that goes into designing a missile system and the underlying concern with program budgeting, cost effectiveness, and the other conceptual tools of the new social accounting movement mentioned above.

As Boguslaw states, "Large-scale industrial, military, and space systems are the new utopias that the age of computers has thrust upon us."[34] He goes on to suggest that they lack only one of "the critical features of classical utopias . . . the humanoid orientation." The deeper, and perhaps more disturbing, lack is that of security. One may discern to an extent the way in which the systems methodology comes to operate as an autonomous form providing its own ends justification, and also how it functions as a *final authority* (a legitimizing "god-term") in the sense that H. D. Duncan uses this phrase. Science, and particularly its ancillary mathematical ritual, becomes a theocratic instrumentality that avoids the need to rely upon the fallibility of human decision making. The ends-legitimizing authority is, again, external to, and constraining upon, man.

Fortunately, the ambitions of the new systems utopians are more directly, and presently, concerned with improvements in physical systems efficiencies. They tend to avoid the more idiosyncratic problems of psychosocial design. Boguslaw's insights are again acute in this regard:

The new utopians . . . tend to deal with man only in his workaday world without prescribing sex practices, child rearing procedures or

methods for achieving the good life. They deal with messages, decisions, commands and work procedures. . . . They receive their impetus
from the newly discovered capabilities of computational equipment
rather than from the fundamental moral, intellectual or even physical
requirements of mankind.

To this extent they do not want to dictate how man should order
his life, but are concerned more with putting the means for order
at his disposal. But the dividing line of human desire and "systems
fit" is often a narrow one.

Our present range of societal institutions for monitoring present,
and anticipating future, changes are markedly inadequate in this
regard. Their kinds of professional expertise in economic projec-
ton, technological forecasting, weaponry analysis, and similar prog-
nostications have proved to be of little service in monitoring and
evaluating the kinds of changes in symbolic trends and social
movements that do not come within the range of their traditional
perspectives.

Moreover, as specialist disciplines operating within a fixed establishment format, they tend to proceed on certain static assumptions
about the continuing centrality and role of various social institutions—the economy, the polity, the military—regarded as relatively unchanging in their central function.

Confronted with the problem of changing life styles, there is a
tendency for these to be regarded as of marginal concern, as
merely end-points phenomena in social processes whose more
causally determinant agencies are to be sought in economic, scientific, technological, or geographical areas.

In terms of accurate near-future forecasting of even material
requirements, which is much more their defined brief, the record
of most such institutional agencies has been rather poor. Predictions have been made at too short a range, too slow, and in many
cases have been altogether wrong, both in the areas where change
was predicted and in the manner in which it was to be effected.

The systems utopian outlook is not wholly confined to the aerospace, missile, and physical systems-planning world, but encompasses an attitude that can be found in the Skinnerian "Walden
Two" type of utopian community, in the experimental city type of
futures scheme, which we have mentioned, and in many other effi-

ciency-oriented future plans that are now circulating. In an abrupt swing away from the administratively convenient world of the establishment prophet and the efficient utopia of the systems theorist, we might consider briefly the new old-utopian schemes particularly favored by the young. The hippie movement with its romantic revival of Art Nouveau, of the old English Digger idea, and the constellation of attitudes, life styles, and unconventional social forms, has also led to the formation of a great many utopian communities. The hippie phenomenon is too complex for more than comment here, but many of the ideas underlying its return to community, to the tribal solidarity, are of great sociological interest.

Our more immediate concern, however, is with the future orientation of this group toward a society that swerves away from many of the premises of their surrounding and supportive social milieu. Though apparently antithetic to the systems utopian, there are many strange interlinkages with the hippies' interest in, and reliance upon, advanced communications technologies as art-form vehicles.

The most recent metamorphosis from hippie to yippie is also based on an acute intuition that the stage of advance technology may enable us to reduce the administrative complexity of fiscal accounting by a free economy, in which access to life maintenance of goods and services is no longer tied to the direct exchange of money or gainful labor tokens.

This proposition may be found also in the more respectable proponents of the guaranteed income,[35] in the observable shift to a service-oriented rather than a market economy, and to the degree that the society largely operates on a credit basis, with payments future-deferred on varying hypothetical bases.

In attitude, organization, and lineage, the hippie and yippie futures are anarcho-syndicalist:

. . . revolutionary theory and practice must now look primarily to the future, rather than to the past, for inspiration and clarity; that a qualitatively new order of possibility faces our generation—the possibility of a free, nonrepressive, stateless and decentralized society based on face-to-face democracy, community, spontaneity, and new, meaningful sense of human solidarity.

We believe that technology has now advanced to a point where the burden of toil and material necessity could be removed from the shoulders of humanity, opening an era of unprecedented freedom in every aspect of life, a nonrepressive civilization and human condition in which man could fulfill all his potentialities as a rounded, universal being.[36]

This quotation is, of course, more representative of the extended wing of the hippie libertarian movement. Associated more closely with the center is a diffuse, extremely varied number of utopian communities.

These vary from the free pad to the family work group of artists, musicians, and actors to larger communities both urban and rural, many of which have attained a more or less stable form. Typical of the large community, for example, would be "Drop City" and "Libre" in southern Colorado, groups of artists, musicians, writers, and others who have constructed their own houses, significantly, out of junk-auto metal but which display sophisticated geometrical forms and building techniques. Their economy is a free one, based almost entirely on locally produced food and various ways of tapping in to the rejected and discarded materials of the local city. Thus, it functions as a kind of recycling and reuse unit, a closed-cycle economy such as that envisaged for the more scientific and prestigious "experimental city" already mentioned.

The growth in numbers of other types of future oriented utopian communities in the United States alone is so relatively great as to support its own journal and directory.[37] The latter lists approximately eighty different communities ranging through the United States, England, Canada, Central America, France, Israel, and New Zealand. Of course many of these are revived models of older forms, such as the Oneida and Owenite types but their importance lies in their number and relative steady growth. In the past two or three years, the hippie and community movement has also begun to establish international linkups with English, German, and French groups, and in particular with the militant "Provo" group in Holland. The latter developed out of a future-oriented art movement, the "Situationists," of the 1950s, whose aesthetic and intellectual lineage may be traced to the Dadaist movement in the 1930s and particularly in terms of their techniques and imagery to the earlier Futurist movement in Italy after World War One.

This brief review of the new prophets and new social movements toward the future has been extremely sketchy and idiosyncratic in its selection. Much more has been omitted than has been mentioned. It is sufficient, perhaps, merely to show that the new prophets of our future are no small band of messianic oracles adrift in the wilderness, but represent rather a wide cross section of our liveliest contemporary minds. The diversity of their thinking and its imaginative reaches assures us, at the very least, that though the future may be neither nightmare nor utopian dream, it will certainly not be dull.

VI
Toward a
Planetary Society

To address ourselves to the questions of a planetary society is no wishful utopian fantasy but a sober recognition of everyday facts. Though we are presently split up into an agglomeration of separate principalities, their larger claims to autonomy and sovereignty are now more apparent than real.

This kind of statement may seem quite unrealistic when we are still enmeshed in a series of interminable wars and international tensions. But these conflicts, however bloody and reprehensible, have an air of stalemate and confusion, which they did not have before. They may be the tail-end convulsions of an old and obsolete system, which seem to be at their fiercest as they become increasingly irrelevant and inimical to the main directions of the world community. While those directions will probably never eradicate the possibility of armed conflict, they already attempt to limit its scale and wider repercussions.

Modern war is not rewarding in the old sense. The adage "to the victor belongs the spoils" has been curiously reversed. Total victory now despoils both vanquished and victor. The acquisition of total power—to destroy a city, a country, or the planet itself—has emasculated military power. The ineffectual employment of less than total means, though awesomely massive by any previous standards, begins to erode the mythology of war itself.

As the physical forces with which we control our environment become increasingly less visible, less tangible, and less effective, so the use of these forces and material power has declined as a measure of superiority. Even their visible display has come to connote weakness and insecurity rather than security and strength.

At each turn in world events, the powerlessness of "powers" and the "leadership syndrome" becomes ever more acute in the

267

face of developments that go beyond their traditional grasp. Most of the formative new patterns of human communication and response, of service networks and new technologies, of new social allegiances and responsibilities are no longer restrained within the old physical, cultural, and geographical bounds. It is a world that has merged into one community, less influenced by political and ideological ideas than by scientific and technological developments.

It is important that we clarify the "one world" theme. Given this truism, most people then assume a one world order—a stable blueprint for a future society in which want will disappear, war will be abolished, and men will work together for unselfish and harmonious ends. We tend to project into the future (or the past) the order, consistency, and regularity that is rarely available in the present. Even if such a society were wholly possible, it is doubtful if it would be humanly desirable—or even palatable. Man is characterized not only by his search for order, but also by his tolerance and need for a measure of inconsistency and disorder.

In referring to a planetary society, therefore, we mean merely one in which the basic forms, institutions, and values of that society are more directly oriented toward the maintenance of the world community.

The following considerations partially define the maintenance aspect of the planetary society:

1. Our major national technological economies now require access to the material resources of the whole earth for their continued operation. No nation or region is wholly self-sufficient and autonomous in this regard. Our economic activities also require an increasingly shared pool of freely available, and swift, information and knowledge transfer for their sustainment.

2. Our use of resources in support of these systems now approaches levels that begin to interfere substantially with the natural cycles of energy and materials in the overall earth system. Air, soil, and water pollution now transcend national boundaries and require transnational coordination for effective control.

3. All advanced technologies are now global in their operation. Their larger-scale requirements increasingly go beyond the capacity of any single nation or consortium of nations to manufacture or wholly maintain. Their operational aspects require common or-

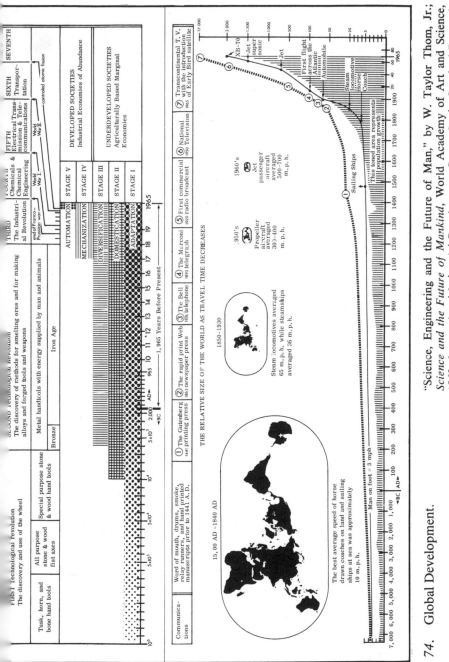

74. Global Development.

"Science, Engineering and the Future of Man," by W. Taylor Thom, Jr.; *Science and the Future of Mankind*, World Academy of Art and Science, 1963; *International Industrial Development Center Study*, Stanford Research Institute, 1962.

ganization and shared personnel and facilities for their maintenance. The regulations for landing and servicing an airliner in
Kabul are the same as those in London or Rio; the telephone,
teletype, and transistor do not work differently in Bangkok or
Birmingham.

4. Commerce, in relation to these technologies, now has to plan
and operate without regard to former bounds.

The final specifications for a computer reflect inputs from at least
twenty countries, so that it may meet the needs of virtually every
market, handle decimal as well as sterling, and print output not only
in Indian, or Japanese Katakana—but in type faces for a myriad different languages.[1]

To such specifications we may add the international trained and
exchanged technicians, equipment, instructions, and programs, plus
the fact that the manufacture, assembly and end uses of various
physical components may be thousands of miles apart. Such undertakings already seek to escape the control of individual nations
and pursue their activities under transnational treaties.

Only thus can global enterprises avoid the stifling restrictions imposed
upon commerce by the archaic limits of nation states . . . and realize
their potential to use the world's resources with maximal efficiency.[2]

5. Though still divided politically and ideologically, human society now has a more common cultural milieu than ever before.

Eskimo children who have never seen a wheeled vehicle can identify
the types of aircraft which fly overhead. The young Dyaks in the
conghouses of the equatorial jungle of Borneo listen to the Beatles,
and the wandering Bedouins with transistor radios, bought by selling
dates to the oilmen of the Sahara, hear Nasser's radio telling how
American planes are bombing Vietnam children half the world away.[3]

Global circulation of cultural styles and artifacts, through new
forms of communication and distribution, has engendered shared
attitudes and experiences in their use. Interpenetrating and diffusing
through locally diverse cultures, these common elements form part
of a transnational (that is, a planetary) culture.

6. Accompanying this diffusion of products, services, and new

sociocultural attitudes has been the almost invisible growth and widening function of world regulatory agencies.

The international postal air and surface transport and the telecommunications services are maintained and regulated through transnationally agreed codes and standards; the intricate network of the World Health Organization monitors the incidence and controls the spread of plague, smallpox, and other hazards. Agencies such as the latter are empowered to close a frontier, seal off a city, and redirect passenger and cargo flights in the air.

The increased dependence of the world's nations on such cooperative services is an invisible check mechanism that transcends political and ideological differences:

Even the Communist Chinese help keep tabs on the weather. They need the world's data and the world needs theirs. So they broadcast what they have to be sure of getting what they want in return. Their little-publicized action points up the moral that, when it comes to the weather, no nation can live unto itself. Their simple fact of earthly life makes the program to establish an effective global weather-observing system one of the smoothest-running international ventures ever.[4]

7. Individual initiative and cooperative action on a global scale is responsible for, and powerfully extends, official regulatory and other services. The number of international associations and professional organizations grows daily. The annual-date listing of their meetings, conferences, and work projects alone now runs to several volumes.

This web of international associational services and interlocked nongovernmental organizations represents a trend and a commitment whose real power is as yet unrealized.

For example, many organizations are scientific and technological in professional composition. As science is consulted increasingly for local legislative guidance in both physical and social affairs, its more responsible and eminent practitioners have begun to question the ethical accountability of their professions for the uses to which sciences and technologies may be put. Such uses have, hitherto, been determined almost wholly by attitudes and predilections of national societies. Many scientists now recognize that their central allegiance to the maintenance of the ecological matrix that sustains world human society may take precedence over the more transient, and possibly dangerous, priorities of national interest.

8. All major problems are now world problems, and most are in no way amenable to national solutions. The nature and scale of many, such as world health, food, and housing, have already gone beyond the stage where they respond to limited internation solutions; they are transnational in both their dimensions and the range of solutions that may be applied to them.

While emphasizing "one world," "transnational," and similar terms, it is again important to deemphasize any suggestion that the trend toward a planetary society necessarily infers a "world" government of a type represented by any of the present political systems. Those who advocate such schemes usually overlook the oppressive possibilities of centralized power. Our presently divisive system of *symbolically* autonomous principalities at least assures a degree of minimal sanctuary for those whose views and actions may not be in accord with those of their local regime. To impose

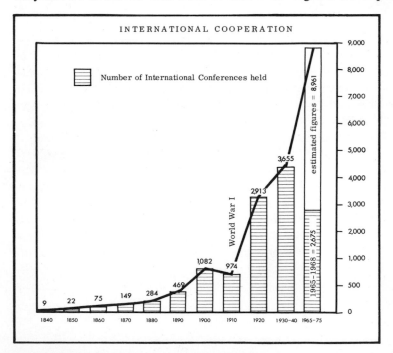

Figure 75.

any model of current government on a world scale in these terms would be folly.

While admitting that we have been pressed into close contiguity by the various agencies of change, we should note also that these agencies (particularly the technological) permit a much greater degree of decentralized autonomy and freedom together with the possibility of central coordination and cooperative control than ever existed before. In effect, given present technical means, a center can be anywhere.*

Turning to the more negative aspects of the planetary society, we may emphasize that it is presently characterized by dire inequity in the distribution of resources and access to the means for adequate living standards. As one writer has put it, we now face two different and coexistent world realities:

Our reality [of] regular meals, education, employment, entertainment and . . . margins of safety against the unexpected; and the *other* reality of the larger human experience compounded of hunger, disease, ignorance, insecurity, daily uncertainty and fear.[5]

The "revolution of rising expectations" presses closely upon our more comfortable Western reality and, if not countered by immediate and innovative means, will certainly engulf us.

International development is still constrained within the same obsolete notions that entangle the separate economic systems. Industrial advance for the have-not nations has been adjusted to the necessary stages of a myth of readiness for advanced technologies. Such myths become particularly transparent when they seemingly do not apply to the transfer of military technologies.

Questions about the impact of too rapid change, the erosion of cultural values, and the lack of proper institutions have been raised, and humane solutions have been resisted, to avoid radical action by the more fortunate nations.

Behind the prevarication and the excuses lie the older but obsolete strategies of the extension of power and vested interests. Despite superficial acceptance of foreign assistance grants and an

---

*This lesson has not been lost on the military, whose "command and control" centers are now airborne, under ocean, or terrestrial, as the mission requires.

apathetic approach toward solving the problems of underdeveloped countries, such aid has been used mostly as a pressure to secure favored terms for the donor nation's investment or access to strategic territory or resources.

There is hardly a region in the world where urgent tasks of development have not had to be deferred or abandoned because of political instability or the prior claim of the military on resources.[6]

Both internal instability and military claims go increasingly hand in hand. The total expenditures of foreign economic aid by all donor countries is equivalent to about 6 percent of the world's defense expenditures.[7]

As a *negative* service network, the global defense establishments

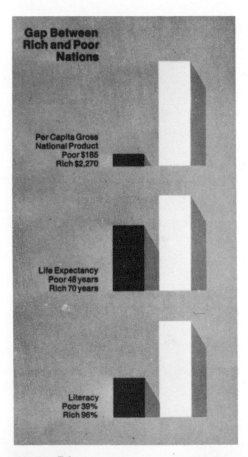

Gap Between Rich and Poor Nations

Per Capita Gross National Product
Poor $185
Rich $2,270

Life Expectancy
Poor 48 years
Rich 70 years

Literacy
Poor 39%
Rich 96%

Figure 76.

NEGATIVE	vs.	POSITIVE
attack submarines at $45,000,000 each	would pay for	1 year of agricultural aid for $178,699,760
e $105,000,000 atomic submarine minus missiles	would pay for	$132,095,000 in famine relief aid including freight costs
e $122,600,000 atomic submarine including missiles	would pay for	$150,000,000 in techical aid
e $275,000,000 aircraft carrier	would pay for	$251,000,000 for 12,000 high school dwellings
$104,616,800 naval weapons plant	would pay for	35 school buildings at $4,000,000 each
$104,616,800 naval weapons plant	would pay for	26 - 160 bed hospitals at $4,000,000 each
e $250,000,000 intercontinental ballistic missile base	would pay for	One 1,743,000 KWH capacity hydro electric dam
standard jet bombers at a cost of $8,000,000 each	would pay for	A school lunch program of $110,000,000 and serving 14 million children
One new prototype bomber fully equiped	would pay for	250,000 teacher salaries this year or 30 science faculties each with 1,000 students or 75 fully-equiped 100-bed hospitals... or 50,000 tractors... or 15,000 harvesters

e 77.
Peace Race," Seymour Melman, Braziller, 1961; *Atlanta Journal,*
11, 1965.

encompass a very large fraction of the highest scientific and technical expertise available in the world. Present expenditures for military purposes and support total almost 10 percent of the world's annual output of goods and services; nearly 50 million people are presently preoccupied with the maintenance of these world networks of armed forces, bases, depots, communications services, research and development, and production facilities.

This certainly demonstrates the presently available capacity of man to design, construct, and maintain massive and extremely complex global facilities. In view of the present size of the military establishment we may well question: Who is defending whom against what?

In general, we need to revise our approaches and our strategies toward the reality of ongoing change. Wholly political and ideological ends are now patently inadequate. Politics is no longer the art of the possible. It is now more the art of attempting to avoid the inevitable.

At a time when organized human knowledge allows man to accomplish the most audacious of yesterday's impossibles, the so-called expediences and realities of the conventional wisdom are dangerously outmoded. Our prime need is to devise new agencies, new organizations, and models of social action that may enable us to escape our largely artificial dilemmas. In seeking to define those factors that constrain positive change and seemingly negate our most inventive social strategies, we would do well to reexamine some of the most cherished social attitudes, institutions, and values that form the basis of human society. The key to many of our difficulties lies in the identification of those social orientations that in the past had great survival value, but which may now endanger our survival in the present, or cripple our approach to the future.

The full significance of the change process is still barely understood, even by those who have largely invented its components, organized its productive capacities, and are responsible for its acceleration.

The End of Economic Man

In advanced societies where the strongest conventions are

anchored in wealth and property, the most characteristic break with past values has occurred in this area.

Human labor is no longer directly related to the production of material goods in these societies; yet most of their fiscal difficulties emanate from obsolete models of the relation of such energy to productivity.

We assess volumes of goods produced relative to man-hours employed in their production, although even in the least automated process this is not a very direct relationship. We produce usable artifacts by applying energy through technical means to the forming of materials. The choice of material, means, and artifact forms are based on prior human energy investment not calculable in the process. In the fully automated plant, the sole forming determinant is *information*—as programed into the tools. In the final analysis, the only unique input into the production process is human knowledge.

To demonstrate the changed relation between direct human labor input and production, one perceptive analyst takes

. . . the extreme example of an automatically controlled electricity-generating plant connected to the British grid system, (in which) the operating crew may not even know whether or not it is producing electricity at a given time, and short of permanent shut down, employment is totally insensitive to fluctuations in demand for electricity.[8]

Though an extreme example, this demonstrates the break in the direct functional relation of human input and actual production, and processing. Many differential lags in various types of industry obscure this trend, which runs through every form of production enterprise from agriculture to aerospace.

As largely predicated on the survival virtues of work and the relation of income and living standards to productive employment, this alters many of the basic premises of our main economic and social institutions. It also tends to erode the allocation of living standards according to earlier related principles of rights, duties, exchange values, and similar antiquation.

From this time forward, man may potentially produce in abundance all his material life-sustaining requirements without the need to exact human labor in equable return. In effect, since science and technology are directly based on the availability of all recorded human knowledge, all human equity is already invested in the whole process. The invention of the zero is as important as that of the transistor. It is therefore a realistic, rather than merely philosophical, premise that the only universal credit card for access to the fruits of the whole enterprise is membership in the human race.

As technological change profoundly alters the nature and centrality of economic activity as a major social institution, capital and business enterprise is no longer a key wealth-producing and innovative force in society.[9] Increased knowledge, based on human resource capital, transferred into many forms of physical and social activities is now more directly the wealth generator.

Less than 25 percent of the United States work force is engaged in primary production, and the overall input of human energies into the production of goods and physical services has declined abruptly in the past few decades.*

*"Between 1950 and 1960, for example, private enterprise accounted for only one out of every ten new jobs that were created in the economy. All the rest were generated by the public or the private, not for profit sectors. . . . Today, a third of the labor force works for some employer other than a private businessman, compared with only 5% in 1929." R. L. Heilbroner, *The Limits of American Capitalism* (New York: Harper & Row, Publishers, Inc., 1965), p. 52.

Production and Man-Hours Worked: Petroleum Refining Industry, 1947-59

(1947=100)

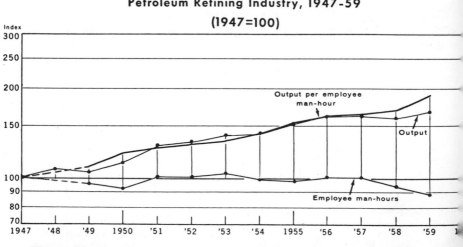

Figure 78.
U.S. Department of Labor.

The emphasis within industry has shifted from manufacture and distribution of products to that of service—whether in service of supplies product or in provision of rentable and service-maintained facilities. This is most apparent in the advanced sectors of industry; airlines, for instance, branch out into motels, hotels, resorts, and other forms of full service. The communications industry of telephone, TV, and radio expands toward the "Comsat" type of service, from personal message to education, health, resource communication, and the like. The trend is toward *people service* networks rather than product-market orientation.

Housing and other more traditional enterprises are still characterized by a low level of technological performance, high cost of fiscal and human energy investment, and product sale rather than product service.

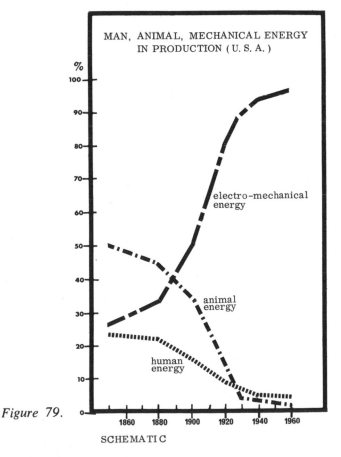

Figure 79.

SCHEMATIC

This is not to denigrate individual enterprise, but to suggest that its present and future characteristics may not be defined narrowly in terms of economic profit and material wealth gain. It may be as vigorously pursued in terms of other types of rewards. For example, though we classically define our free enterprise systems as those in which economic self-interest or direct profit are the main risk incentives and regulatory mechanisms, over 75 percent of their industry is large-scale corporate enterprise tied to banks, insurance, and public finance. The largest ventures—aerospace, communications, and defense—are those in which risk is minimal, profit margins are fixed, and the free market relation is hardly evident! Even the initial capitalization, means of production, and support research may be provided through public funds.

When we consider that most of the research and development in this area is also directly, or indirectly, government-financed, we come upon a form of guaranteed income already operative, and on a much grander scale than we presently conceive. It is noteworthy that no one has so far suggested that the initiative and self-respect of large-scale corporate enterprise has been particularly eroded by such an arrangement, a common charge against such income for the less fortunate.

Much of our futures concern is arrayed around the value of work in the determination of future roles in society. But when we examine the theories more closely, we find that there is a considerable residue of earlier intellectual attitudes to the rise of industry lagging behind the sophisticated critiques and empirical researches that have outmoded them. Much of the sociology of work and leisure is still primarily the study of those social roles that arise from the classification of men by gainful occupation, or in which all other activity is interpreted in relation to work, as traditionally defined. They are based on the model of economic man.

This radical change, which is also occurring in other countries, from product- and market-oriented economies to service- and welfare-oriented systems whose mainspring is no longer economically motivated, profoundly alters the importance and status relation of occupational roles. The more valuable work, even economically, is in human service, whether directly in teaching, welfare, or other public service or indirectly in the expansion of knowledge and the exploration of other physical, intellectual, or social frontiers.

Work, as previously defined, is no longer the central life interest. It has lost its relation to the compulsive work ethic, to the principle of nationality and efficiency, and the notion of time as money, that is, as a scarce commodity and socially significant unit.

Rationality and efficiency in human work were related to the extraction of maximal performance in the attainment of productive ends with scarce resources and variable means. They were the constraints of a primitive period of industrialization. With scarce resources now interconvertible, materials recycling and abundant energies as well as rationality and efficiency in machine production are reduced to routine performance choices from an available array of means offering many types of efficiency; all these are calculated against manufacturing costs, materials investment, reliability criteria, and other factors. The burden of rationality and efficiency is shifted over into the area of nonhuman operational factors.

This, of course, is still masked by the inability of many to understand that machines are intended to "off-load" man and that human time and energies are not required to equate machine time. For those still in the nineteenth century, even the advent of the computer merely presents itself as an additional reason to extract more human conformity—to ease the load of the machine.

Our presently evolving patterns of prolonged education, extended vacation, fringe benefits, and earlier retirement are indicators of the degree to which we are no longer in a work economy or culture. Though the threat of excessive leisure usually raises its head at this point, there is a more subtle transformation occurring even in this area. When human labor is no longer the yardstick of productive wealth, the virtues of hard work toward self-profit, whether in the accumulation of material or spiritual goods, are largely eroded. One of its last strongholds is formal education, which still accords high moral value in due ratio to difficulty and labor in learning. Cultivated aesthetic taste is also associated with the acquisition of hard-won understanding. Even the most recent programed and reinforcement schedule techniques of learning are still curiously biased on the relation of work to profit.

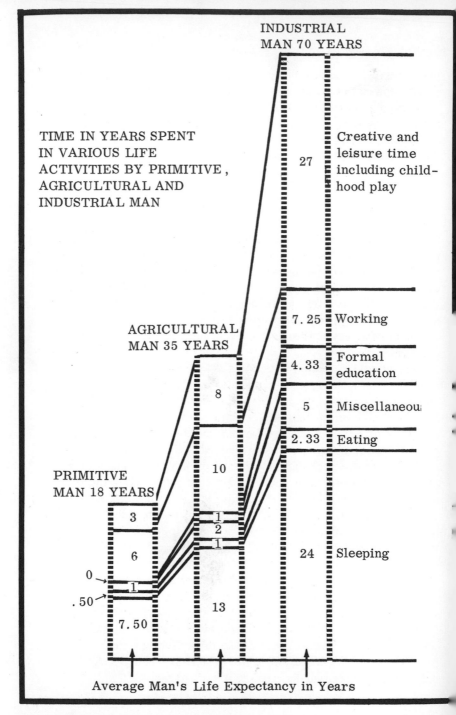

Figure 80.

Clearly, all our notions of the supposed virtues of imposed hard work and self-profit are based largely on the economics of scarcity and on previous standards of marginal survival.

We retain certain illusions and compulsions because we cannot design any other support for the social edifice. In exacting gainful mechanical work as required by preindustrial society in return for sustenance and shelter, many of man's more important activities were relegated to marginal status. By still regarding them as leisure, hobbies, and entertainment, we deny them status and their potential value in replacing gainful work as social activity.

Many of these hitherto marginal activities of man are those around which the more central social institutions may regroup themselves. Education, previously thought of as preparation for living is now more pervasively viewed as an *ongoing* aspect of living itself. Research, another devalued term, may be recast into a form that encompasses many types of individual and social exploration, of which specialized scientific research is only one type. Art and other more individually creative pursuits are currently transforming into quite different modes of participative experience.

Emerging Life Styles

We may define life style, at its simplest, as the form of living— the interweaving of activities, spaces, apparel, equipment, and their communicative aspects which characterize a way of life.

Historically, life styles were defined by economic class and occupational status factors. The peasant had a fixed style of life (in clothing, food, housing, mobility, language), much different from that of the soldier, the noble, or the king.

By and large, modern life styles have lost this mandatory component and inflexibility. Work and occupational role no longer determine so directly the life styling of individuals in a nonwork-oriented culture. The detachment of the way of life from the way of earning life, or living, does not replace work with leisure, but alters the meaning of both terms; it is not nonwork *or* leisure, but the decline of exclusively economic measures for human activities.

Ways of earning a living, occupational status, economic and geographic location, and other categories are no longer constraining factors on the style of life. Occupation, location, environmental, and social milieu may be changed many times in a lifetime.

Even more characteristically, a number of coexistent but exclusive life styles may be enjoyed at the same time; that is, in the same time sense, vacation, weekend, and work life style may be quite different yet coexistent. They are no longer wholly meaningful as separate, compartmentalized sequences. This is reflected in the interchangeability of apparel, equipment, and of the physical enclosures and spaces that are associated with such different time uses.

The overlapping of work/vacation/weekend living is also accompanied by the flexible adoption of appropriate styling for the many different social roles that the individual now occupies.

In terms of physical mobility, this greater diversity of styles requires differential use of an extended number of physical facilities. This is most marked in the service industry trends. Increased social and physical mobility detaches ownership from access to the use of a great range of facilities and encourages other types of use relations. Large numbers of social goods are shared and in the public domain; essential services such as water, energy, and sewage have long been in this category. National parks and other developments are of a similar nature. For more personal items, rental supplants ownership as use relation, from rent-a-suit to rent-a-car or airplane to a dinner service, a bridal gown, a set of family heirlooms, or skis. Often these may be grouped in package services—with the rented-service dwelling may go the ditto car, boat, lawnmower, trailer, television, golf clubs, or dinner jacket.

In relation to the service aspect of the changes in life style, the fiscal operation of economies, traditionally regarded as conservative, is increasingly based on long-range expectancy, operations, and plans. In rental and hire-purchase, future income expectations are exchanged for present use relations. A key feature of such developments is their accompaniment by guarantees of future performance—product life, durability, service maintenance, and the like. The trend of "enjoy now—pay later" is a curious reversal of the deferment of gratification implicit in the Protestant business ethic.

The rise of the complex insurance and credit structure is another aspect of this, in which expectation of return on investment may be deferred for long periods into the future. Business in futures, traditionally connoted by those of grain, cotton, and other commodities, is extended to the more ephemeral futures in the latest electronic and other developments—even to the knowledge industry as such. The balance of investment in education, research, in "creativity," where return is indirect and certainly in a speculative future, is now relatively common in areas of corporate enterprise.

The supposed acquisitive materialism of a technological society has an oddly contradictory flavor when the trend seems to be toward less acquisition and less attachment and domination by the "value" of physical possession. Beyond a certain level of material development, it seems more obvious that the value of material goods, in the sense of their pursuit and exclusive ownership, declines as they become more freely available. In this sense the revolutionary exhortation, "from each according to his abilities, to each according to his needs," is already partially reached in advanced societies. Present conflicts in such societies are less about ownership of the means of production than about access to, and control of, the human services of the society.

These features—lack of material attachment, decline of economic self-interest and possession, diversity of life style—are most marked in the young. The present youth versus authority confrontation is not a material but a moral conflict. It is less about the physical acquisition of more material means than about the moral and philosophical questions relating to the individual and societal use of such means.

In many senses, the younger generation has not rejected the traditions and precepts handed down to them by their elders. They have, indeed, taken them seriously! They have believed what was told to them about inalienable rights, the pursuit of truth and justice for all men, and other shibboleths. They are clamoring their acceptance of these truths as self-evident, and their singular determination to strive for them in the face of considerable discouragement. Both the acceptance and the striving arise from their position as a generation that has been routinely exposed for the first time in history to the enormously organized capabilities of man, and to the full knowledge of his responsibility to deploy this to positive or negative purpose.

In terms of life styles, the so-called youth culture offers an extraordinary range. Within its diversity there is an assumption of availability to all, and the conviction that each participant may engage in, or "opt out," according to his individual preference. Styles and social milieux are *inclusive* rather than exclusive and are *interpenetrative* of one another in location and communications mode.

The diversity of dress, personal styling, and communications is particularly characterized by the manner in which these use elements from other roles, periods, and situations simultaneously and in juxtaposition. Artifacts and means are displaced from their original contexts and purposes and used autonomously to any preferred purpose. The classical ends and means dichotomy and its alienative connotations are dissolved by a prior assumption that human needs and desires are the determinants, rather than fixed and unalterable relation of techniques and forms leading to some predetermined end.

One may approach other aspects of changing life style by way of this concept of the autonomism of means. Marx originally used this to describe the alienation of the worker from both the means of production and its products, since they were autonomously separated from his labor. In later social theory this has been extended to the notion of alienation, generally as inherent in a technological society in which the scientist is separated from the ownership of the means of his work, the administrator from his means, and so on.

Autonomism has been somewhat overemphasized. It has been used more as a crutch to avoid responsibility—that is, it has been presumed to be inherent in the system and beyond individual control—than as an insightful concept through which such alienation may be avoided by the redemption of more participative control.

The autonomism of means is also a normal function of symbolic transfer. The separation or distance between a raw biological urge and its social expression in symbolic form may be considerably extended; thus, in lyric poetry, the form may be practiced effectively in the absence of any specific object to whom it is addressed, or may be adopted for its own sake.

In Georg Simmel's sociological rephrasing of autonomism,

. . . it happens that these materials, these forces and interests, in a peculiar manner remove themselves from the service of life that originally produced and employed them. They become autonomous in the sense that they are no longer inseparable from the objects which they formed and thereby become more available to our purposes. They come to play freely in themselves and for their own sake.[10]

We may also apply this concept to life styles. The particular style of a given life mode is initially formed through the pressures and urgencies of naked survival; for example, as in a hunting economy of a nomadic society. Gradually, the most efficacious practices and styles of hunting, riding, and dressing become the most favored and ideal. On the one hand, they are sanctified through traditional usage, and on the other, as core survival strategies they furnish the preferred style that is taught, played, and refined for its own sake.

The stirrup, the sword, or spear form the "dressage" in correct riding; the trappings of the hunt emerge as forms in their own right, and their style comes to function as the correct form defining the knight or the caballero. In modern times and modes, the "city gent," the costermonger, or the "man in the gray flannel suit" represent the chosen image.

This separation between utility and life style may be seen at its greatest autonomy in military life, where the trappings, practices, and minute differentiation of rank, styles, and ceremonial observances bear little or no relation to the military ends of actual warfare.

The present transformation of many obsolete work or survival skills into leisure skills is another area of the extension of life-style range. It is most evident in skiing, surfing, horseback riding, sailing, sky diving, and skin diving, where previously localized survival-craft skills are developed into complex techniques requiring much greater coordination, training, and persistence than in their earlier forms.

The more autonomous the form and the further removed from

the survival imperative, the closer it approaches an art form, and the more demanding its performance.

The traditional argument has usually gone the other way. As an activity became detached from its original need context, and was ritualized into a play or art form, its performance was correspondingly degraded. The underlying premise is that without the real exigencies of the hunt, war, and competitive physical survival, man becomes soft and degenerate. Again, as with many such arguments, the reverse may be true. In the archaeological record, there is evidence to suggest that in many ways our present-day man is tougher, more adaptable, and more resistant to stress and disease than were his ancestors.

We may carry this discussion of life styles forward into the area of sex in much the same way. In earlier periods of marginal survival, deviance from the group norms of "increase and multiply" was in many ways physically threatening to the continuity of the society. It is no longer so. With less value attached to the reproduction aspect of sex, and the detachment of the act from procreative responsibility through conception, the range of permissible deviance in the act itself is no longer related to group survival but to individual factors of choice, aesthetics, and other considerations. Most forms of socially disapproved deviance, in this regard, will probably return to the province of personal concern.

In the more public emphases on sex there is also a similar trend toward its status as a private art form, life-style development that was earlier reserved to more decadent elites.

Perhaps the most fundamental revolution in this area is the oral contraceptive. One may analyze this, rather unaesthetically, in terms of control of the means of production having been taken over by women. Probably no single factor made women more subject to men than the fear that they might be impregnated without their consent. This was manifestly expressed in their earlier chattel status and in the latent rape theme in many marriage rituals. Previous forms of women's equal suffrage had little in common with the privileges accorded by the kinds of new social roles that women may now enjoy in the post-pill era.

Such changes in life styles, as we may see, are more than mere changes in external form. They emerge from, and are expressions of, changes in the core institutions and value systems of our society. As such, they are more important indicators of change than those in technologies, economic and market orientation, in weaponry, and other activities. They are more determinative of the future directions in which these means will be employed.

As we have reiterated, our major problems in facing the future are no longer those of physical means and technologies, but of conceptual attitudes.

In keeping with the future development of new forms of human activity, we need to rethink much of our physical and social planning of the kinds of facilities required. Though such future planning is being pursued most vigorously, and has come to be both an occupational role and life style in its own right, it is still tied in many areas to sets of obsolete premises and conceptual schemes that invalidate much of its work.

The city, for example, has been a specific focus of much planning concern for over a century, but our thinking is oriented to the "urbs" in an agricultural society or one in early transition through an industrializing economy. The city is now only one kind of way station or temporarily preferred center in an extended transportation, communication, and service facilities net. As no longer determined by such networks (to the extent they go where people are), or by other physical considerations such as defense or access to production, planning has no one ideal form. Our current urban dilemmas partially result from pursuit of such an all-encompassing ideal.

The Future City

While the more obvious obstacles to the wholesale replanning of cities are those of financial and real estate interests, much of our present failure to conceive of new city forms lies with our traditional ideal model. This has become curiously restricted to the nineteenth-century version of the multipurpose city as a static agglomeration of commercial enterprise/industrial production and distribution points related to materials transportation and warehousing. Urban living was tucked into the interstices of a system for earning a living or controlling the production and flow of material goods and wealth.

It has hardly been considered that the city may not evolve further as a multifunctional aggregate, but may in the future take many special forms for varied social purposes. The traditional concept of one type of urban form has been singled out and abstracted from a number of past examples that were evolved in relation to a specific set of needs.

The needs still exist, and have expanded rather than contracted. Their larger compaction in one form is no advance, but might further erode the city as a form.

The earliest cities were central depositories of power, specialized skills, of wealth in terms of agricultural surplus stored against future needs, or converted into royal/religious treasure or other symbolic wealth. They functioned also as communications centers in the administrative and trading networks, and as exchange and market points. They were often, and necessarily, walled-in fortresses which could survive for varying periods as autonomous units when under siege by enemies.

The ecology of such preindustrial cities was relatively stable. Their maximal growth was governed by factors of public health, sanitation, and food supply which limited them to a particular size and location in both aggregate population and facilities.

The preceding description is one specific and synoptic abstraction of the city form, but we should remember that, coexisting with such living urban centers from the earliest times, there were other city forms. For example, large enclosures of many types developed not as living centers but as religious and ceremonial centers—the neolithic ceremonial centers of the (Stone)henge, the Egyptian cities of the dead, the American Indian cities constructed for communal religious functions. There are the more recent examples of Angkor Wat, the pilgrimage centers of Mecca, and the Vatican City. In our own period we may also note various types of partially specialized forms: the capital city, such as Washington, London, Moscow, Paris, as both a ceremonial and administrative center with its symbolic residence for the chief dignitary; the manufacturing city often identified with a product, such as Detroit; the neutral meeting place and conference center of Geneva, which also functions as an international wealth depository; New York and Los Angeles as communications cities.

A remarkable pure specialized form would be Las Vegas as the "fun" or recreative city (the "pop spa") continuing the specialized functional purposes of socially recreative activities, of presentation, display, and ostentation, which were previously available in Bath, Carlsbad, or Saratoga.

One might then continue these developmental examples to include many emergent forms of "urbs," which are presently collapsed into a single abstraction—*the city*. The danger in clinging to this abstraction as a supposedly multifunctional model is that we may constantly fail in attempting to re-create something that never actually existed autonomously, but evolved slowly in response to necessities and historical exigencies.

Much of the implosive compaction of both large numbers of people and many types of urban function into one form occurred in the nineteenth century under the accelerated pressures of industrialization. This specific evolution of the urbs has continued into the post-industrial period, and shows signs of grave instability and obsolescence. The present attempts to revive and re-create this no longer viable type of multipurpose city seem to be curiously ill-fated.

In terms of our available transportation and communication technologies, the standard of living that was previously available only in cities may now be enjoyed in remotely deployed locations. The services of the city are available *without* the need to go within the city walls. For many, the city is where one goes to the theater, to shop, to transact business, to talk with a legislator, or to have fun.

We may suggest, therefore, that much of our present concern with designing and planning the ideal city form may indeed be misdirected. We should rather reconceptualize our model of the urbs and reduce our level of abstraction to allow for a number of possible and alternate models. The types noted below were all viable and coexistent forms in the past and are presently reemerging in the more developed and industrialized societies (they should, of course, not be considered as mutually exclusive forms, but as having various overlapping functions):

The Ceremonial City. Now in secular form as the administrative and political capitals. But there are other subcapitals for various communal ceremonies and public observances.

The University City. Presently evident where the older form has continued in sustained growth or where such centers have been created by the establishment of new universities, colleges, and institutes. These latter centers have often been in relatively remote locations and are of proven viability for such further development.

The Scientific City. As an outgrowth of the university form but often purely evolved as an aggregate of research and development center. Space, atomic energy, and other research areas have given rise to such cities in the U.S., U.S.S.R., and Europe.[11]

The Festival City. The festival, or "arts," city could be related to the university or ceremonial capitals, but shows signs of a developing autonomous form, as in Edinburgh, Venice, and Salzburg.

The Recreation, or "Fun," City. This already exists in its purest form as Las Vegas, but the category includes many other vacation cities: the whole of the Cote d'Azur, the Costa Brava, or Miami Strip development may be considered as such forms. This degree of specialization may extend to the ski city, the sea city, or the theater/opera or cinema city.

The Communications City. Again, by circumstance, this may also be functionally part of the capital or the university form. New York is probably one of the prime examples, the center for communications industries of television, radio, newspapers, advertising, publishing.

The Convention/Conference City. Many of the core facilities of some major cities, their hotels, railroad and air networks, and ancillary services now depend for their major revenues on the yearly conventions or succession of conferences, which bring thousands of transient residents for periods of a few days, a week, or a month.

The Museum City. This is the city in, and of, history, and there are many examples. The main capitals come immediately to mind, but there are countless smaller and purer examples such as Florence, Bruges, Rome, and Athens. There are also the growing number of actual or reconstructed historical sites around which facilities for the tourist, the scholar, and the casual visitor grow up.

Williamsburg and Angkor Wat are separable in time and geographic space, but share more functional features than Paris and Chicago.

The Experimental City. This type is presently enjoying a catchword vogue, but the concept needs to be extended *not only* toward forms within which the physical social functions of urban living may be experimentally studied, as in a variable controlled laboratory environment. We need, even more, other forms where people may go to experiment *socially*, to explore different life styles, different kinds of social relationships, varied tempos of living, and the possibilities of many innovative life strategies, which they may not otherwise experience or try out.

To a degree, such experimental city forms may take on the functions of the therapeutic or health community, organized around large-scale medical facilities, or may be connoted as alternate modes for the re-creative city form.

The categories discussed above could be extended considerably and cross-related in function to create new forms. Their only present validity may be to provide a fresh conceptual framework for reconsidering the city of the future or the future of the city.

Within that conceptual frame, as in all futures consideration, there needs to be a more rigorous acceptance of the full range of human idiosyncratic requirements. The "aseptic and well-lighted" place characteristic of many current city-planning practices is not accommodative of many human desires and proclivities. Planning for those that fall out of the normal range is relegated to means of *controlling* deviance and the seaminess of the bohemias, and the bar strip may be avoided. Yet, a considerable measure of aberrance may be expected in any human group. To plan only for the *control* and *surveillance* of those areas of human behavior that do not accord with present norms is not future- but past-oriented.

Education in Reality

Many of our present discontinuities and our traumatic collisions with change processes are due to the conceptual failure of those institutions whose larger responsibility lies with the orientation and guidance of society. The transmission of values and attitudes and the continuity of standards and order within change have been eroded less by those who have sought to change them than by those responsible for their traditional maintenance.

Education has, for example, been one of our more laggard institutions in this regard. The response to change has been largely confined to the adoption of technologies that have been administratively convenient, with little attention to the radical nature of required educational changes in themselves.

As we noted earlier, in confronting the future the students of today are less concerned with rejecting the past than with the meaningful relationship of the present to that past and to their future.

. . . the generation which was born into the atomic age, had their births registered by computer, and had Sputnik as their zodiacal sign . . . take for granted the marvels which still bewilder their elders. They are also more aware that most of the arguments of what we call "international" politics are irrelevant. . . . Mankind has become an entity, interdependent through our common necessities. The post atom generation senses all this: their elders are still schizophrenic—recognising the facts of a shrunken world but rejecting the implications which upset outworn creeds.[12]

Education is one of the core institutions charged with the transmission of values, meaning, and the understanding of change in human society. Its largest deficiencies have been in this area, where it has dealt with the symbolic and value content of our culture almost entirely in terms of the past. There has been little real attempt to convey standards of critical assessment commensurate with our present cultural realities. Such standards are still almost exclusively occupied with the older traditional modes and with the type of knowledge and training through which cultivated choice and participation was exercised in these modes.

Any common charges of lowered standards and mass manipulation through the newer media, if real, might be traceable to such bias in our educational systems. Television and film may be used as teaching tools, but are seldom related to their extramural function as major culture channels. The printed word is still considered the prime cultural vehicle, whereas much of our contemporary culture is already conveyed in highly developed and sophisticated forms through pictorial images and other expressive modes.

Various gaps are thus consistently maintained between cultural expectations and the wide range of available cultural realities. The anomic blockage of full understanding and participation in our emergent planetary culture is largely due to obsolete educational attitudes. We patently require manifold attempts to demonstrate the ways in which the meaningful and symbolic value systems of man's past are being transmuted in the present revolution of world media, that is, to establish creative continuity between traditional culture and our contemporary cultural situations. We may accomplish this through education in the linkages and meanings, which exist in common through vastly transformed symbols, between our past local heritages and their present metamorphosis in the larger cultural context.

The Planetary Culture

The world we now live in, with its particular qualities of speed, mobility, rapidity of change and communication, has no historical precedent as a cultural context. Man can now see farther, move faster, produce more than ever before. Devices such as high-speed cameras, radio telescopes, and the orbital satellites have extended the range of our sensory experience far beyond that ever imagined. Besides enormously enlarging the extent of the physical world available to our direct experience in an ordinary lifetime, such new means provide us—through the multimedia, TV, motion pictures, picture magazines and newspapers—with what is virtually an extension of our culture world. A constant stream of moving, fleeting images of the world is presented for our daily appraisal. Through these means we extend ourselves psychically, telescoping time, moving through history, spanning the world through unprecedented visual and aural means of experience.

Within this process is the diverse plurality of messages, symbols, products, entertainment, and attitudes conveyed typically through the network of global communications, including within its scope the many physical artifacts designed and produced for world consumption, which comprise our contemporary environment.

The lavish diversity mirrors myriad facets of a period in which rapid and frequent changes in the human condition call for a rich profusion of symbolic images, messages, stories, and impressions that may enable man to locate in, learn, and adapt himself to his society. Their constant re-creation and renewal matches the requirements of his more mobile and changing social experience.

In which way do the characteristics of this form of development culture differ from those of the older, "high," or fine, culture with which it still coexists? The latter arose largely in vertical societies whose main cultural channels—painting, sculpture, literature, music, and drama—served and were maintained by a privileged elite. This might be, singly or concurrently, an aristocracy, a body of free citizens or cultivated bourgeoisie, or a priesthood, which represented and directed most of the cultural goals and preferences. Work in these channels was individually created in the society for a limited group of persons whose position allowed them the material wealth, necessary leisure, and degree of literacy or educated sensibility required for its full enjoyment. In the main, such works were conceived as enduring through time, universally applicable expressions of man's condition. The values of canons within which they were judged are reflective of the societal beliefs and prevailing dogma within which they were created. Such canons included permanence, individual uniqueness, and an assumed accessibility to all men according to personal susceptibility and cultivated taste; they tended to associate aesthetic pleasure with conditions of moral judgment.

Though grossly oversimplified, these are some of the factors that may be used to compare the classical to the newer cultural forms. Our bare outlining is in no way intended to belittle the status of classical culture or minimize its massive contribution to our civilization. The accessibility to all persons in all periods of this type of culture, however, is a doubtful quantity. Its present viability and expansion in many forms stresses the inclusive nature of our present period in which a much wider cultural repertoire is available to the individual.

It should be emphasized, however, that the aesthetic and value assumptions drawn from, and valid within, such classical forms still furnish the bulk of our critical apparatus. They have obvious inadequacies when applied to those forms in the present communications modes, whose creation, context, and qualities are quite different. This accounts for the uneasy adversity with which most academic critics view such material. It is more often the standard of judgment that is inadequate rather than that which is being judged.

Many of the things that constitute the present environment are identical and expendable—a vast range of personal and household objects, for instance, which were previously craft-cultural forms. When they are worn out, lost, or destroyed, they may be replaced by others exactly similar. Or, when they wear out in the symbolic sense, that is, are no longer fashionable, they may be replaced by others with the same functional capacity but of a more typically symbolic form.

Such expendable objects have no intrinsic uniqueness or permanent appeal that could qualify them for merit within the older canons. The capacity of new processes to replicate these artifacts from earlier traditions, not only exactly but also successfully in quite different materials, is also a tendency that has bothered culture-conscious persons since the onset of the industrial revolution. The critical change, then, is that value no longer is attached to material aspects of things. This earlier attitude was based on scarcity and the amount of physical life energy that had to be devoted to the craft creation of many cultural artifacts. Emphasis now is on the symbolic value, not on its rare material or how much it may cost. The new channels of TV, movie, and mass circulation magazines with four-color reproductions, for example, which now carry so much of our cultural communication, did not exist previously. We have no critical precedents to draw upon which are fully adequate to this new situation. These channels also broadcast to the society as a whole and in an immediate manner, whereas previous cultural messages traveled slowly along restricted routes to their equally restricted audience. Creation and production were formerly geared to a small culture-making elite at the top of the social pyramid; they are now directed by the plurality of goals and preferences representing the wider range of society.

The term "mass" used to refer to contemporary culture or audience requires qualifying. The so-called mass breaks down into many cross groupings of minorities, differentiated by age, sex, nationality, education, work, leisure, activities, and so forth. A cursory glance at any large magazine stand will serve to illustrate how many different groups, attitudes, and special requirements go to make up the audience.

The planetary form of culture promises to provide larger-scale availability of cultural products to many more people. The consumption of these products remains more than ever, and more widely, within the province of individual choice, and such choices are less dictated by tradition, authority, and scarcity than they were previously.

Also, and importantly, there is a considerable degree of participation by the consumer in the creation of cultural forms. His appreciation is a critical factor. Production or transmission on a scale involving millions of people and many different audiences must be ever sensitive to acceptance or rejection of that which is presented. This latter point has been expressed by Hauser in his *Social History of Art*:

. . . the cinema goers of the whole world have to contribute to the financing of a big film. . . . By their mere presence at theatrical performances in Athens or the Middle Ages they were never able to influence the ways of art directly; only since they have come on the scene as consumers and paid the full price for their enjoyment, have the terms on which they hand over their shillings become a decisive factor in the history of art.[13]

That pressures on, and manipulation of, such choice does exist in partially due to the present economic and political structure of society, but is to a degree inevitable in any society. Where little or no resistance to, or awareness of, such adverse manipulation is found, it may be related, as we suggested, to deficiency in education.

The cultural messages and symbols that orient man to his environment are now capable of being transmitted at greater speed and in ways which transcend earlier and slower means. A visual language of common but constantly varying symbolic images is in use, which tends to overrun all previous barriers of language and frontier. That so much cultural diffusion occurs in this nonverbal fashion is obviously disturbing to those who have been schooled in strong literary traditions. There is a certain ease of assimilation that is suspect in the view of older standards, which usually assumed progressive difficulty of formal attainment (that is, initially of literacy) as necessary and morally justifiable steps toward full cultural enjoyment.

The facility of transmission-shared symbols and attitudes is a key element in the expansion and diffusion of cultural forms around the globe. They link vast heterogeneous publics. They establish contact between peoples by providing an extended range of common experiences, even where the people stay put. It has been alleged that this development breaks down the different national manifestations of culture, blending customs and beliefs and making for a homogeneous world culture of uniform attitude and appearance in which individual difference will disappear. But loss of local individuality has been more apparent than real.

It is more in evidence that local cultural forms have been revived and strengthened in many parts of the world. Though we refer to the homogeneity and lack of variety, we also complain about the bewildering changes of art styles and musical forms that circulate within our culture. The more denotable uniform and homogeneous society was the primitive enclave, or preindustrial peasant community, with its limited repertoire of cultural forms and possible life-style alternatives.

Though our cursory review has emphasized the large-scale mass aspect of world cultural diffusion, there is also the concomitant increase in individual cultural communication and participation.

The copying machine allows every writer to be his own publisher. It also makes for an extraordinary flow of personalized information exchange between people. In combination with the telephone and other devices, and the frequency of international meetings, there are already a number of invisible college networks* around the world within which an increasing volume of professional work, interpersonal and intergroup exchange, and coordination is carried.

*A unique protoype of this has been pioneered by John Dixon in the United States in the form of a personalized and selective information service to an international network of scholars, executives, and legislators.

Associated with this is the phenomenal rise in the "underground" newspapers, journals, and books, which now form the autonomous information network of the younger generation. Again, this is made possible through the ubiquity and low-cost availability of printing, duplicating, and other means.

Cameras, tape recorders, and movie-making apparatus are more available to more people at less cost. This has spurred a new creative wave in underground movies and other art forms, which have diffused swiftly into the even more complex technologies of the multimedia-theater-dance-music-image-light presentations and collaborations.

At every level, such developments are characterized by individual initiative and direct participation in the control of complex processes and by the fact that such participation is also a premise of the newer art forms in themselves. There are no spectators; everyone is involved in one way or another in the performance.

When one refers to art in this way, it is no longer fine art as previously defined. The arts, as such, are no longer a canonical form of cultural communication restricted to specific elites and conducted according to specified rules and procedures.

Art work, as in the Cage "concert" or the Rauschenberg "combine" is less viewable as a discrete event or series of object relations. The "event" is one of temporal immersion in a continuous contextual flow of communicated experiences. The technological means, media, or channel of that communication is no longer an obtrusive constraining element.

The masterwork in these emerging forms may only be a reel of punched or magnetized tape, or some other invisible sequencing mode of transmitting the experience. As there is little either/or exclusivity, it may also be produced in a durable, replicable, product form for wider circulation.

The future of cultural forms already has many more dimensions of rich diversity. The promise within the newer media is of a greater interpenetration and interaction of life-art-culture rather than the forms-objects-images that preserved and isolated social life.

As for the larger communication and understanding implied in a shared planetary culture, it is more than obvious today that we must understand and cooperate on a truly global scale, or we perish.

References

I THE SENSE OF THE FUTURE

1. Boris Pregel, "The Impact of the Nuclear Age," in *America Faces the Nuclear Age*, D. Landman and J. E. Fairchild, eds. New York: Sheridan House, 1961, p. 26.
2. Daniel Bell, "Twelve Modes of Prediction," *Daedalus* (*J. Am. Acad. of Arts and Sciences*; Summer, 1964), p. 486.
3. Bertrand de Jouvenel, "Utopia for Practical Purposes," *Daedalus* (*J. Am. Acad. Arts and Sci.*; Spring, 1965), p. 444.
4. Hasan Ozbekhan, *Technology and Man's Future*, System Development Corporation (U.S.), Sp.-2494; May, 1966.
5. R. C. Cook, "Truth and Consequences in a New Era," *Population Bulletin*, Vol. XXII, No. 4 (November, 1966), U.S.

II THE FUTURE OF THE PAST

1. Time's Arrow

1. John Cohen, "Subjective Time," from *The Voices of Time*, J. T. Fraser, ed. New York: George Braziller, Inc., 1967, p. 262.
2. Mircea Eliade, *The Sacred and the Profane*. New York: Harper & Row, Publishers, 1961, p. 95.
3. Claude Levi Strauss, *The Savage Mind*. London: George Wiedenfeld & Nicolson Ltd., 1966, p. 236.
4. Fred L. Polak, *The Image of the Future*, Vol. I. Leyden: A. W. Sijthoff; Dobbs Ferry, N.Y.: Oceana Publications, Inc., 1961, p. 23.
5. Max Weber, *Essays in Sociology*. Trans. by H. H. Gerth and C. W. Mills, eds. New York: Oxford University Press, 1958, p. 275.
6. Mircea Eliade, *The Myth of the Eternal Return*. New York: Bollingen Foundation, 1954, p. 104.
7. Max Weber, *Essays in Sociology*. Trans. by H. H. Gerth and C. W. Mills, eds. New York: Oxford University Press, 1958, p. 280.

8. Corinne Lathrop Gilb, "Time and Change in Twentieth Century Thought," *Journal of World History*, Vol. IX, No. 4 (1966), pp. 867–880.
9. H. Stuart Hughes, *Consciousness and Society: The Reorientation of European Social Thought 1890–1930*. New York: Alfred A. Knopf, Inc., 1958.
10. E. J. Hobsbawm, *The Age of Revolution 1789–1848*. New York: New American Library, Inc., 1962, p. 91. (A Mentor Book.)

2.   The Industrial Revolution

1. H. E. Friedlander and J. Oser, *Economic History of Modern Europe*. Englewood Cliffs, N.J.: Prentice-Hall, Inc., 1953, p. 64.
2. R. Buckminster Fuller, *Ideas and Integrities*. Englewood Cliffs, N.J.: Prentice-Hall, Inc., 1963.
3. W. and H. Woodruff, "Economic Growth: Myth or Reality," *Technology and Culture*, No. 4 (Fall, 1966).
4. Manning Nash, *Machine Aga Maya: The Industrialization of a Guatemalan Community*. New York: The Free Press, 1958, p. 116.
5. Peter A. Munch, *Economic Development and Conflicting Values*, Manuscript, Department of Sociology, Southern Illinois University and the Maxwell Graduate School, Syracuse University, Syracuse, New York.
6. Emile Durkheim, *The Division of Labor in Society* (1893). Trans. by George Simpson. Glencoe, Illinois: The Free Press, 1947, p. 229.
7. Juergen Schmandt, "On the Emergence of a Second-Generation Science Policy in America," *Science and Policy: A Changing Union*. Paper for the Organization for European Cooperation and Development (OECD), April, 1967.
8. Dennis Gabor, *Inventing the Future*. London: Secker and Warburg; New York: Alfred A. Knopf, Inc., 1963.
9. Ossip K. Flechteim, *History and Futurology*. Germany: Verlag Anton Hain K.-G., 1966.

III   THE FUTURE OF THE PRESENT

1.   The Dimensions of Change

1. John Wilkinson, *Futuribles: Innovation vs. Stability*, Center for the Study of Democratic Institutions (U.S.), 1967.
2. Warren G. Bennis, Kenneth D. Benne, and Robert Chin, eds.,

The Planning of Change. New York: Holt, Rinehart and Winston, Inc., 1962, p. 3.

3. Hugh D. Duncan, *Communication and Social Order.* New York: Oxford University Press, 1968, p. 1.

2. An Ecological Overview

1. R. B. Fuller, "Prospects for Humanity," *Saturday Review* (August 29, 1964).
2. *Energy Resources.* Washington, D.C.: Natl. Res. Council, Natl. Acad. Sci. Publ. No. 1000-D, Committee on Natural Resources, 1962.
3. Erich W. Zimmermann, *Introduction to World Resources*, Henry L. Hunker, ed. New York: Harper & Row, 1964.
4. O. T. Duncan, "Social Organization and the Ecosytem," in *Handbook of Modern Sociology*, R. L. Faris, ed. Skokie, Ill.: Rand McNally, 1964.

3. The Environ Systems

1. R. Doane, *World Balance Sheet.* New York: Harper & Row, Publishers, 1957, p. 27.
2. G. Borgstrom, "The Human Biosphere and Its Biological and Chemical Limitations," *Global Impacts of Applied Microbiology*, Mortimer P. Starr, ed. New York: John Wiley & Sons, Inc., 1964.
3. H. Boyko, "Salt Water Agriculture," *Scientific American* (March, 1967).
4. A. Kantrowitz, *Electronic Physiologic Aids.* New York: Maimonides Hospital, 1963.
5. Adelbert Ames, Jr., Institute for Associated Research, Hanover, N.H.
6. R. B. Fuller, *Ideas and Integrity.* New Jersey: Prentice-Hall, Inc. 1963.
7. Zygmunt Baunan, "Image of Man in Modern Sociology," *Polish Sociological Bulletin* No. 1, 1967, p. 14.
8. W. La Barre, *The Human Animal.* Chicago: University of Chicago Press, 1954, p. 92.

4. Man Plus

1. Giovanni Pico della Mirandola, "Oration on the Dignity of Man" (1486). Trans. by E. L. Forbes from *The Renaissance Philos-*

ophy of Man, E. Cassener, ed. Chicago: University of Chicago Press, 1948, p. 225.

2. Robert J. White, "The Isolated Brain," *Industrial Research Inc.* (April, 1968), p. 65.

3. Manfred Clynes, Foreword to *Cyborg: Evolution of the Superman*, D. S. Halacy, Jr. ed. New York: Harper & Row, p. 8.

4. Jacques Ellul, *The Technological Society*, trans. by John Wilkinson. New York: Alfred A. Knopf, Inc., 1964.

5. Richard R. Landers, *Man's Place in the Dybosphere*. New Jersey: Prentice-Hall, Inc., 1966, p. 4.

6. L. Zotova and A. Voskreseusky, *Bionics, A New Science*. Izv. (Russia), July 16, 1961.

7. *Unimate*, Unimation Inc., a subsidiary of Pullman, Inc. and Condec Corporation; *Versatran*, AMF Thermatool Corporation, subsidiary of American Machine and Foundry Co.

8. Henry D. Block and Herbert Ginsberg, "The Psychology of Robots," *Psychology Today*, Communications/Research/Machines/ Inc. (April, 1968), p. 54.

9. Henry D. Block, "Simulation of Statistically Composite Systems," from *Prospects for Simulation and Simulators of Dynamic Systems*, George Shapiro and Milton Rogers, eds. New York: Spartan Books, Inc., 1967.

10. M. W. Thring, "The Place of the Technologist in Modern Society," *J. Roy. Soc. Arts* (April, 1966).

11. General Electric Company, Schenectady, N.Y., 1966 .

12. Professor E. Carlson, UCLA, AP Wire Service, April 10, 1966.

13. Warren M. Brodey, "Human Enhancement Through Evolutionary Technology," *IEEE Spectrum* (September, 1967), p. 90.

5.   The New Symbiosis

1. Business Week special report (1966).

2. B. V. Akhlibininsky and N. I. Khrallenko, *Cybernetics and Problems of Development*, (Lenizdat Publishing House, 1963), U.S. Department of Commerce, OTS Report 64–215–17.

3. Information Release, U.S. Strategic Air Command (402) 294–2544/4433.

4. Wm. R. Corliss, *Scientific Satellites*, Scientific and Technical Information Division, Office of Technology Utilization, NASA, SO-133, 1967.

5. W. O. Roberts, "Peaceful Uses of the Earth's Atmosphere," *Science*, Vol. 152, No. 3119 (April, 1966).

6. Homer E. Newell, "Current Program and Considerations of the Future for Earth Resources Survey," 5th Symposium on Remote Sensing of Environment, April, 1968.
7. NASA news release, June 26, 1968.
8. Philip L. Johnson, *Remote Sensing as an Ecological Tool*, Symposium on Ecology of Subarctic Regions, UNESCO (Finland, 1968).
9. Robert N. Colwell, "Remote Sensing of Natural Resources," *Scientific American* (January, 1968), pp. 54–69.
10. E. R. Spangler, "Results of Space Research 1957–1967," *TRW Space Log* Vol. 7, No. 3 (Fall, 1967), p. 52.

6.   Problems and Prospects

1. Derek de Solla Price, *Little Science, Big Science*. New York: Columbia University Press, 1963, p. 5.
2. John Wilkinson, *The Quantitative Society*. Center for the Study of Democratic Institutions.
3. Donald Bogue, "End of the Population Explosion?," *U.S. News & World Report* (March 11, 1968).
4. Arnold J. Toynbee, "New Windows into History," *Think*, (September-October 1965), p. 4.
5. M. King Hubbert, *Energy Resources*. Washington, D.C.: Natl. Research Council, Natl. Acad. Sci. Publ. No. 1000-D, Committee on Natural Resources, 1962.

IV   THE FUTURE OF THE FUTURE

1.   Outer Space

1. Kenneth Brown and Lawrence D. Ely, *Space Logistics Engineering*. New York: John Wiley and Sons, Inc. 1962, p. 9.
2. Report of study contracted February, 1968, by NASA, Langley Research Center, Hampton, Virginia.
3. James M. Gavin, "Perspectives and Prospects in Space," Honors Convocation, American Institute of Aeronautics and Astronautics, Boston, Mass. December, 1966. (Chairman of the Board paper: Arthur D. Little, Inc. p. 14).
4. Space Science and Applications Program, E. P. 47, Fiscal Year 1968, Washington, D.C.: Natl. Aeronau. Space Admin.
5. Y. N. Sushkov, *Flights into Space, Nauchn.-Populyarnaya Biblioteka*, Moskva, 1963. (Edited machine translation FTD-MT-64–227, U.S. Department of Commerce, 1964.)

6. *Ibid.*, p. 15.
7. V. Trobolev, "Trolley Bus Lines in Space," *Znaniye-Sila* (Nov. 2, 1964).
8. Ward J. Haas, "The Biological Significance of the Space Effort," in *Planetology and Space Mission Planning*, Robert D. Enzman and Edward M. Weyer, eds. (New York: Academy of Sciences, 1966), p. 446.

2.   Inner Space

1. John L. Mero, "Mineral Wealth from the Oceans," *Science Journal* (incorporating *Discovery*), (July, 1964).
2. Boundless Frontiers, U.S. Department of the Navy Report No. OP–09D2/jj.
3. W. McLeod Chapman, "Ocean Fisheries: Status and Outlook," transactions of Second Annual Conference of Marine Technology Society, 1966, pp. 15, 20.
4. J. L. Mero, *The Mineral Resources of the Sea.* New York: American Elsevier Publishing Co., Inc., 1965.
5. Robert E. Hillman, "Drugs from the Sea," *Oceanology International*, Industrial Research, Inc. (September-October, 1967), p. 35.
6. Andreas B. Rechnitzer, "Deep Submersibles," *Oceanology International 1968 Yearbook Directory*, Industrial Research, Inc., p. 24.

3.   The Resources of the Planet Earth

1. Erich W. Zimmerman, *An Introduction to World Resources*, H. L. Hunker, ed. New York: Harper & Row, 1964.
2. R. B. Fuller and John McHale, *Inventory of World Resources: Human Trends and Needs*, Phase I (1963), Document 1 of World Design Science Decade, World Resources Inventory, Southern Illinois University, Carbondale, Ill. 62901.
3. B. V. Akhlibininisky and N. I. Khrallenko, *Cybernetics and Problems of Development*, USSR: Lenizdat Publishing House, 1963.
4. Thomas J. Watson, Jr., Senate Subcommittee on Manpower and Employment Report, (IBM Corporation, Nov. 12, 1963).
5. W. Taylor Thom, Jr., *Major Oil and Gas Deposits of the Coastal Lowlands and Continental Shelves* (unpublished paper, American Institute of Geonomy and Natural Resources), May, 1967.
6. Boris Pregel, "The Impact of the Nuclear Age," in *America*

Faces the Nuclear Age, D. Landman and J. E. Fairchild, eds. New York: Sheridan House, 1961, pp. 28–29.

7. *Ibid.*

8. C. Guy Suits, Vice President and Director of Research, General Electric Company, Seventh Panel on Science and Technology, 89th U.S. Congress, January, 1966.

9. Sir Harold Hartley, "The Recovery of Metals from Scrap," *Advancement of Science*, Vol. II, No. 7 (1942). (Despite the date, this remains one of the classical and most informative papers in this area.)

10. "Restoring the Quality of the Environment," *Report of the Environmental Pollution Panel*, President's Science Advisory Committee, The White House, November, 1965.

V   PROPHETS OF THE FUTURE

1. Hugh D. Duncan, *Language and Literature in Society*. New Jersey: The Bedminster Press, 1961, p. 15.

2. Louis Pauwels and Jacques Bergier, *The Morning of the Magicians*. New York: Stein & Day, 1967.

3. John R. Pierce, "Communications Technology and the Future," *Daedalus* (J. Am. Acad. Arts and Sci.; Spring 1965), pp. 506–507.

4. C. C. Furnas, *The Next Hundred Years*. Baltimore: The Williams & Wilkins Co., 1936.

5. C. C. Furnas, "The Next Hundred Years—Thirty Years Later," Address to 45th Annual Meeting of the American Petroleum Institute, Nov. 9, 1965.

6. Boris Pregel, *Daily News* (Miami, Florida) Jan. 12, 1941.

7. Boris Pregel, "Peaceful Uses of Atomic Energy," *Social Research: International Quarterly of Political and Social Science* (March 1947), p. 42.

8. Boris Pregel, *L'Energie Atomique et L'Abondance*. Paris: L'Ecole Libre des Hautes Etudes, 1948.

9. Arthur C. Clarke, "An Elementary Mathematical Approach to Astronautics," *J. Brit. Interplane. Soc.* (January, 1939).

10. Dennis Gabor, *Inventing the Future*. London: Secker and Warburg; New York: Alfred A. Knopf, Inc., 1963, pp. 207–208.

11. Dennis Gabor, "Technology, Life and Leisure," *Nature*, Vol. 200, No. 4906 (Nov. 19, 1968).

12. Alvin Weinberg, "Can Technology Replace Social Engineering,"

Information Forum on Technology and Nation, Atoms and U.S., Inc., No. 3 (Second Quarter, 1967), p. 1.

13. Henry Winthrop, "The Sociologist and the Study of the Future," *The American Sociologist,* (May, 1968), p. 136.

14. Bertrand de Jouvenel, *On the Surmising Forum* (mimeo copy 1965), p. 11.

15. ———, *The Art of Conjecture.* New York: Basic Books, Inc., 1967, p. 5.

16. R. B. Fuller, *Nine Chains to the Moon.* Carbondale: Southern Illinois University Press, 1963.

17. ———, "Vision '65," keynote address. Carbondale: Southern Illinois University, October, 1965.

18. Marshall McLuhan, *Understanding Media: The Extensions of Man.* New York: McGraw-Hill Book Co., Inc., 1966.

19. "Mankind 2000," Preparatory International Secretariat (London, May, 1966).

20. R. Jungk, *Outline of a European Lookout Institution* (draft, 1967), Institut Fur Zukunftsfragen, Vienna, Austria.

21. Adapted from: Erich Jantsch, "Technological Forecasting in Corporate Planning," *Long Range Planning,* Vol. 1, No. 1, Sept., 1968, pp. 40–50. (Published by Pergamon Press, Oxford [U.K.], and Long Island City, New York).

22. Arnold Buchholz (draft manuscript 1968); see also, Buchholz, Neue Wege sowjetischer Bildung und Wissenschaft. Methodische und organisatorische Probleme, Koln, 1963, 93 S.

23. *Soviet Life,* No. 5 (140) (May, 1968), pp. 56–58.

24. Robert Boguslaw, *The New Utopians: A Study of System Design and Social Change.* New Jersey: Prentice-Hall, Inc., 1965.

25. Herman Kahn, *On Thermonuclear War.* New Jersey: Princeton University Press, 1960. Also, *On Escalation: Metaphors and Scenarios,* New York: Frederick A. Praeger, Inc., 1965.

26. ———, *Working Paper,* Part I, H. Kahn, W. Pfaff, and J. Wiener, eds. (mimeo copy) New York: Hudson Institute, Inc.

27. Daniel Bell, "The End of Ideology" in *On the Exhaustion of Political Ideas in the Fifties,* (1960). New York: The Free Press, 1965, p. 15.

28. Daniel Bell, "The Future as Present Expectation," *Current* (November, 1967), p. 6.

29. ———, "The Year 2000—Trajectory of an Idea," *Daedalus* (J. Am. Acad. Arts and Sci.; Summer, 1967), p. 643.

30. Harold D. Lasswell, "Strategies of Inquiry, The Use of Observa-

tion," *The Human Meaning of the Social Sciences*, Daniel Lerner, ed. Cleveland: The World Publishing Company, 1959. (A Meridian book).

31. Bertram M. Gross and Michael Springer, "A New Orientation in American Government," *Ann. Am. Acad. Political and Social Sci.* (special issue devoted to "Social Goals and Indicators for American Society"; May, 1967), p. 7.

32. *The Minnesota "Experimental City"; Smithsonian Papers on "Future Museums"; "Designing Education for the Future".* An eight-state project (one among six major programs) sponsored by the U.S. Dept. of Health, Education and Welfare, 1966.

33. Hans H. Landsberg, L. L. Fischman, and J. L. Fisher, *Resources in America's Future*. Baltimore: The Johns Hopkins Press, 1963.

34. R. Boguslaw, *The New Utopians: A Study of System Design and Social Change.* Englewood Cliffs, N.J.: Prentice-Hall, Inc., 1965, p. 5.

35. R. Theobald, ed. *Social Policies for America in the Seventies.* New York: Doubleday and Company, Inc., 1968.

36. Editorial, *Anarchos*, No. 1 (February 1968).

37. "Directory of Social Change," *The Modern Utopian*, Tufts University, Mass.

VI TOWARD THE PLANETARY SOCIETY

1. *New Scientist* (England, Oct. 26, 1967).

2. George W. Ball, November, 1967 (former U.S. Undersecretary of State).

3. Ritchie Calder, "The Speed of Change," *Bulletin of the Atomic Scientists* (December, 1965).

4. R. C. Cowen, Science Editor, *Christian Science Monitor*, February, 1968.

5. Hasan Ozbekhan, *Technology and Man's Future*, System Development Corporation, 1966.

6. Report on the World Social Situation, United Nations, N.Y., March, 1966.

7. *World Wide Defense Expenditures and Selected Economies Data*, U.S. Arms Control and Disarmament Agency, 1967.

8. E.R.F.W. Crossman, *Automation, Skill and Manpower Predictions*, Seminar on Manpower Policy and Program, U.S. Department of Labor, April 15, 1965.

9. B. F. Massell, "A Disaggregated View of Technical Change," RAND Corporation, 1966, p. 1.

10. "The Sociology of Georg Simmel," trans. by Kurt H. Wolff, ed. New York: The Free Press, 1950, p. 41.
11. J. McHale, "An International Scientific City." Architectural Design, London (October, 1965), p. 482.
12. Ritchie Calder, "The Speed of Change," *Bulletin of the Atomic Scientists* (December, 1965).
13. Arnold Hauser, *The Social History of Art*, Vol. 4. London: Routledge & Kegan Paul Ltd.; New York: Alfred A. Knopf, Inc., 1951, 1958, p. 250.

Bibliography

BOOKS

Bennis, Warren G., Kenneth D. Benne, and Robert Chin, eds., *The Planning of Change*. New York: Holt, Rinehart and Winston, Inc., 1962, p. 3.

Boguslaw, R. *The New Utopians: A Study of System Design and Social Change*. Englewood Cliffs, N.J.: Prentice-Hall, Inc., 1965, p. 5.

Brown, Kenneth, and Lawrence D. Ely., *Space Logistics Engineering*. New York: John Wiley & Sons, Inc. 1962, p. 9.

Clynes, Manfred (Foreword to *Cyborg: Evolution of the Superman*, D. S. Halacy, Jr., ed.) New York: Harper & Row, 1965, p. 8.

Cohen, John, "Subjective Time," from *The Voices of Time*, J. T. Fraser, ed. New York: George Braziller, Inc. 1967, p. 262.

de Jouvenel, Bertrand, *On the Surmising Forum* (mimeo copy, 1965), p. 11.

————, *The Art of Conjecture*. New York: Basic Books, Inc., 1967, p. 5.

"Directory of Social Change," The Modern Utopian, Tufts University, Mass.

Duncan, Hugh D., *Communication and Social Order*. New York: Oxford University Press, 1968, p. 1.

————, *Language and Literature in Society*, Totowa, N.J.: The Bedminster Press, Inc., 1961, p. 15.

Durkheim, Emile, *The Division of Labor in Society* (1893), trans. by George Simpson. Glencoe, Ill.: The Free Press, 1947, p. 229.

Eliade, Mircea, *The Myth of the Eternal Return*. New York: Bollingen Foundation, 1954, p. 104.

Friedlander, H. E., and J. Oser, *Economic History of Modern Europe*. Englewood Cliffs, N.J.: Prentice-Hall, Inc. 1953, p. 64.

Flechteim, Ossip K., *History and Futurology*. Germany: Verlag Anton Hain K.-G., 1966.

Fuller, R. Buckminster, *Ideas and Integrities*, Englewood Cliffs, N.J.: Prentice-Hall, Inc., 1963.

Fuller, R. Buckminster, *Nine Chains to the Moon*, (Carbondale, Ill.: Southern Illinois University Press, 1963.

————, and John McHale, *Inventory of World Resources: Human Trends and Needs*, Phase I (1963) Document I of World Design Science Decade, World Resources Inventory. Carbondale, Ill.: Southern Illinois University.

Furnas, C. C., *The Next Hundred Years*. Baltimore: The Williams & Wilkins Co., 1936.

Gabor, Dennis, *Inventing the Future*. London: Secker and Warburg; New York: Alfred A. Knopf, Inc., 1963, pp. 207–208.

Gardner, John W., *Self Renewal*. New York: Harper & Row, 1964.

Haas, Ward J., *"The Biological Significance of the Space Effort,"* in *Planeotology and Space Mission Planning*, Robert D. Enzman and Edward M. Weyer, eds., New York: Academy of Sciences, 1966, p. 466.

Hartley, Sir Arnold, "The Recovery of Metals from Scrap," *Advancement of Science*, Vol. II, No. 7 (1942).

Hobsbawm, E. J., *The Age of Revolution 1789–1848*. New York: New American Library, Inc., (A Mentor book). 1962, p. 91.

Hubbert, M. King, *Energy Resources*. Washington, D.C.: National Academy of Sciences, National Research Council Publ. No. 1000–D, Committee on Natural Resources, 1962.

Hughes, H. Stuart, *Consciousness and Society: The Reorientation of European Social Thought 1890–1930*. New York: Alfred A. Knopf, Inc., 1958.

Kahn, Herman, *On Thermonuclear War*. New Jersey: Princeton Unversity Press, 1960. Also, *On Escalation: Metaphors and Scenarios*. Frederick A. Praeger, Inc., 1965.

Kantrowitz, A., *Electronic Physiologic Aids*. New York: Maimonides Hospital, 1963.

La Barre, W., *The Human Animal*. Chicago: University of Chicago Press, 1954, p. 92.

Landers, Richard R., *Man's Place in the Dybosphere*. Englewood Cliffs, N.J.: Prentice-Hall, Inc., 1966, p. 4.

Landsberg, Hans H., L. L. Rischman, and J. L. Risher, *Resources in America's Future*. Baltimore: Johns Hopkins Press, Inc., 1963.

Lasswell, Harold D., "Strategies of Inquiry: The Use of Observation," from *The Human Meaning of the Social Sciences*, Daniel Lerner, ed. Cleveland: The World Publishing Company, 1959. (A Meridian Book.)

Levi-Strauss, Claude, *The Savage Mind*. London: George Wiedenfeld and Nicolson, 1966, p. 236.

McLuhan, Marshall, *Understanding Media: The Extensions of Man*, New York: McGraw-Hill Book Company, Inc., 1966.

Mankind 2000, Preparatory International Secretariat (London), May, 1966.

Massell, B. F., *A Disaggregated View of Technical Change*. RAND Corporation, 1966, p. 1.

Mero, J. L., *The Mineral Resources of the Sea*. New York: American Elsevier Publishing Co., Inc., 1965.

Nash, Manning, *Machine Age Maya: The Industrialization of a Guatemalan Community*. New York: The Free Press, 1958, p. 116.

Pauwels, Louis, and Jacques Bergier, *The Morning of the Magicians*. New York: Stein and Day, Inc., 1967.

Polak, Fred L., *The Image of the Future*, Vol. I. Leyden: A. W. Sijthoff; Dobbs Ferry, N.Y.: Oceana Publications, Inc., 1961, p. 23.

Pregel, Boris, "The Impact of the Nuclear Age," in *America Faces the Nuclear Age*, D. Landman and J. E. Fairchild, eds. New York: Sheridan House, 1961, p. 26.

————, L'Energie Atomique et L'Abondance, L'École Libre des Hautes Études, 1948.

Social Policies for America in the Seventies, R. Theobald, ed., New York: Doubleday & Company, Inc., 1968.

Sushkov, Y. N., "Flights into Space," *Nauchno-Populyarnaya Biblioteka*, Moskva, 1963. (Edited machine Trans. FTD–MT–64–227, U.S. Dept. Commerce, 1964.)

Weber, Max, *Essays in Sociology*. Trans. by H. H. Gerth and C. W. Mills, eds. New York: Oxford University Press, Inc., 1958, p. 275.

Wolff, Kurt H., ed. and trans., *The Sociology of Georg Simmel*. New York: The Free Press, 1950, p. 41.

Zimmermann, Erich W., *Introduction to World Resources*, Henry L. Hunker, ed. New York: Harper & Row, 1964.

Zotova L., and A. Voskreseusky, "Bionics, A New Science," *Izv.* (July 16, 1961).

ARTICLES AND PERIODICALS

Ames, Adelbert, Jr., "Experiments in Perception," *Progressive Architecture* (December, 1947), p. 20.

Anarchos, Editorial No. 1, February 1968. (Publisher Box 466, N.Y.)

Ball, George W., *Time* (November, 1967). (Former U.S. Undersecretary of State.)

Baunan, Zygmunt, "Image of Man in Modern Sociology," *Polish Sociological Bulletin*, No. 1, (1967), p. 14.

Bell, Daniel, "Twelve Modes of Prediction," *Daedalus* (J. Am. Acad. Arts and Sci.; Summer, 1964), p. 486.

————, "The End of Ideology," in *Exhaustion of Political Ideas in the Fifties* (1960). New York: The Free Press, 1965, p. 15.

————, "The Future as Present Expectation," *Current* (November, 1967), p. 6.

————, "The Year 2000—Trajectory of an Idea," *Daedalus* (J. Am. Acad. Arts and Sci.; Summer, 1967), p. 643.

Block, Henry D., "Simulation of Statistically Composite Systems," in *Prospects for Simulation and Simulators of Dynamic Systems*, George Shapiro and Milton Rogers, eds., New York: Books, Inc. (Spartan Books, Inc.), 1967, p. 31.

————, and Herbert Ginsburg, "The Psychology of Robots," *Psychology Today*, Communications/Research/Machines/Inc. (April, 1968), p. 54.

Borgstrom, G. "The Human Biosphere and Its Biological and Chemical Limitations," in *Global Impacts of Applied Microbiology*, Mortimer P. Starr, ed., New York: John Wiley & Sons, Inc., 1964.

Boyko, H., "Salt Water Agriculture," *Scientific American* (March, 1967).

Brodey, Warren M., "Human Enhancement Through Evolutionary Technology," *IEEE Spectrum* (September, 1967), p. 90.

Colwell, Robert N., "Remote Sensing of Natural Resources," *Scientific American* (January, 1968).

Clarke, Arthur C., "An Elementary Mathematical Approach to Astronautics," Brit. Interplanet. Soc. (January, 1939).

Cook, R. C., "Truth and Consequences in a New Era," *Population Bulletin*, Vol. XXII, No. 4 (November, 1966).

Cowen, R. C., Science Edition, *Christian Science Monitor* (February, 1968).

de Jouvenel, Bertrand, "Utopia for Practical Purposes," *Daedalus* (J. Am. Acad. Arts and Sci.; Spring, 1965), p. 444.

Duncan, O. T., "Social Organization and the Ecosystem," in *Handbook of Modern Sociology*, R. L. Faris, ed. Skokie, Ill.: Rand McNally & Co., 1964.

Fuller, R. Buckminster, "Prospects for Humanity," *Saturday Review* (Aug. 29, 1964).

Gabor, Dennis, "Technology, Life and Leisure," *Nature*, Vol. 200, No. 4906, p. 7.

Gilb, Corinne Lathrop, "Time and Change in Twentieth Century Thought," *J. World History*, Vol. IX, No. 4 (1966), pp. 867–880.

Gross, Bertram M., and Michael Springer, "A New Orientation in American Government," *Ann. Amer. Acad. Political and Social Sci.* (special issue devoted to "Social Goals and Indicators for American Society," May, 1967), p. 7.

Hillman, Robert E., "Drugs from the Sea," *Oceanology International, Industrial Research, Inc.*; (September–October 1967), p. 35.

Jungk, R., *Outline of a European Lookout Institution* (draft 1967), Institut Fur Zukunftsfragen, Vienna, Austria.

Kahn, Herman, *Working Paper, Part I*, H. Kahn, W. Pfaff, and J. Wiener, eds., Hudson Institute Inc., N.Y., 1966.

McHale, J., "An International Scientific City," *Architectural Design* (London; October, 1965), p. 482.

Mero, J. L., "Mineral Wealth from the Oceans," *Science Journal* (incorporating *Discovery*), (July, 1964).

New Scientist (England), Oct. 26, 1967.

Pico della Mirandola, Giovanni, "Oration on the Dignity of Man" (1486), trans. by E. L. Forbes in *The Renaissance Philosophy of Man*; E. Cassener, ed. Chicago: University of Chicago Press, 1948, p. 225.

Pierce, John R., "Communications Technology and the Future," *Daedalus* (J. Am. Acad. Arts and Sci.; Spring, 1965), pp. 506–507.

Pregel, Boris, "Peaceful Uses of Atomic Energy," *Social Research International Quarterly of Political and Social Science* (March, 1947), p. 42.

————, *Daily News* (Miami, Florida), Jan. 12, 1941.

Rechnitzer, Andreas, B., "Deep Submersibles," *Oceanology International 1968 Yearbook Directory*, Industrial Research, Inc., p. 24.

Schmandt, Juergen, "On the Emergence of a Second-Generation Science Policy In America in Science and Policy, A Changing Union." Paper for the Organization for European Cooperation and Development (OECD), April 1967.

Soviet Life No. 5, (140), (May, 1968), p. 56–58.

Spangler, E. R., "Results of Space Research 1957–1967", *TRW Space Log*, Vol. 7, No. 3 (Fall, 1967), p. 52.

Thring, M. W., "The Pace of the Technologist in Modern Society," *J. Roy. Soc. Arts* (April 1966).

Toynbee, Arnold J., "New Windows into History," *Think* (September–October 1965), p. 4.

Trobolev, V., "Trolley Bus Lines in Space," *Znaniye-Sila* (Nov. 2, 1964).

Weinberg, Alvin, "Can Technology Replace Social Engineering," *Information Forum on Technology and Nation*, Atoms and U.S., Inc., No. 3 (Second Quarter 1967), p. 1.

Winthrop, Henry, "The Sociologist and the Study of the Future," *The American Sociologist* (May, 1968), p. 136.

White, Robert J., "The Isolated Brain," *Industrial Research Inc.* (April, 1968), p. 65.

Woodruff, W., and H., "Economic Growth, Myth or Reality," *Technology and Culture*, No. 4 (Fall 1966).

REPORTS

Akhilibininsky and N. I. Khrallenko, *Cybernetics and Problem Development*, Trans. U.S. Dept. Commerce, OTS Report 64–215–17 (Lenizdat Publishing House, 1963).

Boundless Frontiers, U.S. Dept. Navy Report No. OP-09D2/jj.

Business Week, special report (1966).

Calder, Ritchie, "The Speed of Change," *Bul. Atomic Scientists* (December, 1965).

Corliss, William R., *Scientific Satellites*, Scientific and Technical Information Division, Office of Technology Utilization, NASA, SO-133, 1967.

Nat. Aeron. Space Admin., Space Science and Applications Program, E. P. 47, Fiscal Year 1968.

"Restoring the Quality of the Environment," Report of the Environmental Pollution Panel, President's Science Advisory Committee, The White House, November, 1965.

United Nations Report, World Social Situation, March, 1966.

U.S. Dept. of Health, Education and Welfare, *The Minnesota "Experimental City"; Smithsonian Papers on "Future Museums"; "Designing Education for the Future."* An eight-state project, 1966.

Watson, Thomas J., Jr., Senate Subcommittee on Manpower and Employment Report (IBM Corporation, Nov. 12, 1963).

World Wide Defense Expenditures and Selected Economies Data (1967), U.S. Arms Control and Disarmament Agency.

OTHER SOURCES

Buchholz, Arnold, draft manuscript (1968).

Carlson, Professor E., UCLA, AP Wire Service (April 10, 1966).

Chapman, W. McLeod, "Ocean Fisheries, Status and Outlook," transactions of Second Annual Conference of Marine Technology Society (1966), pp. 15–20.

Crossman, E. R. and F. W. Crossman "Automation, Skill and Manpower Prediction," Seminar on Manpower Policy and Program (U.S. Dept. of Labor, April 15, 1965).

Fuller, R. Buckminster, "Vision '65," keynote address, Southern Illinois University, October, 1965.

Furnas, C. C., "The Next Hundred Years—Thirty Years Later," address to 45th Annual Meeting of the American Petroleum Institute (Nov. 9, 1965).

Gavin, James M., "Perspectives and Prospects in Space," Honors Convocation, American Institute of Aeronautics and Astronautics, Boston, December, 1966, (Chairman of the Board paper: Arthur D. Little, Inc.), p. 14.

General Electric Company (1966).

Information Release, U.S. Strategic Air Command (402) 294–2544–4433.

Jantsch, Erich, "Integrating Forecasting and Planning Through a Function-Oriented Approach," from *Technological Forecasting for Industry and Government*, James R. Bright, ed. Englewood Cliffs, N.J.: Prentice-Hall, Inc., 1968.

Johnson, Philip L., "Remote Sensing," Symposium on Ecology of Subarctic Regions, UNESCO (Finland, 1968).

Munch, Peter A., "Economic Development and Conflicting Values," manuscript, Department of Sociology, Southern Illinois University and the Maxwell Graduate School, Syracuse University, Syracuse, New York.

NASA News Release, June 26, 1968.

Ozbekhan, Hasan, "Technology and Man's Future," System Development Corporation, 1966.

———, *Ibid.* (U.S.) Sp.-2494, May, 1966.

Suits, C. Guy, Vice President and Director of Research, General Electric Company, Seventh Panel on Science and Technology, 89th US Congress January 1966.

Thom, W. Taylor, Jr., "Major Oil and Gas Deposits of the Coastal Lowlands and Continental Shelves," (unpublished paper, American Institute of Geonomy and Natural Resources, May 1967).

Wilkinson, John, "Futuribles: Innovation vs. Stability," Center for the Study of Democratic Institutions (U.S.) 1967.

Index

Against the Grain (Huysmans), 35
"Âge of Gold" (Saint-Simon), 259
Air pollution, 141, 156, 157, 231
American Institute of Planners, The, 258
American Revolution, 31
Ames, Adelbert, 249
Andromeda Nebula (Yefrenov), 193
Art of Conjecture (de Jouvenel), 247
Asimov, Isaac, 155, 242
Atmospheric environ system, 75–76
Atomic energy, 244
Automatic Picture Transmission service (APT), 136, 142
Automation, 123–24, 224; *see also* Computer technology; Cybernetics
Autonomism, and changing life styles, 286–88

Baade, Fritz, 253
Baudelaire, Pierre Charles, 35
Beardsley, Aubrey Vincent, 36
Bell, Daniel, 255
Bellamy, Edward, 243
Berkeley George, 249
Bestuzhev-Lada, Igor, 253
Beyond Tomorrow (Cole), 193
Bioelectrochemical technologies, and synthetic materials, 229
Bioengineering, 110, 119, 120
Biogeochemical cycles in the ecosystem, 81–82
Biomass, as source of stored solar energy, 207
Bionics, 108, 128
Biosphere: and man, 68, 71–74; tropospheric layer of atmosphere in, 75; available waters in, 75–76; major cycles in, 81–82; "noosphere" layer in, 91, 167*n*
Biosynthesis of food materials from fossil fuel bases, 213–14
Block, H., 111, 114
Bogue, Donald, 162
Boguslaw, Robert, 254, 260
Bratsk Hydroelectric Power Station, 210
British Interplanetary Society, 245
Buchholz, Arnold, 252–53

Carrel, Alexis, 105
Center for Technology and Culture, University of Toronto, 249
Change: disorienting nature of, in today's society, 19–20; major agencies of, 25; dimensions of, 57–65; and choice, 59; pace and notion of, 59–60; increased frequency of, 60; long-range and large-scale effects of, 60; expanded impact and awareness of, 60–61; differential rates in acceptance and use of, 61; revolutionary, and evolutionary, 62; two crucial aspects of, in mid-20th century situation, 62; and need for understanding past change and past-change agencies, 63; and ecological revolution, 63–64
Christianity, redemption as key progressive concept of, 27–29
Church, role of, in study of future of society, 259
City: experimental, 259, 261, 263, 293; of the future, 289–93; the capital city, 290; ceremonial type of, 290, 291; the communications city, 290, 292; the convention/conference city, 290, 292; the manufacturing city, 290; the recreation, or "fun," city, 291, 292; the festival, or "arts," city, 292; the museum city, 292; the scientific city, 292; the university city, 292
Civilisation at the Crossroads, 253–54
Clarke, Arthur C., 245, 252, 253
Clynes, Manfred, 106
Cole, D. M., 193
"Commission on the Year 2000, The," 255–56
Communications: speed of, 59; use of satellite systems in, 143–47, 245
Composites, 228–29
Computer technology, 120–22, 123–24, 141, 248, 257, 260, 281; *see also* Cybernetics
Comte Auguste, 27, 30, 34*n*, 36, 167*n*
Constructivism, 38
Contamination of earth by organisms brought back by interplanetary probes, 193
Continuous neighborhood, man's world changed to, 59
Cooper, Fenimore, 249–50
Corporate industry, future orientation of, 259–60
Cost effectiveness of futures, 9
Cousteau, Jacques-Yves, 203, 206
Cryogenics, 120
Culture system of man, 89
Cybernetics, 96–97, 120–22, 166–67, 254; and the new symbiosis, 123–48; *see also* Computer technology
Cyborg, 106

Dadaism, 38, 263
Davidson, Frank P., 251n
De Bakey, Michael, 104
de Chardin, Teilhard, 91n, 167n, 259n
Deep River of Ocean Systems, Inc., 203
de Jouvenel, Bertrand, 246–47, 250, 251, 252
Desalination of sea water, 198
Development of World Thinking on the Future of Man and His Earth, The (Bestuzshev-Lada), 253
Dixon, John, 299n
Dr. Jekyll and Mr. Hyde (Stevenson), 35, 50
Donne, John, 59
"Doomsday: Friday, 13 November A.D. 2026" (Von Foerster, et al.), 155
Duncan, H. D., 260
Durkheim, Émile, 30, 36
"Dymaxion" principles of R. B. Fuller, 226n, 248

Ecological revolution, 63–64
Ecology: and the future, 231–37; technological systems as organic part of, 231; objectives in redesigning ecological undertakings, 236; *see also* Planetary ecology
Economic man, 46–47; end of, 276–83
Eddington's phrase, "Time's arrow," 19
Education: satellite-relayed, 147; in reality, 293–95
Electrochemical industries, and synthetic materials, 229
Electromechanical circuitry within man, 110
Eliade, Mircea, 21
Ellul, Jacques, 94, 108
Energy, 208–20; solar, 208–13, 214–15, 236; stages of exploitation of, related to course of human society, 208–10; world production and consumption of, 211, 214; water power, as source of, 214, 236; tidal power, as source of, 214, 236; geothermal sources of, 214; nuclear power, as source of, 215–17, 236; conversion and transmission of, 217–20
Environmental Health Task Force, 157–58
"Establishment prophets" of the West, 254–55, 258
Ethics, the world in terms of, 24
"European Lookout Institution," Jungk's outline of, 250–51
Evolutionary teleology, 167
"Expo '67" dome, of R. B. Fuller, 248

Fisheries, increase in yield of the world's, 197–98
Flechteim, Ossip K., 52
Food cycle, refashioning of, 236
Ford, Henry, 43n
Fossil fuels: extractive depletion of, 78, 229, 236; as source of stored solar energy, 208; increase in use of, 212–13; use of chemicals derived from, 229
Fourier, François Marie Charles, 27, 34
Frankenstein, or the Modern Prometheus (Shelley), 35
Free enterprise systems, 280
French Revolution, 31, 63
Freud, Sigmund, 22, 30
Fuller, R. Buckminster, 167n, 210, 226n, 228n, 247–48
Furnas, C. C., 243
Future, the: the sense of, 3–15; as integral aspect of the human condition, 3–6; cyclical model of, in Eastern societies, 4; Western view of, 4; prediction, 6–8; social futures, 8; aspect of choice in, 8–15; time sense intimately linked with sense of the future, 19; reevaluation of the past, in study of, 29–30, 52; "inventing the future," 52
Future of Man, The (de Chardin), 259n
Futures: research, 10, 62–63, 241, 246–47, 250, 252, 257; collective, 10–11; priority, and reevaluation and redesign of social forms and possibilities, 11; thinking, areas of, 15; machine-derived forecasts, 257; *see also* Technological forecasting
Futurist, The, journal of The World Futures Society, 258n

Gabor, Dennis, 52, 245
Galton, Sir Francis, 7
Garbage disposal, problem of, 157
Gardner, John W., 35n
Gauguin, Paul, 36
General Electric's Space Technology Center, 193
Geothermal sources of energy, 214
Ginsberg, H., 111
Global ecology, *see* Ecology; Planetary ecology
Global services, 220, 271
Greeks, and development of intellectual and rational vision of the city of man, 26
Growth law, phases of, 150–53
Guaranteed income, 262, 280

Halacy, D. S., Jr., 107
Hallucinogenic agents, 119
Hauser, Arnold, 298
Hegel, Georg Wilhelm Friedrich, 32
Heilbroner, R. L., 278n
Helmer, Olaf, "Delphi" method of, 257
Hippie movement, 262–63
Hudson Institute, 254
Human enhancement, 122
Human system, 82–97; biophysical, 83–85; psychosocial, 85–91; technological, 91–97
Hume, David, 249
Huysmans, Joris Karl, 35
Hydroelectric power, 214

Industrial growth and materials use: phases of, 222–24; future phase of, 224–26
Industrial Revolution, 31, 39–53, 63, 222
Industrialization: as global phenomenon, 43; first phases of, 46–47
Industry, shift of emphasis within, to service, 279
Inequities between have and have-not peoples, 13
Institute of Defense Analysis, 254
"Integrative Planning of Technology" (Jantsch), 252n
Interdependent global relationships, 59, 142, 223
International associations and professional organizations, 271
International Congress of Futures Research, 252
International Secretariat of Futures Research, 252

Jantsch, Erich, 251–52
Joyce, James, 250
Judaic tradition, and the world to come, 26–27
Jungk, Robert, 250–51, 252, 253

Kahn, Herman, 254
Kylstra, Johannes, 206

La Barre, W., 92
La Biosphere (Vernadsky), 91n
Landers, Richard R., 106, 108
Lasswell, Harold, 257–58
Lawrence, D. H., 32, 250
Life, existence of, elsewhere in our solar system, 193–94
Life expectancy, increase in, 84, 103, 104, 164
Life styles, emerging, 23, 261, 283–89
Limits of American Capitalism, The (Heilbroner), 278n
Lindbergh, Charles A., 59
Link, Edwin A., 204
Living organisms, and balanced symbiotic relations, 66
LSD, 119
Lunar base, 189

Machine, fear of, 34–35
"Macro-Engineering: A Capability in Search of a Methodology" (Davidson), 251n
Man: present image of, 30; and the overall ecosystem, 67–68, 73–74; and the biosphere, 68, 71–74; and man/machine relations ("Man Plus"), 98–122; extension of, into horizontal and vertical space, 98–99; and chances of survival, 170; see also Economic man
"Man and Society in the Scientific-Technological Revolution," Prague 1968 conference, 253

Management science, 120
Manhattan Project, 244
"Manifest destiny" of nation-state, 14, 37
"Mankind 2000" project, 250
Manned orbital space stations, 189
Marine environ of man, 79–81
Marine pharmacology, research into, 199
Marx, Karl, 22, 27, 30, 33, 36, 258, 286
Mass production, 40–42
Material resources, 220–31; contained within the land surface, 78, 221–22; of the oceans, 80–81, 197–200, 221; of the atmosphere, 221; use of, and industrial growth, phases of, 222–24; restructuring of, 224; reserves and future uses of, 226–28; recycling and reuse of, 231, 234, 236
Materials synthesis, 228–30
McLuhan, Marshall, 128, 249–50
Mechanical Bride, The (McLuhan), 249
Mechanical revolution, 68
Medical drug controls, 159
Medievalism, revival of, in 19th century romanticism, 34
Melville, Herman, 36
Metals: found within land surface, 78, 221–22; reuse of, through successive use/scrap processes, 78, 225, 234, 236; oceans as potential source of, 198–99; continuing centrality of, within the industrial ecology, 225
Microminiaturization, 162, 183–84, 187
Mineral resources: of ocean, 197, 198; of earth's crust, 221
"Moral Spectrum of Machines" (Thring), 117
Morning of the Magicians, The (Pauwels and Bergier), 242
Morris, William, 34
Myth, element of, in individual and social time, 21–22, 24

National Academy of Science, 170
National socialism, 37
Nation-state, self-sufficiency and "manifest destiny" of, 14, 37
Neighborhood, continuous, man's world changed to, 59
New Utopians, The (Boguslaw), 254
Newcomen, Thomas, 40
"Next Fifty Years 1967–2017, The" conference of The American Institute of Planners, 258
Next Hundred Years, The (Furnas), 243
Nietzsche, Friedrich Wilhelm, 32
Nodule deposits of ores on ocean floor, 198
"Noosphere" layer in biosphere, 91, 167n
Nuclear power, 215–17, 236

Ocean research and development, 200
Ocean technology, 200–03
O.E.C.D. (Organisation for Economic Cooperation and Development, Europe), 251
Offshore drilling for oil and natural gas, 199
"One-World-Town Plan," of R. B. Fuller, 247–48
"One world" view of the future, 12, 268, 272
Operation Hindsight, of Department of Defense, 61–62
Orbital space stations, manned, 189
Organ transplants in man, 103–04
Osgood, Charles, 257
Outer space, 175–95; convergence of sciences in space research, 176–77

Pareto, Vilfredo, 30
Past: the future of, 17–53; reevaluation of, in study of the future, 29–30, 52; need for understanding past change and past-change agencies, 63
Pearl, Raymond, 151
Pearson, Karl, 7
Personality system of the individual, 88–89
Petty, Sir William, 7
Phenomenon of Man, The (de Chardin), 91n
Philosophical Institute of the Czechoslovak Academy of Sciences, 253
Philosophy, the world in terms of, 23–24
Pico della Mirandola, Giovanni, 99
Planetary culture, 295–300
Planetary ecology, 64–65, 123, 142, 150, 232; *see also* Ecology
Planetary society: maintenance aspects of, 268–73; negative aspects of, 273
Plastics, 228; developed from fossil fuel bases, 213–14, 229; structural, 229
Plato, 26
Poe, Edgar Allan, 36
Polak, Fred L., 23
Polymers, structural, 229
Popper, Karl, 246
Population control, 84, 154, 163; and the population explosion, 153–54, 162
Positivism, 48–49
Predicting the future, 6–8; *see also* Futures
Pregel, Boris, 244
Present: the future of, 55–171; problems and prospects of, 149–71
"Presidential Address to the British Association" (Ramsay), 210
Price, Derek de Solla, 151, 160
Profiles of the Future (Clark), 245
Protein gained from the sea, 195
Psychoanalysis, and reordering and reinterpreting past experience, 21
Psychosymbolic aspects of the future, 15

Public funds, allocation of, to long-range social programs, 9

Race to the Year 2000, The (Baade), 253
Radioactive energies, 244
Ramsay, Sir William, 210
RAND Corporation, 254, 257
Recreational use of the sea and shore "interface" area, 207
Reformation, 63
Religion, the world in terms of, 23
Religious conversion, relation of, to past, present, and future, 21
Renaissance, 31, 63, 99
Republic, The (Plato), 26
Resources in America's Future (Landsberg, et al.), 259
Revolutions: of rising expectation, 31, 273; of the present, as global in spatial and quantitative aspects, 63
Rimbaud, Arthur, 35, 36
Robots, industrial, 110–11
Rocket-rail system of interplanetary travel, 192
Romantic Revolution, and Romanticism, 31, 32–34, 48
Rousseau, Jean Jacques, 249
Ruskin, John, 34
Russian Revolution, 31, 57

Sacred societies, 24
Saint-Simon, Claude Henri de Rouvroy, Comte de, 27, 36, 247, 255, 259
Sapir, Edward, 249
Sarnoff, David, 146
Satellites: man-made, circling the globe, 59, 128; use of, in the new symbiosis, 123–48
Schopenhauer, Arthur, 32
Science: ascendancy of, over religion, 3; the world in terms of, 24
Science fiction, 193, 241–42, 245
Scientific revolution, 39
Secular societies, 24–25
Self Renewal (Gardner), 35n
Sex, and changing life styles, 288
Shelley, Mary, 35
Simmel, Georg, 287
"Situationists," future-oriented art movement of, 263
Skalak, Richard, 110
"Social accounting" movement, 258
Social behaviors of man, and maintenance of the ecosystem, 89–90
Social effects of new technologies, 8
Social engineering, 120
Social Forecasting Research Institute of the Soviet Sociological Association, 253
Social History of Art (Hauser), 298
Social pathology of uncontrolled growth in urban density, 159
Social progress: related directly to changes in immediate past, 25; view

Social progress (*cont.*)
of, derived from Greek and Judeo-Christian traditions, 25–29
Social sciences: formulation and academic definition of, 30; and estrangement from modern society, 36; and futures research movement, 246–47; language of, 255
Social system of man, 89
Social telesis, 167
Social unrest, current, 31
Sociodicy of amelioration, 25
Sociology, and study of the future, 246
Soil pollution, 141, 156, 157, 231
Solar energy, 208–13, 214–15, 236
Soviet Union: work in space of, 189, 192; futures planning of, 252–53
Space exploration, questions of social and cultural nature related to, 193
Space research: convergence of sciences in, 176–77; by-products of, 187
"Spaceship Earth Game," of R. B. Fuller, 248–49
Spencer, Herbert, 7, 30, 258
Sputnik, 57, 128
Stevenson, Robert Louis, 35, 50
"Stress syndrome," 159
Structural aspects of spacecraft systems, 186
Structural plastics, 229
Structural polymers, 229
Surrealism, 38
Synergy, concept of, 167
Systems Development Corporation, 254
Systems science, 120

Technological forecasting, 241, 251–52
Technological Society, The (Ellul), 108
Technology, the world in terms of, 24
Teleology, evolutionary, 167
Telephony, satellite, 145–46
Television coverage, worldwide, through satellite relay transmission, 143
Terrestrial environ of man, 76–79
Theodicy of suffering, 24–25
"Think tanks," 254, 256
Thring, M. W., 110, 114, 117
Tidal power, 214, 236
Time magazine, compact essay of, on "The Futurists: Looking Toward A.D. 2000," 256
Time sense: intimately linked with sense of the future, 19; variability of time relations, 19; and the present, 20; individual subjective relation to the past, 20–21
"Time's arrow," Eddington's phrase, 19
Tomorrow Is Here Already (Jungk), 250
Toynbee, Arnold J., 46, 167
"Tribalism" advocated by leaders of youth, 37, 262
Tropospheric layer of atmosphere, 75
"Twenty-First Century, The," CBS documentary program, 256
Typee (Melville), 36

Ulysses (Joyce), 38
Undersea living, 203–07
Understanding Media (McLuhan), 249
Underwater breathing apparatus, 206
Underwater research, 197
Unimate industrial robot, 110
U.N. International Cooperation Year, 130
U.S. Applied Technology Satellite (A.T.S. 1), 136
U.S. Ocean Systems, Inc., 203
Utopia of the Virgin Mother, The (Comte), 34n
Utopian communities, 23, 261–63
Utopian novelists, 241
Utopian systems of age of computers, 260, 261

Van Allen radiation belts, 207
Van de Velde, Henry, 35
Velikowsky, Immanuel, 242
Verlaine, Paul, 36
Vernadsky, W. I., 91n
Verne, Jules, 242
Versatran industrial robot, 110

Wall Street Journal series on expected social and technological changes, 256
Walter, Grey, 111
Wanigan mobile bases in use in Arctic, 189n
Ward, Lester, 167
Wasteland, The (Eliot), 38
Water pollution, 141, 156, 157, 231
Water power, 214–20, 236
Watt, James, 40
Weather-monitoring information, satellite-reported, 130–31, 137, 271
Weber, Max, 24, 30, 36, 258
Weinberg, Alvin, 246
Wells, H. G., 242, 243, 245
"Werkbund" to elevate aesthetic taste of lower classes, 35
White, Robert J., 105
Whorf, Benjamin L., 249
Wilde, Oscar, 36
Wilkinson, John, 61, 153
Winthrop, Henry, 246
Women, as cosmonauts, 189
Work, value of, in determination of future roles in society, 280–83
"World Design Science Decade" program, 228n
World Futures Society, The, 258n
World Health Organization, 156, 271
World Wars I and II, and the 20th century world, 57
World Weather Watch, 130, 131, 142
Worlds in Collision (Velikowsky), 242
Wright, Wilbur and Orville, 59

Yippie movement, 262–63
Younger generation: and emerging life styles, 285–86; "underground" newspapers, journals, books of, 300

Zimmerman, Erich W., 209